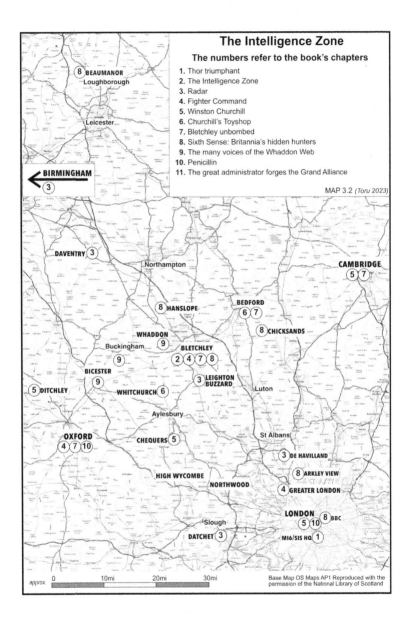

The Intelligence Zone

The numbers refer to the book's chapters

1. Thor triumphant
2. The Intelligence Zone
3. Radar
4. Fighter Command
5. Winston Churchill
6. Churchill's Toyshop
7. Bletchley unbombed
8. Sixth Sense: Britannia's hidden hunters
9. The many voices of the Whaddon Web
10. Penicillin
11. The great administrator forges the Grand Alliance

MAP 3.2 *(Toru 2023)*

approx. 0   10mi   20mi   30mi

Base Map OS Maps AP1 Reproduced with the permission of the National Library of Scotland

The Intelligence Zone

Churchill's secret sites and what they gave the world

Alan Biggins

with Maps and Illustrations by Kai Toru

Previous books by Alan Biggins
A Normandy Tapestry: a portrait of rural France
Selling French Dreams - tales of property, France and family
30 Great days out in Brittany
A New World after Pearl

First edition March 2023
Published by Kirkdale Books
Website - theintelligencezone.com
Contact - intzoneuk@gmail.com

ISBN; 978-1-7393299-0-7 – Paperback
ISBN; 978-1-7393299-1-4 – eBook

About the Author

Alan Biggins served in the Royal Air Force until the age of twenty one. He then worked in the newly-emerging world of computing. He rose through the ranks of that fascinating profession to become a specialist in the installation of trans-European systems for international (mainly American) clients. Fluent in French, a beginner in German and not bad in English, his work for clients such as Universal Studios took him to much of Europe. His travels developed his interest in military history, as well as German beer and French food (but not the other way around).

In his spare time in the 1990's (computer contracting sometimes gives too much of that!), he wrote three books about France. These went into various editions and were widely featured across radio, local and national press and magazines.

While in Britain, he was the I.T. Manager for the Milton Keynes Development Corporation, the body which oversaw the building of that new English city. Bletchley Park lies within 'M.K'. Alan walks a lot; and while exploring the area came upon many sites related to the war; and especially to communications, computing, spies and the special forces. Discovering how this treasure trove of sites were linked together; and how they related to Europe and America, resulted in this book and its sequel '*A New World after Pearl*'. They have been written with the help of many museums and institutions. To show his gratitude he has put together a website www.theintelligencezone.com for his readers to learn more about these astonishing places. He has spent the first five years of his retirement writing – and hopes to spend the next five brushing up his knowledge of German beer.

Freedom is the sure possession of those alone who have the
courage to defend it.
Pericles

*This book is dedicated to those who fought; and those
who thought; for our freedom.*

Contents

Necessity is the mother of invention.
(The phrase was first recorded in English in 1519)

Introduction

From David and Goliath onwards, the endless tale of man's conflicts has shown again and again that brains can sometimes beat brawn. Britain has never been short of brains. The island has been home to some of the worlds' great scientists; the greatest of them all being Isaac Newton, who laid down much of the foundations on which pre-atomic physics rests. It was also the place where man's first great leap into the modern world – the Industrial Revolution - took place. With the Second World War – indeed with the threat of it - British inventive genius reached a new level. Necessity – proverbially the mother of invention – led to world-changing British developments in fields as diverse as computing, communications, medicine, radar and atomics.

Most of that invention took place in a small area north of the river Thames, bounded roughly by the cities of London, Birmingham, Oxford and Cambridge. This is the area that I have called the Intelligence Zone. Its centre is roughly at Bletchley Park; the birthplace of the intelligence revolution which shortened the war. Bletchley Park was not alone, but the centre of many sites. The scale and complexity of the interception, decoding and distribution of intelligence in this area was breath-taking.

Not only were British inventions crucial in winning the war, they have also shaped the modern world. The Intelligence Zone during the Second World War was a uniquely important time and place in world history. But the cauldron of invention is but part of the story. At the same time, in the same area, the spies and saboteurs who Churchill ordered to "set Europe ablaze" were being trained and controlled. Here, too, were the exiled governments of half the countries of Europe. Cheek-by-jowl were based many of the commanders of the Allied armed forces.

The story of the Intelligence Zone is not dry history: it is an epic made from the experiences of men and women. Some of their stories are profound, some are humbling, some terrifying.

Being human, they are shot through with the stuff that shapes us all – love, hate, doubt, certainty, invention, work, the search for a better world and – sometimes - British dry humour.

To give some examples of what you will find in these pages:

- It is June 1940. The defeated British army has recently returned from Dunkirk with practically no weapons. In London, in a room overlooking Horse Guards a soldier studies Churchill's face. The soldier – Edward Spears - wonders how long 'the weary, tired and shattered' old man can carry on:

  'The news was bad, agonising... the gods of Hitler's Germany had taken charge of heaven. Perhaps the old Norsemen were right in their belief that one day evil would prevail in the world.' Big Ben had just chimed. It was one o'clock in the morning. 'I did not take my eyes off the heavy hunched figure in black. The strong light under a green shade caused the pale face to look paler than usual. For the first time in my life I understood the agony of Gethsemane, what it meant to carry absolutely alone an immeasurable burden.'

- From a bomb-scarred London railway station, a mission departs for America to hand over Britain's military secrets – atomic, radar, jets and more. This is knowledge on which the very freedom – and arguably the soul – of man depends. The Pax Britannica has ended, the Pax Americana will soon begin.

- At Bentley Priory, Hugh Dowding builds and wields RAF Fighter Command to narrowly defeat the Luftwaffe – and is promptly sacked.

- On Bletchley railway station a girl in a green jumper - the nineteen year old Mavis Lever - cooks chips for the survivors of Dunkirk and goes on to consign the Italian fleet to Davy Jones' locker.

- A resistance heroine in France sends messages to a lonely hilltop cabin in North Buckinghamshire which will lead to the destruction of the German rocket programme designed to pummel London to dust.

The 'A' list in my story: Churchill, Roosevelt, Turing and Dowding: are major figures of history. Others such as Watson-Watt, Ian Fleming, Hugh Dowding and Bomber Harris, are well known. Yet others are all but forgotten or not generally known – Sinclair, Winterbotham, Cheshire, Delmer, Millar, Cotton, Rock, Lever, Pile and Fourcade to name but a few. These were actors in an epic of endeavour, courage and genius which has shaped the modern world. I am privileged to recount some of what they did.

My story starts with the head of MI6 – 'Quex' Sinclair – 'the wickedest man in London'

1: Thor triumphant

O Lord our God arise,
scatter our enemies,
and make them fall.
Confound their politics,
frustrate their knavish tricks,
on Thee our hopes we fix,
God save us all.
Verse 2 of the British National Anthem.

Quex Sinclair

It's generally thought that the Second World War came as a bit of a surprise to Britain and that somehow 'Blighty' muddled through it by a masterly mix of bloody-mindedness and stiff upper lip. Actually the story is a bit more complicated, and a whole lot more interesting, than that. The real reason why Britain – narrowly - escaped being invaded by Nazi Germany was because she had spent several years preparing for the attack. That was mainly down to warnings from the Secret Intelligence Service (SIS); and the man who banged the drum hardest was its boss, Rear-Admiral Hugh Sinclair.

The SIS is more commonly known as MI6 these days; but they are one and the same organisation. It was begun in 1909 because of concern at Germany's imperial expansion. Hugh Sinclair was its second director. He had been educated at

Quex at sea

1

Stubbington House, a boarding school on the south coast of England which was known as the cradle of the Royal Navy. From it, in 1886, at the age of 13, he went to sea.

At the beginning of the First World War, he entered the Royal Navy's Naval Intelligence Division (NID), becoming its director in 1919.

Among his peers, Hugh Sinclair was known as 'Quex' – a nickname derived from Sir Arthur Pinero's play – 'The Gay Lord Quex' - first performed in 1900. Like his namesake 'the wickedest man in London' Sinclair was a bon vivant with a stormy private life – long remembered in the navy for the violent rows he had with his wife in his cabin in HMS *Renown* when he served as her captain in the first war.

Sinclair became Director of the SIS in 1923. It was he who started the tradition of always referring to the head of the service as 'C', this being a tribute to Captain Mansfield Cumming, Royal Navy, the first Director, who died at his desk the year Quex took over. The link between the Royal Navy and the (at first English and then British) secret services, goes far back into history. This is hardly surprising considering that, pre-aeroplane, all British contact with foreign lands was by ship.

Although secretive in some ways – he forsook naval uniform and wore a slightly too small bowler hat - 'rammed as firmly as possible on his head' – Quex's ancient open topped Lancia car was hard to miss. He had his office in Broadway Buildings, in London. His visitors had first to knock on a hatch in his outer office. When admitted by a secretary they would then wait for the green lightbulb outside his office (reminiscent of the green ink he used for his correspondence) to come on. He lived next to the office and went to work through a connecting door. However, secret locations are rarely so to taxi drivers and delivery men. One morning Quex was shocked to see a large arrow painted on the pavement with the words 'To the British Secret Service Office.'

In the 1930s, Quex became increasingly interested in what was happening in Germany. At that time, after the carnage of the first war, Britain and France were largely pacifist. Pacifism is a worthy aspiration which has a giant flaw: to be successful it requires everyone else to be pacifist too. In Germany, the Nazi party was not pacifist but aggressive. Before I return to Quex and what he did for Britain – and mankind – I will start by looking at the rise of that aggression through the eyes of Sefton Delmer.

Sefton Delmer

Sefton Delmer was, deservedly, the most widely read and influential foreign correspondent writing in English in the 1930s. He described clearly, grippingly and chillingly what was happening in Germany and, indeed, in Europe as a whole, at the time. He was close to Hitler and his court during their rise: a fact that was to cause him to be investigated by MI5, the British domestic security service.

Those who met Delmer thought him a native German. There was nothing in his accent or vocabulary to suggest otherwise. He was born in 1904 in Berlin (where his Australian father was a professor at the university), grew up and was schooled there and spoke German as his mother tongue. He lived through the first war in Berlin – his father being in an internment camp for a short while - until the family was allowed out of Germany into Holland and thence England. Delmer (Tom to his friends) then went to school in London, from where he won a history scholarship to Lincoln College, in Oxford.

He went back and forth to Germany throughout the 1920s where, he tells us, the general feeling among the German populace was that the first war was unfinished business: 'There was hatred of the allies, hatred of the socialists and above all hatred of the Jews.'

His father was now writing for the *Daily Express* – and, after graduating from Oxford, so did Sefton Delmer. Lord Beaverbrook, the proprietor, offered him a job covering Germany.

Eagerly courted by potential sources as a journalist writing for the newspaper with the largest circulation in the world, intelligent and conscientious, outwardly German, no-one could have been better placed than Tom Delmer to get under the skin of events in Germany:

'And what a scene it was! Berlin in 1928 had just about everything which the editor of a popular daily yearns for – sex, murder, political intrigue, money, mystery and bloodshed. Particularly bloodshed. In fact, as time went on, the street battles between the up and coming Nazis and the almost equally up and coming Communists became so frequent that whenever the paper was hard up for an action story someone would ring me up and ask "Tom, old boy, could you let us have a riot?" And most nights I could.'

The 1920s and 30s in Europe saw a bitter and often violent struggle between communism and fascism. Nowhere was this more obvious than in Berlin. One of Delmer's own reporters, Charles Mackay, was shot in a riot by a police cadet. Mackay had put his hand in his pocket for a pass and the cadet, mistaking the gesture, had shot him with an automatic. He was left on the pavement:

'It took him half an hour to die. No one dared intervene. The police cadet was one of more than 4,000 teenage police cadets drafted in to keep the lid on communist agitation. The communists had been inciting workers to class war and revolution. The socialist police chief who was in charge of the action claimed – perhaps correctly – that the action was a communist attempt to launch a civil war.'

This was the Berlin of Isherwood's Sally Bowles, on which the film *Cabaret* was based. The largest city in continental Europe was in a moral vacuum, fought over by communists and nazis and with a rot and decadence that, as well as titillating the *Express* readers, Delmer himself seems to have relished. Here he is on the school days of his then-girlfriend Betty:

'…Betty herself was very soon one of the leaders at this extraordinary school. She became the captain of a clique which among other activities, practised a weird erotic ritual compared with which the orgies of Caligula would have been granted a U Certificate. Betty was the high priestess. To be admitted to her select circle every candidate, whether boy or girl, had to spend twelve hours locked up in a shack with Betty, who would give her verdict whether the candidate was ripe for initiation or not. Similar circles, I knew, existed among teenagers in Berlin. But what struck me as outstandingly peculiar about this clique at Wickendorf was that one of the school mistresses was a member of the ring and encouraged its practices.'

Betty was a Jewess and fled Germany for Paris. She committed suicide there. She is buried in a pauper's grave in Pere Lachaise cemetery. Persecution of the Jews was a mainspring of Nazi ideology. The identification of imaginary enemies as a reason for their country's woes is, of course, one of the standard tactics in a rogue political party's seizure of power.

Sefton Delmer's first book, *Trail Sinister*, gives a disturbing insight into the rottenness, violence and cross-currents of political life in Europe which led to the Armageddon of World War Two. In Delmer's reports from Germany, Spain, France, Poland and Russia, the seeds of the evil harvest which all-but choked the world are evident. The most rampant of those weeds was the German Nazi party.

And Delmer, was in a very, very powerful position. He soon became the *Express's* Chief Reporter in Germany. As such, and as a representative of Britain, the country that the Nazis most wanted to influence, he was courted by the Nazi high command. His insights into the rise of the Nazis are key – and astonishing.

Delmer first saw Hitler speak in 1929, in Berlin:

'I sat as close to him as I could, and stayed from beginning to finish. I do not remember what he said. What fascinated me were his staring hypnotic blue eyes which seemed almost to be popping out of his head. The perspiration streamed down his cheeks, as he worked on the crowd. His starched collar became wet and limp. Then the dye from his cheap blue serge suit came off on to the collar, staining it a dirty purple. I watched his effect on the audience. To me they looked like ordinary comfortable middle class Germans; but he shocked and stirred them into a state of aggressive exultation. It was frightening. When, at the end of it all, they stood singing the 'Deutschland über Alles' anthem, I did not sing or put my hand up to the Nazi salute with the rest. A tiny little fat man beside me wanted to knock me down. 'You just wait.'

Delmer was introduced to Ernst Röhm, the head of the Nazi private army – the *Sturmabteilung* (SA, or 'Brown Shirts') at a Nazi party rally. The SA were Hitler's bully boys: 'A reporter will shake hands with the devil himself for a story.' Röhm wanted Delmer to introduce him to the British secret service to get approval for German rearmament. He invited Delmer to the Brown House, the new Nazi headquarters in Munich, to meet Hitler:

'A week later I drove down to Munich, not down the Autobahn which had not yet been built, but across the Thuringian mountains and through the lovely old towns and villages of Thuringia and Franconia, watching the gables of the houses grow steeper and steeper the further south I got.

The Brown House, ...built with part of the money from Hitler's rich industrial backers, was not the aesthetic climax of my journey south, but it was certainly brown. On the pavement fronting it stood two sentries in the black breeches, brown shirts and black shirts which were the uniform of Hitler's own newly formed elite bodyguard, the SS. There was none of that Buckingham Palace reticence about these SS sentries, no standing still while the tourists tickle you. "Get down off that footpath," the sentry roared at me and motioned indignantly towards the gutter: "Pedestrians are not allowed on the footpath before the Brown House."

"But I would rather like to come in and visit some of your Herren," I answered mildly, and produced the visiting card which 'Major Ernst Röhm, Retd.' had given me in Berlin. That electrified him all right.

"Heil Hitler!" he cried, snapping to attention and giving me the outstretched arm salute. "Heil!" I answered with friendly condescension, but without raising my arm. "Where do I go in?"

As I entered the sacred portal, a highly ornate, much be-swastikad affair in heavy bronze, I asked myself where else in the world could a political party win votes by bullying the public into the gutter.'

Hitler spoke with passion and volubility. Delmer saw, as many others did, how he could change instantly from being a normal person to a raving lunatic and back again as if he had an internal switch which he turned on and off at will. Hitler told him that Germany must expand into 'the empty spaces of the east'. i.e. Poland and Russia. Hitler's aggressiveness was no surprise to Delmer:

'He had the ruthlessness which Germans of my generation had been taught in their school readers and history books to admire as a virile virtue... (the Nazis were) ...out for power, for blood and for human lives... a nest of snakes constantly writhing and biting for advantage.'

'There were many occasions on which I talked with Hitler after this conversation, both for quotation and not for quotation, but I found that every time the same thing happened. I would put a question. He would reply, and his reply would swell out into an oration.'

Delmer did indeed meet Hitler frequently. The Führer liked him as he spoke native German, understanding every nuance. He used him to gauge popular feeling in Britain – for example: "Does Britain want the royal family restored in Germany?" Delmer even flew on Hitler's private plane. He filmed one of the trips, from Tempelhoff Airport in 1932. It's on YouTube. Hitler is accompanied by his propaganda Minister, Joseph Goebbels. During the outing, they ran the gauntlet of some communist workers shouting 'down with Hitler' (though this is not on the film).

'...but Hitler's leather coated bodyguard had already leaped out of the car and were lashing out with rubber truncheons and blackjacks... what struck me was that Hitler's police escort took no notice of the strong arm men taking the law into their own hands. Apparently the police considered the use of truncheons and pistols against catcalls justified. Not for nothing had the police chief been among the welcoming dignitaries.'

7

A charming vignette of a day in the life of the Führer.

Delmer wrote of the attacks on Jewish business by Röhm's SA:

'It was the Polish and Eastern Jews who had come into Germany who were the main target of the Stormtroopers in those early days of the Third Reich. The Polish legation gave me a carefully documented list of more than 250 Polish Jews whose shops, offices or homes had been looted by the Stormtroopers, while the Jews themselves were carried off to Stormtrooper cellars where they were beaten, tortured and in some cases killed. I sent a long and detailed dispatch to my paper, but for some reason unknown to me it was never published. So I passed the information on to Professor Lindemann – later to become Lord Cherwell – for him to convey to the proper authorities in London. Lindemann had come to Germany to recruit German Jewish Scientists for Britain, an operation probably even more valuable in its contribution to Allied victory in the second war than Lord Cherwell's very important work as Churchill's scientific adviser.'

Adolf Hitler became the Chancellor of Germany in January 1933. Within weeks there was an attempt – which the Nazis blamed on their communist opponents - to burn down the German parliament. This was the Reichstag Fire. Sefton Delmer, a first-class reporter 'gatecrashed' the fire as Hitler, Goering and Goebbels arrived to see its results. He went round with them, a chilling sign of how accepted he was in Nazi high circles.

Who was behind the fire? Delmer thought it really was a communist who had started it. Curt Riess in his book *Joseph Goebbels* argues (convincingly) that it was Goebbels himself, Hitler's 'Minister for Public Enlightenment and Propaganda', who was behind it. 'The Ministry of Public Enlightenment' has a terrifying Orwellian ring to it. Whoever was behind the fire, there is no argument about the result. The Nazis arrested their communist opponents and anyone else they didn't like. In Delmer's words:

'Thousands of non-communists too were taken in – lawyers, doctors, actors, journalists – all of them men and women known for their pacifist or anti-Nazi views. The newly opened concentration camps began to fill up.'

The Nazis called a snap election. They were returned as the party with the most seats, but didn't quite have a majority. Hitler achieved power in alliance with a smaller right-wing party. By the end of the year he had banned the communists and all other parties, including his ex-allies (many of whom then joined the Nazi party). Hitler now had complete power in Germany.

As well as Hitler, Goebbels and Röhm, Delmer met Heinrich Himmler too. The revelations in his book are mind boggling. For example, when Röhm invited Delmer to dinner with Himmler, who was then the police chief in Bavaria (this was in 1933). Delmer questioned him on the new concentration camp he had opened, at Dachau. Himmler claimed that Dachau was a model institution:

'All reports of brutalities being committed there were, he claimed, an invention. "...but if that is the case, Herr Himmler, why don't you let me spend a few days there? Let me be treated as an ordinary internee and see what happens to me. If things are as you say they are this would be the ideal way to nail the lies. What do you say?"

"...it is a masterly idea," laughed Röhm. "We'll put you through the whole process from the initial beating up to the last bit where you get shot while escaping. Prost!" And roaring with convivial laughter we all downed another vodka. All except Himmler who was rather shy and did not join in the drinking beyond raising his glass.'

Himmler decided that after all it would not be a good idea for Delmer to visit Dachau, as there was cholera there. Delmer promptly wrote an article 'cholera in a concentration camp.' The Nazis were not amused.

Lord Beaverbrook, Sefton Delmer's boss, told him that he, Delmer, was the best reporter the *Daily Express* had ever had. He wanted him to stay in Germany, but Delmer felt it was time to move on:

'I had been on good terms with the Nazis while they were in opposition, being friends with them when they were in power and acting the way they did was another matter … from the summer of 1933 I had not only the Germans suspecting me of being a British agent, but the British suspecting me of being an agent of the Germans …officers of MI5 seized opportunities to interview me….'

Ernst Röhm was dead by now, shot, ironically, by the commandant of Dachau – the aforementioned Nazi concentration camp - on Hitler's orders. That was after 'The night of the long knives' when Hitler suppressed the Brown Shirts (SA) and had its leaders shot. The nest of snakes had devoured one of its own. It was soon to devour many, many, more.

Delmer served briefly in Paris, where he gave reign to his epicurean tastes;

'I love being host to my friends ..there is no better way of getting someone to spill the beans than over a drink in your house or a meal at your table. I therefore kept a good cook and a pleasant dining room in my Paris apartment, but I also installed a bar. I was only 32 at the time, but I had begun to put on so much weight ...that my friends had begun to call me 'Uncle Tom.'"

From there, Sefton Delmer went to Spain, covering the Spanish Civil War. I will bring him back into the tale in a little while.

Frederick Winterbotham

At about the same time that Sefton Delmer left Germany (in 1934), a British spy arrived there. His name was Frederick Winterbotham and he worked for the SIS (Secret Intelligence Service). His role was not to titillate the Great British public as they sliced the tops off their breakfast' eggs. He was in Germany to find out what Britain needed to know to prepare for war. His boss, Quex Sinclair, was already sure that war was coming. A year earlier, when Hitler took complete power of Germany, he had said that: "Unless a miracle intervenes" there would be a war between Germany and Britain in a very few years.

Frederick Winterbotham will return again and again to these pages. As I shall describe, he got to know many of the top Nazis, meeting Hitler on a number of occasions. It was partly – and perhaps largely - due to his information about Germany and particularly the Luftwaffe, that British air re-armament began. He introduced vastly improved spy planes. He was one of the first staff at Bletchley Park, where he organised the units which distributed intelligence to the generals in the field. It was due to his book of 1974, *The Ultra Secret,* that the story of Bletchley Park, secret for 30 years, became public. This led to the rewriting of the history of the Second World War.

Fred Winterbotham joined the British army in 1914, at the start of the First World War. He was 17. He later transferred from the cavalry into the army's air force, the Royal Flying Corps (RFC). It was while flying as an escort to a 'somewhat suicidal' photo reconnaissance flight that he was shot down in 1917, at Passchendaele, in Flanders, on the Western Front.

The attack was suicidal because the RFC used the same rudimentary tactics as much of the rest of the British army – bald-headed courage and attack at any cost. When Winterbotham spoke to his captors, he quickly realised that 'they had obviously given much more thought to air strategy than we had.' The German pilot who had shot him down presented him with the bullet-ridden cushion he had been sitting on and said jovially "just one more inch and you would have been a soprano." Winterbotham did not forget this.

It was as the Adjutant in his prisoner of war camp that Fred Winterbotham learned German. His thoughts on the character of his German captors – he said there were two distinct types, the brutal and the kindly – are most interesting.

The British army and naval air forces (the RFC and RNAS) were joined to become the Royal Air Force (RAF) on April Fool's Day 1918. This was the world's first independent air force. Flying had come of age.

On returning to England, Winterbotham continued his interrupted education and took a law degree at Oxford. In 1929 he was head-hunted by the RAF who had decided to set up an

Air Section within the SIS. Fred and his secretary were the founder members. Winterbotham, who was highly intelligent and who spoke 'reasonable German and good French', was a natural for the task. He was, incidentally, SIS's first ever graduate. He was given the rank of Wing Commander. Here are his first impressions of his new boss, Admiral Sinclair ("Quex to his friends, 'C' to the establishment, to me the chief"):

'A short, stocky man with the welcoming smile of a benign uncle and very alert dark eyes.' From him, he received the advice: "If you can listen to someone important telling somebody else equally important about some event of importance and, knowing the story to be quite inaccurate, you can keep your mouth shut, you may in due course make a good intelligence officer."

At that time, Russia was seen as Britain's chief enemy. However, reports were arriving of a resurgence in militarism in Germany – and that German air force (Luftwaffe) pilots were being secretly trained in Russia.

The SIS's chief agent in Germany was Baron Wilhelm von der Ropp. Bill de Ropp (as Winterbotham knew him) was a German aristocrat who had studied in England and taken British nationality. De Ropp was being paid by both sides. He was acting in Britain for Alfred Rosenberg, the chief Nazi ideologue and political philosopher, as an influencer. The Nazis were seeking an accommodation with Britain and France so that Germany could invade the east without fighting in the west. De Ropp advised Winterbotham that, if he wanted to know what was happening in Germany, it would be a good idea to get to know Rosenberg.

In 1932 Winterbotham wrote to Alfred Rosenberg on Royal Air Force club notepaper (he had an office in the Air Ministry), inviting him to London. Winterbotham had let it be known that part of his job was writing reports for the Foreign Office. This made him a very attractive person for the Nazis to talk to, for the British Foreign Office would not, at that time, speak directly to the Nazis whom they regarded – rightly enough – as a set of thugs.

Rosenberg was delighted to accept the invitation and came to London. Winterbotham introduced him to the editor of The Times, took him to his old public school (Charterhouse) introduced him to a couple of MPs and generally treated him as an important visiting dignitary. Rosenberg, for his part, promised to introduce Winterbotham to his own boss, Adolf Hitler.

Bill de Ropp gave Fred Winterbotham rule number one for survival in Nazi Germany. Give the Nazi salute when others are doing so. You will be beaten up if you don't. Many foreign visitors learned that painful lesson. To Germans the cost was often higher. Their lives.

Fred Winterbotham went to Germany, as I've said, in 1934:

'In 1934 the 'Heil Hitler' was one of the most extraordinary manifestations I have ever seen. It was, of course, based on the old Roman greeting, but out on the streets of Berlin to see the whole population greeting each other with this unlikely gesture made them look rather like a chorus in a Hollywood musical, and from the looks on their faces many of the more elderly citizens treated it as such.'

What Winterbotham was seeing was far from comical. It was the outward manifestation of the reprogramming of a people. Hitler was being marketed as a new god. The masters of the program were Rosenberg and, increasingly, Joseph Goebbels. Goebbels' Propaganda Ministry would eventually fill a 500 room complex. From it, content was dictated to all radio stations and newspapers on a daily basis. Consequently all German newspapers looked alike.

The more elderly citizens might have been amused; but to the young what they heard and read was gospel. It was illegal to listen to foreign radio – those caught doing so were imprisoned, those convicted of spreading negative foreign news that they heard were liable to be killed. The Germans were told that they and their fellow Nordic peoples, the blue-eyed (and preferably blonde) Aryans, were the Master Race – the chosen ones. Their Fuhrer (leader), Adolf Hitler was all-powerful. Shrines were erected to him in many houses, many sons were named after him. 'Heil Hitler' was the common greeting. The Hitler salute was compulsory. Slogans, Nazi banners and pictures of Hitler were everywhere.

Most foreign peoples – starting with the Jews – were sub-humans worthy only of slavery or death.

One reason why Winterbotham thought Berlin was 'like a Hollywood musical' was the Nazi use of theatrical techniques: striking uniforms and flags and pageantry on a grand scale; climaxing at the annual Nuremberg Rally. The 1934 rally was filmed by the Nazi film maker, Leni Riefenstahl under the title 'Triumph of the will.' It can be seen on YouTube. It is an ominous, powerful and seductive film. Hitler was flanked by two bishops, (one of whom was wearing an iron cross). Gigantic red, white and black swastika flags, torchlight, singing, chanting goose-stepping soldier-ants, simple slogans endlessly repeated, Hitler working himself into a frenzy. The Nazi Party used it for 'political education', in cinemas and schools. Pupils' attendance was mandatory.

The 1941 parody to the tune of the Lambeth Walk (also on YouTube) is priceless.

Geoffrey Cox, a fellow reporter of Sefton Delmer at the *Daily Express*, was at the rally. He thought Hitler 'dangerous and evil'. He was beaten up for not giving the Nazi salute. The man who patched him up in the nearby chemist assured him that: "you will understand such actions when Mosley (leader of the British fascist party) wins power in Britain."

Fred Winterbotham took to carrying a lot of small change as 'brown-shirted males' constantly shook collection boxes under his nose. He was summoned to the holy-of-holies, Hitler's Reich Chancellery to meet the Fuhrer in 1934. Winterbotham was treated as a VIP, with a Mercedes motorcade and outriders clearing all before him. He, too, was treated to the Nazi genius at theatre:

'Here in the great hall with its large black and white marble squares were neatly arranged a score of tall figures in faultless black uniforms, their white-gloved hands resting on either side of their belts. Each was standing stiffly to attention on his allotted white marble square …as a black pawn stepped smartly forward to inspect the party I fully expected the black queen to come skipping down the stairway. The black pawns also extended up the stairs, one on either side every three steps.'

The first thing that impressed Winterbotham about Hitler was his protruding eyes. Hitler told him that:

'There should be only three major powers in the world, the British Empire, the Americans and the German Empire of the future...all we ask is that Britain should not interfere with German expansion.'

He also said that the Luftwaffe, the German air force, was to be substantially increased. At this first meeting, Winterbotham remarked to the Fuhrer that he didn't seem to like the communists. Hitler's eyes bulged out, his face flushed and he began to yell and rant against them. Noticing that Winterbotham was not impressed, he became normal again. This 'switch' of Hitler's had been remarked on by Sefton Delmer and many others.

It may seem incredible that Hitler should reveal his thoughts so clearly to a foreigner. As I've said, Hitler wanted a neutral Britain and the interview with Winterbotham was a means of passing that message to the Air Ministry and the Foreign Office. For his part, Winterbotham now had it 'from the horse's mouth' that the Luftwaffe was to be increased. He wrote up a report on Air Ministry notepaper and circulated it to the Foreign Office and Rosenberg. The latter wrote of the meeting with Hitler and the report in his diary:

'The conversation took a satisfactory course and Winterbotham made a brilliant report in London.'

The report that Winterbotham showed to Rosenberg dealt with aircraft numbers rather than Nazi intentions. He did not show him the other report that he wrote – for Quex Sinclair - which outlined his profound and growing unease at what was happening in Nazi Germany.

Perhaps sensing a convert, Rosenberg explained to Winterbotham his own mystic beliefs; the spiritual side of the Nazi ideology: "If the great Nordic races are to survive, there will be no place for weaklings or fools." He took him to see the great cultural centre 'rather on the lines of an enlarged Vatican city' he was building in Southern Germany, where the new Nordic religion was to have its temples. This would replace Christianity, the weak Jewish religion that Rosenberg hated. This was no religion of love. A century earlier, the German (Jewish) philosopher, Heinrich Heine had made a remarkable prediction:

'Should that subduing talisman, the cross, be shattered, the frenzied madness of the ancient warriors, that insane Berserk rage of which Nordic bards have spoken and sung so often, will once more burst into flame. ... The old stone gods will then rise from long ruins and rub the dust of a thousand years from their eyes, and Thor will leap to life with his giant hammer and smash the Gothic cathedrals. Thought precedes action as lightning precedes thunder. German thunder ... comes rolling somewhat slowly, but .. its crash ... will be unlike anything before in the history of the world. ... At that uproar the eagles of the air will drop dead, and lions in farthest Africa will draw in their tails and slink away. ... A play will be performed in Germany which will make the French Revolution look like an innocent idyll.'

The moment had come. Thor was rising.

The Nazis meant to erase or enslave the lesser peoples. They started by smashing Jewish shops and synagogues. In 1933 – when Hitler came to power - Jews had been removed from their positions in government, the army, and at universities and newspapers; 1935's Nuremberg Laws stripped them of citizenship and eventually their right to own businesses and properties.

The Nazis brought work. Many Germans had been unemployed for years. Now came vast programs of building - new roads, airports, armament production. The Nazis gave theatre: striking uniforms, torch-lit processions, simple slogans 'Germany awake', 'One Reich, one Fuhrer'. The Nazis bought a credo - a vision for a blonde, blue-eyed, Aryan future for those of pure blood 'the future belongs to us'. Chillingly, it was working. Winterbotham says: 'It is just no good suggesting that National Socialism was thrust upon the German people: the great majority swallowed it hook, line and sinker.' Hitler,

Rosenberg and Goebbels were telling them that they were the Master Race – and by and large they agreed.

With Hitler's blessing and Rosenberg's help, and accompanied by his friend Bill de Ropp for translation when needed (Winterbotham's German, which had been fair, was becoming good, but he needed verification), Winterbotham met many of the German leaders. General Kesselring told him of German plans to invade Russia:

'...the conversation was startling... in the coming invasion of Russia, speed and surprise were to be the elements of victory... they would drive vast tank spearheads into Russia at a distance of around 200 miles a day... it was the first time I had ever heard the word 'blitzkrieg.'

Winterbotham duly wrote up what he heard for Quex, who passed the reports on to central government. The reports were not well received there, particularly by Sir Samuel Hoare, soon to be the Foreign Secretary...

'This ostrich attitude of a senior Cabinet minister was the first indication I had of the way in which the British Government were apparently determined to ignore the whole problem of German rearmament: a policy which was to put us in mortal danger when we found ourselves unprepared for a second world war.'

Indeed Winterbotham was ordered by his British political masters to stay out of Germany.

Winterbotham invited a group of German pilots over to Britain. He was, of course, playing a dangerous game. The German pilots were keen to learn all about the Royal Air Force. They learned nothing about radar or the Spitfire. If they had, the Battle of Britain could have been lost before it began. The Luftwaffe boys liked the RAF (officers) Club in Piccadilly so much that they built one of their own. It was in this Luftwaffe Club that Winterbotham – now allowed back into the Reich – picked up interesting information – such as, for example, that the great 'G' force on the Stuka dive bomber could pull their wings off or cause the pilot to black out.

Winterbotham was fortunate to receive, via the British embassy, information that was to make his reports even more

17

relevant. It was marked GEHEIM (secret) and it was a page from a Luftwaffe manual. It gave a list of all Luftwaffe flying schools. This was soon followed by another page listing the complete establishment of a fighter squadron. With it came the request that the information should not be shared with the French intelligence service. Although Winterbotham had a close working relationship, and friendship, with Georges Ronin, his opposite number in the *Deuxième Bureau* – the French secret service – he understood why the mysterious German traitor should be worried. Ronin was 'not sure' about the General Staff of his own army. That had come as no surprise to Winterbotham. Rosenberg had told him that the Nazis had a very extensive spy network in France.

The pages, around 30 in all, kept on coming through 1936, 1937 and 1938. The demand for payment – a big one – came after the fifth or sixth page. Quex Sinclair paid. The information was extremely useful in persuading London that the phenomenal growth in the Luftwaffe was real.

As I've said, information was coming to Winterbotham not only about the Luftwaffe, but about all of their armed forces. That meant a lot of work. Some of the pressure was taken off him by Desmond Morton. Morton became head of the Industrial Intelligence Centre in 1931, and was responsible for providing intelligence on the plans and capabilities for manufacturing munitions in other countries. Morton was a protégé and friend of Winston Churchill. Indeed he had been appointed to his post in Military Intelligence by that remarkable man back in 1924, when Churchill had been Chancellor of the Exchequer. Morton lived less than a mile from Churchill, in Chartwell, Kent and was often a guest there for Sunday lunch. He was helping his friend in writing his history of the First World War. He also passed information to Churchill which helped his fight against the rise of fascism. Churchill used the information to ask difficult questions in parliament.

Politically, things were moving. Quex briefed the newly elected Prime Minister, Stanley Baldwin. Baldwin, who had been elected on a promise to strengthen national defences, ordered an investigation into the scale of German rearmament. In June 1935, Winterbotham and Morton were summoned to appear before a Cabinet committee chaired by the newly appointed Secretary of State for Air, Phillip Cunliffe-Lister (later Lord Swinton):

> 'Morton rose to his feet and gave chapter and verse on the vast extensions being built at all the German aircraft factories. He quoted the great areas of land now turned into factory floor space, the tools supplied.'

Lord Swinton was receptive. As a result of the meeting, funds were voted for the building of Shadow Factories and fighter aircraft production. It has been said that Britain was unready for war in 1939. In fact, a good deal of preparation had been done by then.

Shadow factory roof line

Shadow Factories share a common design. Some are still round today and can be recognised by their distinctive roof line. They were built and tooled up for armament production – primarily aircraft mainframes and engines - and lay idle until they were needed.

Lord Swinton is one of the unsung heroes of World War Two. As a result of his championing of RAF expansion, British governments progressively released more and more money to match German expansion. In all, there were to be six upwardly revised Air Force Budgets sparked off by this process before war started.

While Winterbotham and Morton were the main sources of information, the SIS had others. For instance, in 1937 the principal designer of the Bristol aero-engine, Roy Fedden, was invited for a tour of the Messerschmitt factory. Winterbotham spoke to him afterwards:

> 'He told me that he'd never been so frightened in his life both by the rate of production and by the performance of the ME109 and the twin-engined ME110.'

Then there was František Moravec, the head of Czech Intelligence. We will meet him in a later chapter.

The SIS passed on information to other branches. The development of radar was inextricably linked with the attempt to find an antidote to German aerial rearmament.

As time went past, German sources became more reluctant to speak to Winterbotham. When he visited Germany in 1938, he noted that the Propaganda Ministry had lost interest in him. They had turned their sights on America. Goebbels had a great deal of success with the press on both sides of the Atlantic. Hitler was voted *Time* Magazine's 'Man of the year' in 1938. Now, it should be noted that *Time* chose him (it was always a man back then) as the man who had had 'the greatest impact on news for good or evil' – but it shows how Hitler dominated world events.

Winterbotham's reception from Rosenberg was rather chilly, a repeat of the usual lecture about Britain staying out of Germany's way which summed up:

'…the policies that the Nazis had been trying to put across to the British government with a mixture of bluff, persuasion and threats for the last four years. It was not surprising that the Nazis had been surprised by the lack of reaction in Britain; there had been none.'

Fred Winterbotham believed that the Italians knew that he was a spy; and Rosenberg seemed to confirm this by stressing heavily that the German security services now had close co-operation with Italian intelligence. In these circumstance, he told Winterbotham, it would be better if he left Germany. Winterbotham did so in the summer of 1938.

Quex Sinclair was operating on a shoestring. His staff had no pension but paid no income tax (but that is another story). As late as 1935 his total budget amounted, in his words 'only to the annual cost of keeping a destroyer in home waters'. To put that into perspective, the Royal Navy started World War Two with 164 destroyers – as well as hundreds of other vessels.

Sinclair knew - and stressed again and again – that war was approaching. The nearer it came, the less he was hearing from Germany. More and more agents were 'disappearing' or shutting up. After Winterbotham left, they were more or less reliant on Bill De Ropp. In 1938 the head of the SIS's Political Section estimated that fully 70% of SIS's information on Germany was coming from him alone. (De Ropp wisely spent the war in Switzerland – and survived.)

In December 1938, Sinclair was asked to prepare a dossier on Hitler for the Prime Minister and Foreign Secretary. Quex reported that Hitler possessed:

'Fanaticism, mysticism, ruthlessness, cunning, vanity, moods of exaltation and depression, fits of bitter and self-righteous resentment; and what can only be termed a streak of madness; but with it all there is a great tenacity of purpose, which has often been combined with extraordinary clarity of vision.'

The dossier was received poorly by Sir George Mounsey, the Foreign Office Assistant Under-Secretary—who believed that it did not gel with Britain's policy of appeasement.

Thor had shaken off the dust and had risen. For those who cared to look, there was no missing him now. The appeasers – who were in the majority - believed the best policy was to ignore him and hope he might go away; or pick on someone else.

A few politicians thought differently; Lord Swinton for one. Winston Churchill was another. He wasn't looking the other way, he was raising the alarm with ever greater vigour. His answer to Thor was to fight him and his weapon was, for the moment, the spoken word.

The road to catastrophe

What was it that concerned Quex and Churchill? A series of events which started with Hitler's accession to power in 1933 and ended in the most bloody war in history six years later.

In 1935, Germany took back control of the Saar, her main industrial area, which had been placed under Allied administration after the First World War. In 1938, the German army marched into Austria and integrated it into Germany. In the same year came the Munich Agreement, when France and Britain allowed Germany to take over part of Czechoslovakia.

This she did in October 1938. In March of 1939 she took over the rest of the country.

In August 1939 Hitler signed a peace treaty with Russia's leader, Joseph Stalin. Between them they agreed to carve up the states that separated them. Russia would have the Baltic states Estonia, Latvia and Lithuania. They would divide Poland.

Poland, however, was protected by treaty by both Britain and France.

Two mass murderers on the make.
A cartoon by David Low in the
London Evening Standard said it all.

On the 22nd of August 1939, the day before the pact was signed, Hitler was at his headquarters at Obersalzburg. There he announced to his generals that the destruction of Poland would begin within days. His speech was recorded by his chief of intelligence, Admiral Canaris (Quex's opposite number):

"In a few weeks I shall stretch out my hand to Stalin at the common Russian-German frontier and with him undertake to rule the world ...after Stalin's death – he is a very sick man – we will break the Soviet Union. Then will begin the dawn of the German rule of the Earth."

Hitler dismissed the British and French Prime Ministers as 'poor worms' who were too cowardly to fight him.

August 1939 found Sefton Delmer, always at the forefront of danger, in Poland as the Russian and German pact was announced on the radio. An exultant German who had just heard the broadcast gave him the news:

"Now all is well. The Fuhrer has won. The British and French will never dare fight us now that the Russians are on our side. The Poles will have to give way! There will be no war."

Hitler launched his legions into Poland on the 1st of September 1939. Two days later Britain and France declared war on Germany. Two weeks later, with the agreement of Hitler, Stalin invaded Poland from the east; the two dictators sharing that unfortunate country between them.

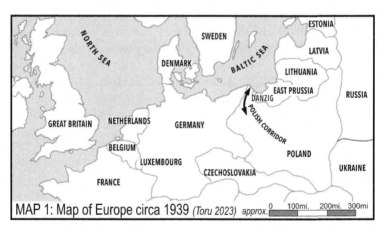

MAP 1: Map of Europe circa 1939 *(Toru 2023)* approx.

The Americans called the first months of the conflict 'the Phoney War' as the Allies made no attempt to attack Germany. The Nazis were quite happy with that as they were busy digesting Poland. When they had done so, in April 1940, they invaded Denmark and Norway. This prompted Britain and France to send troops to Norway. The Allies were defeated there.

Unsurprisingly, all Allied troops in France (about a tenth of them were British) came under overall French command. No attempt was made to attack Germany from France.

France was a country which was deeply divided between the far right and the far left. That wasn't just a French phenomenon, of course. Germany, Spain and Italy all had fascist dictators. Russia had a communist dictator. There was also a large fascist party – Oswald Mosley's - in Britain.

Appeasement and pacifism were the norm in both France and Britain. Both countries had suffered a bloodbath in the First World War and those who spoke against appeasement were generally branded as war-mongers. The majority of the British public only changed their minds with the invasion of Poland. At that point it became crystal clear that Churchill, the main opponent of appeasement in Parliament, had been right all along. Hitler's series of 'final demands' would only cease when he had what he wanted, which was world power.

The war was not a phoney one for Hitler's propaganda genius Joseph Goebbels. He put in a lot of work to soften up the next target, France. One of his main targets were the troops in the Maginot Line – the formidable in-depth string of forts and underground tunnels that reached from the Swiss mountains to the border of Luxembourg. This was France's fixed defence against Germany, constructed to avoid a repeat of the carnage of the trenches in the first war.

Nazi radio broadcasts were tailored for the Line and pornographic leaflets were distributed there. The message to the French troops was that this was not their war, but Britain's. That Britain was providing hardly any troops - and that those troops were overpaid and sleeping with the wives and daughters of the French soldiers. The 'Big Lie' was the phrase that Adolf used for this process. As far back as 1924 he had written:

'If you wish the sympathy of the masses, you must tell them the crudest and most stupid things. Tell a lie long enough and loud enough and the people will believe it.'

The French communists, allied with Hitler (until it was their turn to be attacked), also preached against resistance to

1: Thor triumphant (1929 - June 1940)

MAP 2: The Maginot Line *(Toru 2023)*

Germany. They, too, targeted the French army. Their leaflets were often printed in Germany.

In May 1940, the German armies invaded neutral Holland, Belgium and Luxembourg. To break into France, they sent troops and tanks through the forested Ardennes, drove round the end of the 'impregnable' Maginot Line, and crushed or bypassed at whim the French defences. The defences were weak there, as the French high command had believed the Ardennes impassable to armour. That the French military leaders could base the fate of their country on such a foolish belief was symptomatic of just how rotten they were.

One must not forget their attackers, of course. The German Panzer generals Guderian and Rommel were far superior to their French and British counterparts. Their weapons were better too.

And there was Goebbels. Sefton Delmer was, as ever, on the scene. His descriptions of French morale make clear the other cause of the rapid collapse of the French armies:

'Again and again I had seen the men (in the Maginot Line) ignore the orders of their officers, and the officers ignore that they had been ignored... brilliantly clever

German 'Peace' propaganda… had done its bit to undermine the morale of the French army.'

Hitler himself had said:

'Our real wars will be waged before the military operations… through propaganda before the armies go into action.'

Goebbels was as effective a general in the conquest of France as Heinz Guderian or Erwin Rommel.

Allied troops fell back on Dunkirk, from which around 338,000 of them were evacuated by sea to England, around 110,000 of them French.

Contrary to what is now the generally accepted belief, Dunkirk was far from being the end of British fighting on the continent. One hundred thousand British troops still remained in France. Within days, sixty thousand more British and Canadian troops were shipped over to join them. A large number of the evacuated French troops also went back. As these troops made their way northwards, towards the advancing German armies, their advance was severely hampered by the fact that a large proportion of the civilian population of northern France and Belgium were fleeing south.

Panic

Panic gripped the people, old, young, men and women They were driven by history; not the dry history of the schoolroom – but the family memory of bloody and recurring blows from the east that had torn apart their lands and families again and again with the unpredictability of an erupting volcano. They knew what to expect from the waking of Thor – this was the third German invasion in seventy years. It is worth briefly recalling the bloody past that fuelled their pell-mell flight…

In 1870 a confederation of German states, led by Prussia, invaded France and annexed part of that country. This was the Franco-Prussian war. The German states (except Austria) then unified to become Germany.

In 1914, Germany again invaded France and (neutral) Belgium. At that time, the French held the Germans back from Paris. Then the British arrived and the war settled down into trench warfare across northern France and Belgium. The French lost 1.5 million dead, the British about a million. The landscape was ravaged and many towns and villages were destroyed.

Now, in 1940, hardly more than twenty years after the last time, while the land was still a moonscape of old trenches and the main harvest from many field was explosives from the earlier fighting, they were here again. Run! Run south, or west, but run from the invaders! Small towns, villages, hamlets, farms and manors were totally deserted. Dogs, cats and pigs wandered the villages looking for their owners and for food. Unmilked cows died in agony.

Ten days after the Dunkirk evacuation had finished, German troops entered Paris. A good part of the city's population had already joined the endless streams of refugees.

The Parisians had their own memories. Seventy years earlier, in the war of 1870, the Germans had lain siege to the city for twenty weeks, leading to bitter fighting between the citizens within the walls. And starvation. Their grandparents had had to eat horses, dogs, cats, rats, even the zoo elephants. The Parisians of 1940 didn't want a repeat of that. Their unease was stoked up – quite literally – by their own government. As the German armies approached Paris, the French Foreign Office began to make great piles of their records, burning them in the open air. The smoke was seen for miles – many thought the Germans had already arrived. When the people learned what was causing the smoke, unease turned to panic. Two million Parisians (three quarters of the population) fled the city, clogging all roads to the south and the west. Among them were virtually all of the British who lived in Paris – business men and women, civilians, diplomats, journalists.

It was Winston Churchill who had ordered British reinforcements into France after Dunkirk. He had come to power on the day of the German assault on France, when, after enraged scenes in a finally-awakened Parliament, Neville Chamberlain resigned and Churchill had become Prime Minister. The reinforcement was unsuccessful. The German armour was unstoppable and the British were forced to re-embark from any port they could along the Atlantic seaboard, mostly Cherbourg, Brest and Bordeaux. French troops died as

27

rear guards to protect some of the evacuations. Largely forgotten today, it was a massive naval operation. More than 230,000 were evacuated. This happened in mid-June 1940, two weeks after the Dunkirk evacuations (Operation Dynamo), had ended.

The journalists of the *Daily Express* were among those who fled Paris. Sefton Delmer was in one car, with his wife and friends. Two other *Express* journalists who would distinguish themselves in print and in battle, George Millar and Geoffrey Cox, were in another. Delmer recalls:

'We had not got more than fifteen miles out of Paris before we were bogged down in the endless immovable stream of refugees that was clogging the roads for scores of miles. Horse-drawn farm carts, private cars with mattresses on the roof, delivery vans, motorcycles, all were tangled up in a frightened… stampede, which denied these vital roads to the French armies. Slowly we inched forward and whenever there was a chance to overtake, I grabbed it.'

(Like most of us when stuck in traffic, Delmer, never thought that he himself was part of the problem.)

Cox wrote of the journey:

'Broken down cars had been tipped into ditches to clear the road. Every food shop was stripped bare of produce. In farmhouse courtyards exhausted children slept under hay carts, whilst haggard women queued to get water from farm pumps. A nation disintegrating into a mass of squabbling, exhausted, desperate individuals at the one time when it needed cohesion in the face of the enemy.'

Delmer's party made their way to Bordeaux where they had been told there would be British ships ready to take them to England.

Bordeaux – the breaking of the alliance

The French Prime Minister and Cabinet were already in Bordeaux. They too had fled from Paris. They too were ready to put to sea to escape from France.

Since the hammer-blow of the Nazi offensive, France and Britain had been in constant talks about how to stop the German army. Churchill's liaison officer with the French was the Conservative Member of Parliament for Carlisle, Major-General Sir Edward Spears. Spears was one of 'Churchill's clique' who supported Winston over his opposition to the British and French surrender of Czechoslovakia to Germany at Munich. He was so strongly pro-French that he was referred to within the House of Commons as 'the member for Paris'. He and Churchill had first met in the First World War, in the trenches. Spears, bi-lingual in English and French, had been a liaison officer then, too. The friendship could easily have been a short one as Churchill had almost shot him – or possibly himself. It had happened when Spears was taking Winston through the trenches and the latter's pistol – hanging from a lanyard - had gone off by accident, randomly spraying bullets and causing Churchill to dance a jig. The 'automatic revolver' was a Churchillian invention that did not pass field trials.

During the First World War, Spears had been a great admirer of the French leader Clemenceau and of the French army. The second war gave him different views. His book *Assignment to Catastrophe* is illuminating on the political intrigues, appeasement, defeatism and incompetence in the French high command and government that led to the fall of France. Spears was with Churchill right from the start of the second war. When they toured the Maginot Line together, Churchill had voiced the fear that the line might be bypassed by an armoured attack through the Ardennes......

Sir Edward Spears puts the blame for the military downfall of France largely on the shoulders of the supreme French army commanders, Maurice Gamelin and, after he was sacked, his successor Maxime Weygand. He is no more charitable about French politicians, hoping, if there should be a French defeat that:

'The invasion would clean the land of the scum that had ruined it.' And, of Bordeaux he said: 'all the sewers of France had burst and their nauseating mess was seeping into the beautiful city.'

His account of his time with the French Cabinet as it fled south from Paris reads at times like a French farce. He respected

Paul Reynaud, the Prime Minister, but had little time for his mistress, a noted appeaser. She routinely put her head around the door of Cabinet and military meetings to see what was going on. When she was found to have hidden a secret telegram in her bed, Reynaud threw two glasses of water over her.

Churchill was omni-present. He made five visits to France in the six weeks between the invasion and the French surrender. Realising that defeat was inevitable, he wanted the French to continue the struggle from their colonies (the French Empire was second in size only to Britain's). He spoke to the French Cabinet with the fire and conviction that only he, on the Allied side, was capable of, promising them that: "If we win the war we will one day restore (France) to her power and dignity." He even offered immediate union between the two countries, each as equal citizens of the other. Paul Reynaud agreed with Churchill. He wanted to sail with his government to North Africa (probably via England) and continue the fight from there, but he could not persuade his Cabinet.

At the port of Bordeaux, the last point of the French Cabinet's flight, Spears was approached by Eve Curie, a senior official in the French administration. She warned him that he was wasting his time. The Cabinet would out-vote Reynaud who would then resign and his successor would surrender. This was in contravention of the signed accord between Britain and France that neither would surrender separately without the agreement of the other. Eve Curie was in tears: "We must not dishonour France and we cannot betray England."

It happened exactly as Eve Curie predicted. Reynaud was voted down and resigned. His successor, Philippe Pétain, surrendered, saying that, as Britain was dying, joining with her would be like 'fusion with a corpse'.

Not one of the leading French politicians could be persuaded to continue the fight from England. Spears managed to pluck just two people from the wreckage. One was the Under-Secretary of War, an obscure Colonel called Charles de Gaulle, who had led a briefly successful attack against German armour and believed that a fight was possible. De Gaulle, fearing he would be arrested for his views, asked Spears whether he could arrange his escape to England. Spears radioed Churchill in

London, who promised a plane for the next day. De Gaulle hid overnight, the aircraft arrived and Spears – literally – hauled him aboard. For his action in continuing the fight against the Nazis, de Gaulle would be dispossessed of his property and sentenced to death by France's new collaborationist government. Spears said that he was: 'All that was left of the spirit of France.'

Not quite. The other key member of the French administration who left Bordeaux to carry on the fight was Eve Curie, the daughter of Madame Curie, the double Nobel prize winner. For this, Pétain's new French government stripped her of her French citizenship and confiscated her property. (She later took American citizenship.) Eve escaped on a British ship, the SS *Madura*. It was in the bay, finishing loading, as Spears and de Gaulle flew out of Bordeaux. Also aboard was Sefton Delmer and his party.

In order to save de Gaulle, Sir Edward Spears had had to leave his wife – Mary Borden – behind. Mary is one of the forgotten heroines of the wars. An American heiress and suffragette, she had paid for, staffed, managed and worked in field hospitals for the French army during World War One. That's where she had met Sir Edward. She said of that time:

'I did not count the number who died as I knelt beside their stretchers. Great strong broken men who apologised in whispers for the trouble they gave in dying, slender boys whom I held in my arms while they cried for their mothers.'

Mary provided a mobile field ambulance to France in the second war, too. In June 1940, she, like her husband, was retreating across France. The last time Spears had managed to speak with her, he had told her to head for Bordeaux. When he flew out with de Gaulle, her unit of cars, ambulances and nurses was stuck in traffic and still far from the port.

Aboard the *Madura*

The evacuation of British subjects was being supervised by a friend of Sefton Delmer called Ian Fleming. Fleming was working for the Naval Intelligence Division (which, you may remember, Quex had headed up years before). Now, at

Bordeaux, Fleming was in the uniform of a Lieutenant of the Royal Navy. The last time Delmer had met him he had been in 'civvies'. That had been a year ago, in Russia, where Delmer had gone to report on Russian and British trade negotiations. Fleming, with whom he'd travelled, was supposedly reporting for *The Times*:

'Even our very first meeting had a James Bondish touch. We met in a compartment of the Warsaw-Moscow express …by the time that we arrived we were firm friends, so much so that we decided to share a suite at the National, the antique Intourist hotel just opposite the red-brick Kremlin citadel.'

Delmer had hoped to meet up with a reporter from the Russian newspaper, *Pravda*, whom he had known in Spain. He was to be disappointed as the journalist had been 'liquidated' on Stalin's orders.

Delmer wasn't unduly targeted by Russian security, but Fleming was. The climax came when they were leaving the Soviet Union:

'While the officials hardly glanced at my bags they went through Ian's with scrupulous thoroughness, even searching his cases for false bottoms. The climax came when they discovered a carton of contraceptives made of Soviet artificial latex which Ian – the future creator of James Bond …was carrying back to London to have chemically analysed so as to reveal the Soviet formula. Without a grin, without so much as a smirk, the Soviet customs men and NKVD officers held each sample to the light and examined it. Ian blushed a furious beetroot. "You should have swallowed them," I whispered.'

The ship that Fleming put Delmer and his party on was, as I've mentioned, the SS *Madura,* a P & O liner. The *Madura* had been on her way home from East Africa with 120 'mostly empire builders' when it was diverted to Bordeaux on Fleming's orders. In the next 24 hours 1,623 more were crammed aboard; British residents of France, the embassy staff from Paris, 'French men and women who either feared the Nazis or, (like

Eve Curie) were to continue the resistance.' Baron Rothschild was also aboard.

As they had some weeks earlier, at Dunkirk, the dive bombers and fighters of the Luftwaffe were swarming over the evacuation ports. Stukas screamed down on the *Madura* but missed their prey. At the same time, to their north, a bomb went down one of the funnels of the liner RMS *Lancastria*. She went down very quickly taking 4,000 British soldiers to their deaths. A lesson, were one needed, of what was likely to happen to ships which did not have effective aerial defence. This disaster was the largest loss of military life in any British engagement in World War two. The government did its best to hush-up the catastrophe.

Laden until it could take no more, the SS *Madura* slipped its mooring and sailed for England. The screaming Stuka dive bombers came for her again. Again they missed. Looking over the stern as they steamed out of the Gironde, Sefton Delmer and Geoffrey Cox reflected on the journey they had taken so far. While the total and sudden collapse of the great French armies (over 100 divisions) and the smaller British Expeditionary Force (10 divisions) had surprised them, the pattern of Nazi aggression did not. They had been reporting about it in ever more strident voices for years.

The empire builders on the ship did not always welcome the newcomers. "Disgusting rabble," said one matron from Mombasa as she stumbled over Sefton Delmer's feet. After being routed out into the Atlantic to avoid German mines, the ship arrived at Falmouth. The harbour was crammed with ships which had escaped from France. Cox says:

'It was a superb day of high summer, and on the green headland above the harbour they were stacking hay, loading it by pitchfork on to big wagons …a grey church tower rose above thick green trees. That afternoon England looked very much worth fighting for. Now that we were on our own, the war seemed not only a struggle against an evil creed but also a matter of straight-forward patriotism.'

Also on the *Madura* were an English family of three, the Walls, who had fled from France. The daughter, Daphne, was eight years old. Her father worked for an American company in Paris. Daphne remembered:

'No gang-plank, only a rope-ladder. As I got ready to climb down, my precious doll was snatched from me without warning and hurled down the side of the ship where a sailor caught her. I was relieved and impressed. So this was England! Even the dolls were looked after. And in fact as we were processed through formalities in a big hall there was an extraordinary sense of purpose and calm, as if everybody knew what to expect and was braced for the ordeal ahead. Ladies in WVS uniform gave us food, drinks and sympathy. The next thing I knew, we were on a train to London.'

On June the 20th 1940, the day after the *Madura* sailed from Bordeaux, the SS *Broompark*, a British cargo ship, also left the port. On board were two leading atomic scientists (Lowarski and Halbarn) and their families. The scientists worked for Irene Curie and her husband Jean Foliot (both of whom stayed behind). Irene was Madame Marie Curie's daughter and Eve's sister. The fleeing scientists carried with them them all of France's heavy water. This was used as a dampener, an essential in the production of an atom bomb. The scientists would end up at the Clarendon laboratory, in Cambridge (England) the world's leading centre for atomic research.

Mary Borden, Edward Spears' wife, finally got to Bordeaux the day after the Broompark had left. She went to seek aid from Ian Fleming:

'Fleming, whom I had met in London, looking very smart as a naval Lieutenant, came out to the gate. He smiled when he saw the five cars full of females. The smile was not gentle or chivalrous but more of wry humour, perhaps of annoyance… we'd been thrust on him and would probably be a great nuisance.'

Fleming found space for the 26 nurses on the last civilian ship out, the SS *Ettrick*. It was a crowded crossing. There were 3,000 aboard a ship registered for 2,000. Many of the passengers were Polish troops, heading to England to fight again. In the months ahead, Mary Borden was to suffer a recurring nightmare:

'The spectacle of a nation gone out of its mind with fear was to haunt me. Long after I got home, I would wake up in a cold sweat in my London bed to wonder what would happen if the Germans invaded England: and the faces of mad women would start out at me in the dark, women with insane eyes and streaming hair, at the wheels of cars full of children.'

She still believed in France. Not its leaders, many of whom she knew well (she travelled in the highest of circles): "It was all there for those who had eyes to see and ears to hear. The defeatism, the corruption, the treachery that had been eating away the foundation of France." Her belief was in the people of France - and in a man called Charles de Gaulle.

The last man standing

When Mary Borden landed at Plymouth on June the 26th, 1940, Europe was already occupied by the dictators' armies.

The scale and speed of the catastrophe was without parallel in history. A couple of minor neutrals were – for the moment – tolerated by the dictators, the rest of the democracies had been defeated with almost contemptuous ease. Denmark, Norway, Holland, Luxembourg, Belgium and France had fallen in the space of ten weeks. Poland and Czechoslovakia were gone. Austria was part of the German Reich. Germany's ally, Russia, had invaded the three Baltic States: Lithuania, Estonia and Latvia. The shootings and deportations were already in full swing there.

Europe had fallen. Britain was tyranny's final enemy.

America was neutral and looked like staying that way. A month after Mary Borden landed, a Gallup poll asked her fellow Americans whether they should go to war against Germany and Italy. The overwhelming majority - 86% - said they should stay out. Two other Gallup polls taken in America in May and June of that year – 1940 - are equally illuminating. One asked whether, should they beat Britain, the Germans would attack America next. Two thirds of those surveyed (65%) said yes, it would be their turn next. The other poll asked who would win the fight, Britain or the Axis (Germany, Italy, Hungary and Romania). 32% believed Britain would win, 35% thought the Axis would.

However, another poll showed that the majority of Americans were in favour of selling weapons to Britain. Cash on delivery. If Britain was – as was likely – to be defeated, at least her gold would be in America. That was as far as it went, though. The American president, Franklin D. Roosevelt, although he sympathised with Britain, knew that to back her militarily would have lost him his presidency. Such are the perils of democracy.

A few American voices were raised against appeasement. General Douglas MacArthur, the Chairman of the Committee to Defend America by Aiding the Allies, was one of them. In September 1940 he said... 'To face an adversary in detail has been the prayer of every conqueror in history...help ...should be synchronised with the British effort so that the English-speaking peoples of the world will not be broken in detail. Unity of effort (is vital); not too late, not tomorrow, but today.'

Britain had, of course, her Dominions – Canada, Australia, South Africa and New Zealand - and her Empire. Although important sources of men and materials, these in no way matched the strength of her enemies. In particular, Britain's Army was outgunned, outnumbered and outclassed by the German Wehrmacht. If, at that time, the two armies had fought on British soil, the British would have been beaten just as soundly as they had been in France. If anything the rematch would have gone even worse for 'the Tommies', who had abandoned virtually all of their heavy equipment – guns, tanks, lorries – on the continent.

France had taught the British a lesson. The way to beat Thor was not to fight him toe to toe. But so what? "He who fights and runs away will live to fight another day" is a good maxim but it doesn't win wars. Now Britain must stand and fight – not just for her own life – but to save the world from a new age of tyranny, hate, pain and mass murder. And she must fight alone. But how? Thor had triumphed in Europe and was now mightier than ever.

Britain's three advantages

Britannia did, however, have three advantages.

Firstly, she has a moat. The English Channel is twenty-one miles wide at its narrowest point. Not a huge distance it's true: on a clear day you can see the clock tower in Calais from the White Cliffs of Dover. But, even if others are not, the Islanders are fully aware that their Channel has frustrated many an enemy over the years. To defend the moat Britain had the Royal Navy and the Royal Air Force – notably Fighter Command's Hugh Dowding.

JOYOUS GARD "Surrender, or die".
*Bernard Partridge's cartoon in Punch.
Note the Dominion flags of Canada,
Australia and New Zealand on the
ramparts.*

Secondly the British believed in themselves. They would 'muddle through', losing every battle except the final one. You could call this fanciful - 'a fine conceit' - but nonetheless just about everybody believed it, it was real, it was a strength. And their belief was bolstered by a leader. **The** leader; Winston Spencer Churchill, a stirring, inspiring champion in this, the most desperate hour of his country's existence. King Arthur reborn? Even better, his gutsy eloquence was shot through with humour. He alone was worth many a division of troops: or so, fortunately, his countrymen believed. Outsiders, of course might think differently. For all of Churchill's fine words of 'fighting on the beaches and in the streets' and 'blood, sweat, toil and tears' and 'Britain's finest hour' what could he do? What good were words against Thor?

What the outsider (and most insiders) did not know was that there was a good bit more in Britain's arsenal than blood, sweat, toil and tears. Intelligence – in both senses of the word - had been used to forge new weapons that Thor knew nothing of. And that was largely down to Britain's third advantage, 'C' - the head of the SIS - 'Quex' Sinclair.

An homage to Quex – frustrater of knavish tricks.

Hugh Sinclair was, in fact, already dead. He had died of cancer on the fourth of November 1939, aged 66. Fred Winterbotham said of him: 'His absolute personal loyalty and fairness to his staff were qualities which were rarely found in his successors after his tragic death.'

I would like to end this chapter with my homage to him. Without the scientific teams that he instigated there would have been no Bletchley Park and no Whaddon Hall. Without the SIS's Air Section (and Lord Swinton) there would have been no money for radar and not enough to develop the Spitfire and Hurricane. Without these, Britain would have been invaded.

Without Britain, Russia would have fallen. There are many reasons why I say this, the Royal Navy's Arctic convoys and Bletchley Park being two of them. These are subjects I will return to later in the book.

With Britain and Russia under Nazi rule, America would have been next on the Hitler's list. To finish off that last major adversary, the Nazis would have probably used German rockets; topped, perhaps, with an atomic warhead developed from British atomic knowledge. The atom had first been split in 1932, in Cambridge, in England - and Britain was, in 1940, the most advanced nation on earth in atomic development. It is probable that if Britain had fallen, America would have fallen too. Then would have come what Hitler had called 'The German rule of the earth'. Nazi rule. A new Dark Age. Quex saved the world from that.

It is true that Britain had two other leaders - Churchill and Dowding - without whom the war would have been lost. Without Quex, however, they would not have had the tools to fight and win their battles. Without these three, I doubt whether I, or many who read my words, would have ever been born.

The actions that Sinclair and the British government were to take to counter the Nazi threat would change not only the course of the war but also the future of humanity. That story is largely what this book is about.

Before I embark on this epic, though, please allow me a couple of pages to tell you about the area in England where this took place: the Intelligence Zone.

2: The Intelligence Zone

'The Intelligence Zone' is my personal phrase to describe that area of England from which the management of the war took place. A map of the area is at the start of the book. It lies roughly between London, Birmingham, Oxford, and Cambridge. Its southern boundary was the River Thames, which flows through London. This river line could, it was hoped, be held against the German army should they invade southern England. Some of the bunkers and anti-tank defences prepared for this last-ditch defence remain to this day.

In the previous chapter I told how, in 1935, Fred Winterbotham and Desmond Morton briefed the Secretary of State for Air, Phillip Cunliffe-Lister, on the strength of the German Luftwaffe; which had grown to become the most powerful air force on Earth. The bombers were coming; and they were coming for London. Having honed their skills in city-bombing on Guernica and Madrid and with Europe's largest city for their target, they could hardly miss. Consequently those headquarters which remained in the British capital were dug-in, fortified, and hemmed-in by guns. For example, the Cabinet War Rooms (Churchill's War Rooms) were excavated deep beneath Whitehall; while just round the corner the Admiralty built itself a massive bunker (the Citadel), on Horse Guards' Parade.

While much remained in London, much more was moved out to the countryside. In the 1930s, the Royal Air Force was re-organised into three main commands – Fighter, Bomber and Coastal. Their three headquarters were built close – but not too close - to the city. They were strung out to the north west of the capital, about halfway between Whitehall and Chequers, the Prime Minister's retreat in leafy Buckinghamshire. The RAF also set up a fourth, major, linked, base at Leighton Buzzard – 'Q Central' – the secret base which would run Britain's world-wide military communications.

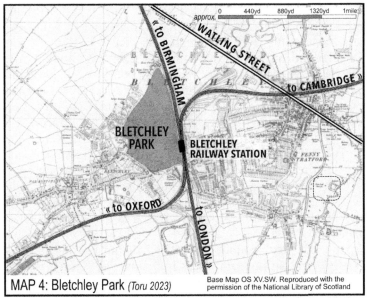

MAP 4: Bletchley Park *(Toru 2023)* Base Map OS XV.SW. Reproduced with the permission of the National Library of Scotland

An Ordnance Survey map of the 1930's showing Bletchley Park, sited next to the crossover of the east west and north south railway lines. Two thousand years earlier the Romans built a fortress (Magiovinium) nearby; on Watling Street, a main artery of England since the dawn of time.

The secret services moved out too. That was down to Fred Winterbotham's boss, 'Quex' Sinclair. In 1937 he had told one of his line managers, the head of the Government Code and Cypher School (GC&CS), Alistair Denniston, that he was now "convinced of the inevitability of war". In 1938 he relocated SIS (MI6) operations a little to the north of the RAF operational HQs, to a country estate where his people could eavesdrop, break codes, make propaganda and generally wreak havoc without being disturbed. The estate he chose was Bletchley Park, in Buckinghamshire, at the exact spot where the south-north railway line from London to Birmingham crosses the east-west rail line from Cambridge to Oxford. Quex recruited heavily from Britain's premier universities.

The 'boffins' from the universities were not the only factor in the choice of Bletchley Park. Less than a mile from the park is Watling Street (or, to give it its more prosaic modern name, the A5). Watling Street is old. It was the first road the Romans built in England (although it predates them) – running in a straight(ish) line from the legions' beachhead in Kent, through London and on to Wales. Along this road ran Britain's main telephone network: cables, repeaters, boosters and switching gear. Bletchley Park, the three Royal Air Force command headquarters and Q Central were all spurred off the same communications backbone, which ran down into London. This network was the central nervous system of Britain's war effort.

Bletchley also fitted in nicely with Quex's leisure pursuit – fox-hunting. The SIS, in the words of the biographer, Christopher Andrew, shared 'a common addiction to London clubs and country sports' – i.e. fox hunting. Quex hunted with the Whaddon Chase. He bought Bletchley Park from a fellow huntsman.

In the next couple of years, secondary sites would mushroom throughout Buckinghamshire, Hertfordshire, Bedfordshire, Northamptonshire and beyond. As will become plain throughout this book, this area was home to a veritable web of intelligence networks and their users. Here advances in intelligence gathering, communications and the first steps in computing were harnessed together to fight the Axis forces. This intelligence revolution was the greatest factor in the Allied victory in the Second World War. It has also shaped the modern world.

The world-changing historical advances of the Industrial Revolution took place in the north of England. Here, a hundred miles further south, this second, intelligence, revolution, was of no less importance for humanity.

In charge of all of this was Winston Churchill who would, during the course of the war, pass the baton of world leadership from Britain to America.

These are events which have shaped the lives of most of humanity. My intent in this book is to give you an inkling of this greatest of epic stories.

3: Radar; the race against time

Radar (noun): a system for detecting the presence, direction, distance, and speed of aircraft, ships, and other objects, by sending out pulses of radio waves which are reflected off the object back to the source.

The naked island

There are very many differences between how Britain was in the nineteen-thirties and how she is today. The past is indeed another country. One major difference, back then, was the legacy of the First World War - when just about every family had lost a father, son, fiancé or close relative. One tenth of British soldiers had been killed and for every death two or three more were badly wounded. The war shaped the peace. Most men (and women) had served in some capacity and just about every man over the age of about thirty-five was an ex-soldier or sailor.

Given this immense shadow of suffering, fear and pain, it is not surprising that the British civil administration (the Civil Service), who had themselves mostly been in the armed forces, were keeping an eye on the rising might of Hitler's Germany. It was from the sky that trouble was expected to come. As I've described in the first chapter, it was at exactly this time that, 'C' - Admiral 'Quex' Sinclair, the head of SIS (MI6) - had sent RAF Wing Commander Frederick Winterbotham to Germany to spy. Winterbotham and others sent back alarming reports of the rapid growth of German air strength. Those reports went to politicians (of their nature transitory) and their more permanent advisors. It was in 1932 that the then Prime Minister, Stanley Baldwin, stood up in Parliament and made a speech in which he said:

"I think it is well also for the man in the street to realise that there is no power on earth that can protect him from being bombed... the bomber will always get through."

Luckily, there were some who did not agree with Baldwin – or at least wanted to test the hypothesis. Politically, the most notable of these were Winston Churchill and his scientific advisor, Frederick Lindemann. I will talk more about them later in the book.

At the same time, a physicist, A.P. Rowe, was looking to find practical answers to the bomber threat. Albert Rowe was working in the Directorate of Scientific Research at the Air Ministry – and he was a worried man. The most advanced aircraft detection devices available at the time were semi-circular concrete 'sound mirrors'. These structures were mostly located in Kent (and aligned towards Paris!). They weren't good enough. The mirrors 'heard' less than half of the aircraft which approached them; and even when they did hear something coming, the object was by then too close to allow much time to do much about it.

Alarmed by this, Rowe read all that he could find on air defence and then wrote a memo (in 1934) to his boss, Harry Wimperis, which concluded that 'we are likely to lose the war if it starts within the next ten years.' Wimperis (who had served with the Royal Naval Air Service and designed what was considered the best bomb sight of the first war) took the report seriously. He contacted every authority that he thought might help, one of which was the Radio Research Station (part of the National Physical Laboratory), at Slough.

RRS Slough was at Ditton Park, Datchet, a couple of miles from Slough itself. Datchet, on the River Thames, is the village where Falstaff was dumped in a ditch in *The Merry Wives of Windsor*. During the war, just as in Shakespeare's time, it was regarded as a bucolic haven.

RRS Slough was concerned with research into, and development of, radio transmission and reception. A large part of its work was pinpointing weather fronts, storms and other atmospheric disturbances. In charge was Robert Watson-Watt, a man in his early forties. Watson-Watt was one of the many men who had developed an interest in radio as a boy. In his case, this had led on to him taking a degree in physics. Physics was, then as now, a very international discipline and Watson-Watt had studied German, which he considered indispensable for keeping up with advances in physics in general and radio in particular. Britain, Germany and America were the world leaders in radio development.

Wimperis asked Watson-Watt if a 'death ray' was feasible to bring down a plane (or kill its pilot). Watson-Watt thought not; but asked his assistant Arnold Wilkins for his opinion. Wilkins replied that he didn't think so either. The power needed was too great for such a weapon to be practical. Watson-Watt then asked Wilkins if there was anything else that they could give the Air Ministry to placate them. Wilkins hummed and hawed and then came up with a thought.

A couple of years earlier (in 1931), General Post Office (GPO) engineers at Colney Heath (in Hertfordshire) had reported problems while engaged in tracking weather fronts with short-wave radio. Overflying aircraft from the nearby de Havilland aerodrome had wreaked havoc with their monitoring equipment. Perhaps this could be put to good use? If so, then possibly aircraft could be detected more rapidly than by using the concrete mirrors. The mirrors operated at the speed of sound – about a mile every five seconds. Radio waves move many times faster than that - at 186,000 miles a second; the speed of light. The difference between the two is, of course, plain in a thunder storm. The lightning flashes; If the sound of thunder comes five seconds later, then that means that the lightning strike was a mile off - and so on. Perhaps lightning could be used rather than thunder to detect aircraft? Watson-Watt reported the possible lead to Wimperis. Thus was the idea of British radar born.

The Tizard Committee

On getting the report back from Slough, Harry Wimperis passed it on to Henry Tizard. Tizard, a mathematician and chemist, was a graduate of Oxford (in 1908) and had then spent some time studying at Berlin university. Like Wimperis, Tizard had seen air service in the first war, serving first as a soldier, then in the Royal Flying Corps, which became the RAF in 1918. After the war, he spent time in the higher ranks of the Civil Service and had been instrumental in appointing Wimperis, who, in turn, set up the Scientific Committee for Air

Defence (usually known as the Tizard Committee), which Tizard chaired. Although it had only five members, it was high powered indeed, counting one actual (Hill) and one future Nobel Prize winner (Blackett).

The report from Slough was the key item on the agenda of the first meeting of the Tizard Committee. They forwarded the report to the Royal Air Force's Air Marshall Hugh Dowding, the Air Member for Supply and Research. Dowding was another man who had had early experience of radio; in the first world war he had been in charge of an experimental station at Brooklands Aerodrome, in Surrey, where he and his team developed early airborne radio (when they were short of components he and an ex-Marconi employee, Mr Prince, would go to Marconi's offices in Aldwych, London and, while Dowding distracted the store keeper, Prince would steal the necessary).

Dowding, who held the RAF's purse strings, was more than interested. He asked Robert Watson-Watt, at RSS Slough, to set up a proper experiment. Just as importantly, he authorised payment for the test. Watson-Watt told Arnold Wilkins to put his theory into practice without delay.

Things were moving quickly and would continue to do so. Since Rowe's letter, Adolf Hitler had come to power in Germany.

Wilkins did the necessary calculations, assembled the equipment and drove north to carry out an experiment.

The Daventry experiment

The experiment took place in Northamptonshire, using the eight year old Daventry Transmitter. This site was a sea of masts holding transmitting aerials (including the world's first longwave transmitting station). For his experiment, Wilkins had arranged that it would transmit a continuous shortwave (50 metre) beam while an aeroplane flew towards it.

Wilkins and his driver drove up in a van from Slough and found a suitable field, which the farmer allowed them to use. By that time it was getting late. It was the 25th of February 1935, the day was short, the interior light of the van had failed and Wilkins and the driver had to set up the equipment by

The Daventry transmitter

candlelight. It was midnight before they got the test gear set up, by which time their van had frozen to the field and they had to dig it out.

Watson-Watt and Rowe arrived on the following day and watched Wilkin's experiment. Radar is the transmission of waves of radio energy and the detection of an object by plotting the 'bounce back' when it crosses the waves' path. Wilkins used a receiver he had prepared at RRS Slough to pick up the reflection from the bomber of the radio pulse sent from the Daventry transmitter. They saw the returned signal when the plane was eight miles distant.

Robert Watson-Watt and Albert Rowe were so excited at the result that when they drove off they forgot Watson-Watt's nephew, Patrick, whom his uncle had bought along for the outing. It was not until they had driven the half-dozen miles to the traffic lights at Towcester that they remembered him. They found Patrick, a level-headed boy who knew his uncle, sitting patiently by the field gate in the winter sunshine.

Rowe coined the acronym RDF as a cover for the work, meaning Range and Direction Finding but it was later changed to Radar (from radio detection and ranging). I shall call it radar from now on.

Also taking place at Datchet was the development of the Adcock HF/DF system which used 4 aerials to track down the source of incoming radio signals. This – 'Hufduff' as the

Americans christened it - was to have a major impact on the submarine war and Hitler's 'V' weapons; subjects which I will return to in later chapters.

Suffolk (and a few pints in the Crown and Castle).

Now that radar had proved to be a possibility, it was necessary to develop it. To do this, Wilkins' section was moved to Orfordness, a remote military site on the Suffolk coast which had lain unused since the end of the first war. Orfordness was only reachable by ferry which was rowed, in the words of one who worked there, by:

"...a taciturn boatman, who, like all good Suffolk folk, was deeply suspicious of 'foreigners'".

Shades of the river Styx.

The move came just three months after the Daventry experiment: the speed being the result of a great deal of pressure on the Slough team from Tizard and Dowding. Both felt that war was coming, both knew that Britain's defences from air attack were virtually non-existent. Visual sighting by the Royal Observer Corps of attacking aircraft would be too late to fly sorties against them – and standing patrols would be quite impossible given the length of the coast and the size of the targets to be defended. The sound mirrors I have mentioned earlier were not only slow, they were often more trouble than they worth. When Rowe arranged a test of one of them for Air Marshall 'Stuffy' Dowding in July 1935, the only clear sounds that were picked up were the horse and cart of the local milkman.

There were just five scientific staff at Orfordness to begin with, including, crucially, Wilkins himself and Edward Bowen. Orfordness was other-worldly: remote and often bracing. 'Bracing' is the euphemism which was used years later to sell nearby Skegness as a holiday destination. Weather-wise in England the divide between east and west is sometimes far harsher than that between north and south. The biting winds that come in over the North Sea from Scandinavia and the Urals are called 'lazy winds' in East Anglia – too lazy to go round a body, they blow straight through you. The erectors (riggers) of the two initial seventy-five foot high lattice towers battled against those winds for weeks. Wilkins commented that:

'Their faces bore witness to the severity of the elements.'

Arnold Wilkins develops Chain Home

The work was very hands-on for the scientists. Wilkins recounts fitting a receiving aerial on top of a two hundred and fifty foot high steel mast. The mast, like an electricity pylon, was a cone on four feet, tapering at the top. His job was to fit the aerial to a wooden cross at the top. He was winched up in a bosun's chair:

'This chair had been designed to last a lifetime, the frame was made of one-inch diameter steel rod which held a thick oak seat and a heavy steel circular band, presumably to prevent one from falling off, and through which one had to climb before sitting down. The dimensions of the whole contraption had been designed so that it would go through the top section of the mast, the cross-sectional area of which was smaller than that of the other two sections. Unfortunately no account had been taken of the passenger's knees and I soon found that one had to be something of a contortionist to negotiate the top section while remaining in the chair. It was, furthermore, quite impossible to work on the aerial when the chair was at its highest point and I had to squeeze out of the chair and stand on one face of the mast while installing the aerials and connecting them to the open-wire lines which I had taken up with me. On completing the work I was not sorry to give the signal to Watson-Watt and assistants to wind me down to contemplate the mess into which my beautiful grey trousers had got through contact with the wet creosote on the mast.'

It was work carried out under high pressure, with long hours. The tiny team often built their own test gear and there was an overly-complex procedure for obtaining materials. Yet in the reminiscences of the period from Bowen, Wilkins and Watson-Watt, there is a profound sense of satisfaction in this wild place of sea, shingle and wind, where they were rowed from the mainland to their work by the taciturn ferryman. Edward ('Taffy') Bowen says:

49

'Many were the nights I spent on a camp bed alongside the transmitter, with a piece of cake and a bottle of beer for supper, and as likely as not the same for breakfast.'

The testing was done using aircraft from nearby RAF Martlesham Heath flying at 15,000 feet, the maximum permitted without the need for oxygen. To start with there was short-circuiting on the aerial wires – sparking so powerful that it could be heard on the other side of the river, half a mile away. This was cured by soldering the wires to the aerials.

While Wilkins, Bowen and the small team continued development of radar at their lonely outpost, Watson-Watt would visit weekly. The meetings were frequently in the lounge of the Crown and Castle in Orford (Rowe preferred the beer in the Jolly Sailor).

Suffolk: a numinous land of lonely curlew and booming bittern. A great eastern window of far horizons and the surge, seals and marsh-pools of the sea. An expectant land of boundless promise at the break of dawn; and tow-headed barmaids, good beer and barn owls at day's end. A magical English county where physicists did great works for their fellows.

Improvements in range and detection went on apace, so that soon Wilkins was able to differentiate between individual aircraft. At this time, the Air Ministry stopped development of the concrete sound mirrors. Some of them lie abandoned along the English east coast to this day.

In December 1935, Lord Swinton (Philip Cunliffe-Lister), the Secretary of state for Air, persuaded the Cabinet and the Treasury to put up £1,000,000 for radar development. Watson-Watt, tireless advocate of radar, had been to see him. Truth to tell, Swinton hadn't taken much persuasion. "My dear boy," he said to Watt, when the latter told him that he planned to write a paper about radar as it was of such great scientific interest: "You are not going to write anything for anybody, except me, for a long time to come." On the back of this, in March 1936 development was moved from Orfordness to nearby Bawdsey Manor, purchased from its owner with 180 acres of prime land for £23,000 by Watson-Watt.

If Watt's claims to have been 'the father of radar' are open to doubt (what about Wilkins?), his vision, popularity, drive and ability to publicise and drive it forward are not. Under his management and using public money released by Swinton (and fuelled by the fears of the Air Ministry and Dowding), a chain of five stations was planned. The requirements for the stations were that they be as high as possible above the sea with flat land behind. These first stations were at Bawdsey(Suffolk), Great Bromley and Canewdon (Essex), and Dunkirk and Dover(both in Kent).

Bawdsey Manor, in Suffolk, where radar development continued, was an odd mix of baronial splendour, poor amenities and a harsh climate. Hard work in hard conditions, but enjoyable. Taffy Bowen says:

'Some of the best technical discussions took place late at night in a timbered hall in front of a roaring fire... we did not care a jot about the absence of refinement in our private lives... for me it was one of the happiest periods of my life.'

Robert Hanbury-Brown, who worked for Bowen in developing air borne radar, described Bawdsey Manor itself as:

'A magical fairy-tale castle with a lawn where there always seemed to be hares (and) a derelict swimming pool on which there were kingfishers.'

Each of the stations of Chain Home were to have transmitting and receiving masts The (metal) transmitting towers were to be 360 feet high and the (wooden) receivers 250 feet. There were to be one or two arrays, each of 4 transmitting and up to 4 receiving towers, at each station.

Chain Home

After a long three-way discussion at the Crown and Castle, Orford, in 1936, 'which went far into one Friday night', responsibilities at Bawdsey were divided. Watson-Watt was, of course, in charge. Wilkins was to design the

51

tall masts (Chain Home) which would stand round the coast of Britain. Bowen was to develop the world's first airborne radar. The names should be remembered and revered. Wilkins forged the shield that saved his country during the Battle of Britain, while Bowen opened the eyes that were to guide the weapons which broke Axis power.

In the corridors of power in London, Bawdsey was backed by the RAF's Director of Scientific Research, Henry Tizard, who was already forecasting that Britain would triumph against daytime attack but needed better night defences. According to Bowen, Tizard was:

'...probably the one man who, in the mid-1930s correctly foresaw how the situation would develop and what should be done about it. He passed these thoughts onto Watson-Watt who passed them on to us at Orfordness.'

As Bawdsey grew, Watson-Watt went trawling for more staff. Recruits were drawn largely from the ranks of young academic physicists. Watson-Watt scouted around the universities and laboratories, requesting, demanding or wheedling the release of high quality research men. Dr A.G. Touch, an Oxford graduate, and the prodigy Robert Hanbury-Brown from Imperial College – 19 years old when he joined in 1936, with a first in engineering and recruited by Tizard – were Bowen's chief assistants in developing airborne radar.

In his book *Three steps to victory*, Watson-Watt tells us that rank did not matter much at Bawdsey:

'It was cynical and earnest, well-informed and enquiring. It was enthusiastic, tireless and hard-working. It was impatient of organisational niceties; it was respectful almost of no one and almost of only one thing – professional competence.'

Its meetings were what Watson-Watt called, his 'Soviets' – where all were heard, all sensible thoughts considered and often worked on.

The first major Air Exercise to demonstrate the use of radar in air defence was held in September 1936. This used large numbers of aircraft and the new radar station at Bawdsey. The speed of development and change meant that demonstrating a stable platform was problematical. The first day of the exercise was a shambles; the incoming aircraft were not detected until they were so close to the coast that their engines could be heard – a sound mirror would have done just as well. Sir Hugh Dowding, who had now been appointed Commander in Chief of the newly created Fighter Command, was there, along with important members of the Air Ministry. Fortunately an impromptu demonstration of airborne radar equipment by 'Taffy' Bowen, and a reversion to an older transmitter saved the day.

For the exercises of 1937 a 'filter' system, to co-ordinate the input of the five listening stations, was introduced. This worked perfectly and radar was vindicated.

As the network was extended round to the Isle of Wight and up to Scotland, Wilkins toured the country searching for sites, encountering some northern bloody-mindedness at Danby Moor in Yorkshire and Ottercops Moss in Northumberland, where landowners did not want their grouse shooting disturbed.

Taffy Bowen develops airborne radar

Tizard and his committee anticipated that the Luftwaffe, thwarted by ground radar during daylight hours, would turn to night bombing. They realised that British fighter aircraft would need airborne radar so that they could get close enough, in the dark, to identify enemy aircraft. Edward Bowen and his team were given the task of developing the world's first airborne radar. The requirements for airborne radar were very different from ground radar. Clearly it would have to be smaller and lighter, but on the plus side it would not need such a long range. However, there was another requirement; it would need to have a much more directional beam so that the fighter pilot would be able to work out the bearing of the enemy aircraft.

The way to meet these requirements would be to operate on a shorter wavelength; not only could the aerial be shorter (aerial length being directly proportional to wavelength) and therefore more aerodynamic, but the shape of the radio beam would be more elongated.

Bowen decided that a viable airborne radar should not exceed 200 lbs in weight, 8 cubic feet in volume and 500 watts in power consumption. The challenge should not be underestimated. In those days most radio components were large, heavy and unsuitable for use in the extremes of vibration, temperature and atmospheric pressure met with in military aircraft. The aircraft power supply was DC, variable in voltage and very limited in capacity. There were a number of other troublesome problems; for example, there were no solid insulated cables to connect the radar equipment to the antennas. But the greatest difficulty of all was to generate enough power at short wavelengths in a transmitter that could be carried in an aircraft.

Bowen and his group tackled and solved most of these problems. To take two important examples, in 1938, with the help of Metropolitan Vickers, he solved the problem of the power supply in aircraft by introducing an engine-driven alternator which gave an 80 volt, 1,000 Hz, voltage-stabilised supply. In 1939 he encouraged Imperial Chemical Industries (ICI) to produce the first radio-frequency cables with polythene insulation, a most important advance. Other great stalwarts of the British engineering industry, EMI at Hayes and GEC at Wembley, were brought into the secret and developed valves and other components. Radar was reaching out into industry. By the end of the war there would be a quarter of a million British men and women working in its production and operation.

Bawdsey's first complete installation of Aerial Intercept radar (AI) was flown on June the ninth, 1939. The radar had a maximum range of 12,000 feet with a Harrow (aeroplane) as a target. In mock interceptions the display seemed easy to use. A week or so later Bowen gave the Commander in Chief of Fighter Command (Sir Hugh Dowding) a successful demonstration; within a few weeks the airborne group was committed to fitting AI into 30 aeroplanes for trials by 25 Squadron at RAF Northolt. Bowen was also busy fitting ASV – Air to Surface Vessel radar - for RAF Coastal Command and the Royal Navy.

The cavity magnetron

A lot of cross-fertilisation between army, navy, air force and civilians took place at Bawdsey. To go forward for a moment, the search for more compact aerials quickly led to the development of the cavity magnetron. This was thanks to the Royal Navy who set up research departments at the universities of Bristol, Oxford and Birmingham. It was at the Admiralty Research Laboratory in Birmingham, in 1940, that two young physicists, John Randall and Harry Boot, who had spent time at the Ventnor radar station on the Isle of Wight, made the breakthrough that made microwave radar a possibility. They invented the first practical cavity magnetron.

Image of a sectioned wartime magnetron. Showing the cavities whose dimensions determine its operating frequency; the permanent magnet is not shown but fits around the magnetron. With thanks to newcomen.com

The magnetron, as its name suggests, uses a magnet. It had been postulated in 1910, in Germany, and improved over the years in Germany, America and Russia. Randall and Boot completed the development of the device with their invention of the cavity magnetron. This was smaller and more powerful than its predecessors – a hundred times more powerful initially and soon much more so - producing high power with a short (10 centimetre) wavelength (a microwave). That meant smaller radar sets which could be fitted into smaller spaces – principally aircraft. The invention would help to give the Allies supremacy in air warfare. Bowen would take a cavity magnetron as part of the gift of Britain's scientific secrets to America, the Tizard Mission, which I shall write about in a later chapter.

These devices are not photogenic; but were not merely war-changing but world-changing. You doubtless have one in your kitchen, as they are at the heart of every microwave oven.

The filter room

As the number of radar sites grew, the task of managing the communications from them was given to Geoffrey Roberts, who had been recruited from the post office (GPO). He, along with one of his staff, Edward Fennessy (who had been transferred from work on the now-redundant concrete mirrors) installed Fighter Command's first Filter Room at the headquarters of the command, Bentley Priory (just North of London), in September 1938.

A Filter Room was a half-way house between Chain Home (and later Chain Home Low) and an RAF Operations Room. The filtering involved putting together all of the inputs from the relevant radar stations (and other sources, mainly the Royal Observer Corps but also from the 'Y' stations, which I will write about later, and Bletchley Park). Then, the now more manageable information was passed to the Operations Room, where RAF operators tracked the aircraft on a plotting table.

Roberts and Fennessy installed the Filter Room at Fighter Command HQ, Bentley Priory, on the day that Neville Chamberlain, Britain's Prime Minister, was flying back from Germany after his first visit to Hitler. They tracked his plane as it crossed the North Sea. A couple of weeks later, Chamberlain flew back to Germany, to sign the Munich Agreement. This he hailed as 'peace in our time'. Churchill called it 'a totally unmitigated defeat'.

As an aside, the process of filtering, then passing the results on to fighter control, then co-ordinating the attacks from squadrons at different airfields, was very complex. The system, further developed between the RAF and Bawdsey staff at RAF Biggin Hill, gave rise to an analysis and design process which was given the name of Operation Research (OR). This was to be spun out and applied with great affect across all of the RAF commands, and later adopted by Britain's ally, America.

Whatever – or whoever – Neville Chamberlain surrendered for peace, Britain must somewhere draw a line against Nazi aggression or finally perish. War was approaching. The bombers were coming. Radar was the shield. The time between the raising of the shield and the launch of the attack was to be very short. Watson-Watt had predicted that war would come in 1938. He had drummed his message home:

'Pressing on Ministers, senior officers and civil servants my slogan, "Every week that passes is one per cent of the time that we are entitled to count our own", I was fortunate to be wrong; even when it turned out to be a half-per-cent instead of a full percent. We were always on the brink of too little and too late; in radar somewhat less than in many military fields. At the best it was Waterloo-like, "a damned close run thing"'.

Highly secret though it was, the pull of Bawdsey was growing. One visitor, in June 1939, was a backbench M.P. who was very interested in aerial matters. His name was Winston Churchill. First he visited RAF Martlesham Heath, the airfield from which the planes that Bawdsey tracked flew. There he was given a (ground based) introduction to air radar by one of Bowen's deputies, the aforementioned Robert Hanbury-Brown. Then Churchill went to Bawdsey where the ground radar defences were demonstrated.

Edward Fennessy, who was in the officers mess when Churchill held forth on the experience, was very impressed at the acuity of the future Prime Minister. Recalling his speech years later, he paraphrased Churchill's words:

'"Gentlemen, what I have seen today is the most exciting thing I've seen for many years. I've seen the weapon with which we're going to defeat the Germans. But you have a problem... I'm a German airman and I've been told to bomb London. As I approach the coast, I'm scared stiff. I know I'm being watched. But once I've crossed the coast I'm a happy German. I throw my flying helmet over the side in glee, for I've flown from the twentieth century into the stone age. That, gentlemen, is the problem you've got to solve." He had got to the root of our problem. Chain Home could see the planes coming in but when they were past our stations they disappeared. Only the Observer Corps, standing on their hillsides, could see them. That's why we had to develop Chain Home Low. Churchill had seen that at a glance and pinpointed it amusingly.'

A tactical retreat

The German air force was showing rather too much interest in Bawdsey. The head of the Luftwaffe's signals organisation, General Wolfgang Martini, had commissioned an airship, the Graf Zeppelin (carrying radio detection equipment) to fly up the English east coast to see what the tall masts which were appearing there were up to. Could it be radar? This was the first military electronics 'spyplane' in history. The 776 foot (237 metre) long dirigible may seem a somewhat old fashioned spy-in-the-sky but the German knowledge of radar was pretty primitive at the time (at the end of the war, Watson-Watt estimated that they were two years behind Britain); and so they needed a lot of room to house their bulky detection equipment. The Graf Zeppelin crawled over Bawdsey (its top speed was 25 knots – about 30mph) twice in 1939. It failed to 'see' the British radar pulses – but the British radar stations did register the airship. They could hardly miss it.

1939 - a rare visitor to our shores - the Graf Zeppelin.

Afraid that Bawdsey would be targeted by the Luftwaffe, and knowing how vital his development teams were to Britain's radar defence, Watson-Watt moved them. He took them out of the front line on the very day that Britain declared war on Germany. Initially he packed them off to Dundee in Scotland. In the next years they were shifted to Wales (St Athans) and then back to England (Worth Matravers in Dorset), before finally finding a home in Malvern, in Worcestershire.

The move from Bawdsey was the end of an era. In nostalgically recalling it afterwards, Wilkins would slip into the accent of Suffolk – a county that he had come to love above all others.

Edward Fennessy takes his section to Leighton Buzzard

One member of the Bawdsey elite refused point-blank to let his section be moved to Dundee. This was Edward Fennessy, who was by now in charge of the construction of, and communications between, radar sites. Such a move would put him too far away from his customers – primarily the RAF headquarter stations to the north of London. He argued his point with his boss (Rowe), who agreed and told him to find a suitable site for his activities. He chose to go to Leighton Buzzard.

Leighton Buzzard is on the main railway railway line between London and Birmingham. Bletchley is one stop (6 miles) further up the line. In the nineteen-thirties this was prime fox-hunting country the hunters being mostly wealthy and often aristocratic (including the occasional royal). The Rothschilds, who were keen supporters, had no less than five stately homes in Buckinghamshire. Many of the best houses in Leighton Buzzard were built as weekend hunting lodges with attached stables. It was one of these roomy properties – Carlton Lodge - that Fennessy commandeered.

Fennessy wasn't interested in hunting, though. He needed to network all of the telephone lines from his ever-growing array of coastal radar stations into RAF Leighton Buzzard – 'Q Central'.

Q Central – the eyes and brains of the RAF

Q Central. The name was deliberately vague. Britain's defence communication network was referred to as 'Q' in the corridors of power; which made the heart of the secret network (RAF Leighton Buzzard) Q Central. The site for this station had been decided before the war as part of Hugh Dowding's RAF expansion scheme. It had no airfield, but plenty of communication masts.

Q Central was spurred off Britain's main General Post Office (GPO) telephone network which ran, as I've said, along Watling Street. As I mentioned in the previous chapter, this complex web of inter-connected sites made up the central nervous system of the British war effort. The three RAF command headquarters were other nodes – as was Bletchley Park and it's satellites. I will look at what Bletchley and its integrated and largely forgotten sites – which have been called 'Bletchley Park's secret sisters' - were up to in later chapters.

Q Central, with a staff of about 600 servicemen and women, had become operational in May 1939. It needed plenty of bandwidth as it was the global communications hub for the British military. Indeed it was the largest telephone and teleprinter exchange in the world. The scale of the operation is staggering. Upwards of a hundred operators were working in the various underground sections at any one time, night and day, seven days a week. The forethought and sheer intelligence of these operations is sobering: one of the sections was solely concerned with sending out dummy traffic, to confuse the enemy.

Q Central received so many teleprinter messages on paper tape (up to 10,000 a day) that a conveyor belt was installed to move them about. The story of the development of these teleprinters is itself a marvel of intelligence. Pre-war, a Wing Commander in the RAF, Oswyn Lywood, had got his hands on a commercial Enigma machine - the same device, of course, that was at the heart of Germans and Italian secure communications and whose output was being decoded at Bletchley - and improved it, partly by adding two rotors and a teleprinter. Lywood called this teleprinter TypeX. It was used by the army and RAF for communicating with the British armed forces in every theatre of war. Alan Turing worked on it for a time. Q Central was the home of Lywood's masterpiece. Unlike the German Enigma, TypeX's messages were never broken by the enemy.

Q Central also handled a large part of Britain's telephone traffic.

Because of its importance, every effort was made to camouflage the site. The personnel were largely underground;

but in case the Luftwaffe was short of somewhere to bomb, dummy roads and buildings were built 'topside', complete with dummy cars. These were, needless to say, at some distance from the subterranean communication halls. Eileen Younghusband was trained there as a radar plotter for the RAF's Fighter Command. In her fascinating autobiography *One Woman's war* she says:

'Everything was highly camouflaged. The buildings were covered by a heavy green fabric …matching the colours of the fields… I wondered what was so important here to receive this treatment.'

As well as disguising the camp from the air, the number of real buildings above ground were kept to a minimum. There were just two station buildings and only twenty-four married quarters. Proposals to build more were quashed so as not to draw attention to the site. Instead, the airmen and women (and more than half of the personnel were women: WAAFs), were billeted in the town of Leighton Buzzard – in the men's case in Marley Tile's disused storage sheds, in the women's (including Eileen) in the old Poor House – neither of which was conducive to cleanliness or comfort.

Fennessy needed to be near Q Central as, quite apart from its role as the centre for Britain's military communications, it was also the heart of the country's radar operations. All of the radar stations around the coast had communication lines leading into it (lines also went to RAF Fighter Command HQ at Bentley Priory). It was this network that Fennessy was expanding at breakneck speed. Leighton Buzzard was also home to the backup Operations Room for Fighter Command HQ. The WAAFs who were to work as plotters at Bentley Priory and the other RAF filter and operations rooms were trained there. Among them was Fred Winterbotham's future wife, Petrea, whom we will meet again in a later chapter.

The one thing about Q Central that could not be camouflaged, of course, were the ninety-foot-high masts that stood above it. There were eventually thirty-eight of them. However, there is safety in numbers. North Buckinghamshire and Bedfordshire were a web of masts. Leighton Buzzard's thirty-eight were little more than a drop in the ocean when compared to the arrays of Whaddon, Chicksands, Bletchley, Hanslope, Beaumanor and all the other sites in the area (which we will visit in future chapters) – not to mention the web on the Dunstable Downs surrounding the Meteorological Office.

The Luftwaffe - no fools - did photograph the site, although they never bombed it. The aerial photographs taken by the Luftwaffe of the 'farmland' overlaying Q Central exist still; but are, unfortunately, not easy to reproduce clearly in a book.

As well as the airmen and women of Q Central, Leighton Buzzard was home to many workers from Bletchley Park – which is, as I've said, one stop up the railway line. The arrival of Fennessy's group from Bawdsey would exacerbate the problem. The population of this attractive little English market town doubled from eight to sixteen thousand during the war.

Sixty Group – build the world's biggest radio network – now!

The radar group that Edward Fennessy moved from Bawdsey to Leighton Buzzard began with a staff of about sixty and quickly spread into more requisitioned houses (and stables) nearby. It was soon taken over by the Royal Air Force, and given the name RAF Sixty Group; Edward Fennessy and a colleague, Doctor Seward being commissioned into the RAF. Fennessy was in charge of planning and constructing the ever-growing Chain Home station network while Seward was in charge of Chain Home Low.

Chain Home Low stations were needed to spot low-flying incoming planes and those which had already crossed the coast. They were the solution to the problem that Churchill had raised of the happy German pilot, metaphorically throwing his flying helmet over the side. Unlike the fixed Chain Home masts they could track inland as well as seawards. They were to replace (but never completely) the Observer Corps' 'eyeball mark one'. The hole in the radar defences was plugged by using an adaptation of gun-laying radar that the army detachment at Bawdsey had developed for use on their cliff-top gun sites. All of the armed forces had a hand in the development of radar.

Chain Home Low masts were erected widely around the coast, often on the same sites as their larger brothers.

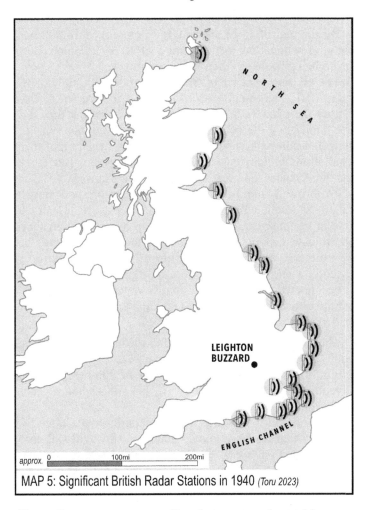

MAP 5: Significant British Radar Stations in 1940 *(Toru 2023)*

Sixty Group grew at a dizzying pace, also taking over around one hundred army and navy radar bases. What it was to achieve was staggering. As 'the father of radar', Robert Watson-Watt put it (a little clumsily):

'… building a radio network several times larger than any other in the world in a time several times smaller than that allowed for building earlier and smaller networks.'

By the end of 1942, Sixty Group employed 18,000 people, many of whom had been trained at RAF Leighton Buzzard before being posted to their radar stations.

The civilian workers of Sixty Signals Group, now members of the RAF, had to conform to irritating service ways. Used to visiting the radar sites at any time of day or night, they did not take kindly to a life of passes, saluting and spit and polish. Nor were they amused at being asked to prove their right to enter installations which they had themselves set up. But the work was in all senses too great to let such things rankle.

To throw a shield around the islands, more and more sites had to be found where masts could be put up. Usually these were in remote places, often on the top of cliffs, often accessed over trackless moors. Then, having found the sites, masts had to be erected, along with buildings, accommodation and searchlight and Ack-Ack (anti-aircraft) gun sites. Services had to be planned and provided: roads, water, sewage, electricity and the crucial connections to Q-Central and Fighter Command headquarters at Bentley Priory.

There is a memorial in the field where Wilkins' original radar experiment took place, near Watling Street, in the delightfully named parish of Stowe Nine Churches, just south of Daventry. Rightly so. Churchill, in his 'finest hour speech' in 1940 said:

'If we fail, the whole world, including the United States, and all that we have known and cared for, will sink into the abyss of a new dark age made more sinister and perhaps more prolonged by the lights of a perverted science.'

Britain did not fail. Radar was ready. The world has Wilkins, Bowen, Hanbury-Brown, Watson-Watt, Tizard, Rowe, Wimperis, Fennessy and Seward and the paymaster, Philip Cunliffe-Lister to thank for that.

Above all, Britain's survival in the Battle of Britain was due to the leader of RAF Fighter Command, Hugh Dowding. In the next chapter, I will talk about how he used radar as the most decisive of his weapons in defeating the aerial armadas which had already caused the downfall of mainland Europe.

4: Fighter Command:

Bentley Priory and Hugh Dowding

Earlier in this book, I mentioned how, largely as a result of the threat from Germany, the RAF was divided into three main 'Commands', Fighter, Bomber and Coastal. I also explained how the headquarters of these (as well as Q Central) were sited in the Intelligence Zone. The headquarters of Fighter Command was at Bentley Priory, on the northern edge of London.

Bentley Priory has an Italianate look. The name suggests that it was once the site of a religious order which was probably suppressed by Henry the Eighth and the land snapped up by some canny developer. The sort of place where some 'honourable' returning from the Grand Tour of Europe in the eighteenth century might proudly hang his Rubens or Canaletto. Outwardly there is nothing that hints at world-shaking deeds. Yet it was here that Britain's greatest airman, Hugh Dowding, planned, executed and won victory in the Battle of Britain; saving not only his country but all humanity from what Churchill called 'the monstrous tyranny, never surpassed in the dark, lamentable catalogue of human crime.'

Hugh 'Stuffy' Dowding had been, as we have seen, the Royal Air Force's chief champion in the development of radar. He, as the Air Member for Supply and Research, conceived and oversaw the development of The Dowding System (of radar usage) by the RAF. When he was promoted to head up RAF Fighter Command, he continued to work with Bawdsey to refine the system.

Stuffy. The nickname is revealing. According to Lieutenant-General 'Tim' Pile (who was in charge of anti-aircraft guns and searchlights), he:

> 'Was the outstanding airman I met in the war. A difficult man, a self-opinionated man, a most determined man, and a man who knew more about all aspects of aerial warfare than anyone ...he treated all visitors to his walking monologues

...and even did the same to the queen ...who could only wait until he had finished, by which time everyone was a good deal behind the clock.'

Dowding was born in Scotland in 1882 and was coming up for retirement immediately before the war (although in positions of high command, retirement dates can be flexible. Churchill was 8 years older than he). Dowding seemed to have imbibed some of the dourness of the Scots covenanters. He was not one to suffer fools gladly. He had, like all those of senior rank in the RAF in the 1930s, begun his flying career in the Royal Flying Corps (RFC), a part of the army which was separated out and amalgamated with the Royal Navy Air Service to become the Royal Air Force on April the 1st 1918.

The lessons of the First World War had a profound effect on Dowding. He learned one of the most important of these lessons – how to avoid frittering away the lives of his men - from his boss, 'The father of the Royal Air Force', Hugh Trenchard. He did not learn it by emulating Trenchard...

Trenchard's nickname in his early days was 'Camel' because he neither drank nor spoke. Later, when he found his voice, this became 'Boom', because of his loud and forceful presence. While not an academic or technical man (he failed his army entrance exams four times), 'Boom' was good at shooting and rugger. He fought in the Boer War and took up flying in 1912, when he was 39. During the first war he (now in charge of the Royal Flying Corps) and his boss, the commander of the British armies, Earl Haig, were closely allied, both favouring constant attack; the way to victory being, in their eyes, the repetition of attack until victory (or defeat). As a result, both the army and the RFC suffered dreadful losses. Haig's nickname was 'the butcher of the Somme'; not for the damage that he inflicted on the enemy, but because of the 420,000 casualties his own army suffered during the Somme battles.

Dowding was of a different mind to Haig and Trenchard. He did not approve of the high number of British losses which resulted from their 'attack, at all costs' policy. Nor was he impressed by what he called Trenchard's 'technical stupidity.' The primary lesson that Dowding took from the carnage of the

Western Front was that bravery, aggression and 'morale' are not sufficient in warfare. Unless they are allied with good weapons and proper planning, they are more likely to lead to death than victory. Siegfried Sassoon, in his poem *'The General'* summed up the results of such idiocy:

'Good-morning, good-morning!" the General said
When we met him last week on our way to the line.
Now the soldiers he smiled at are most of 'em dead,
And we're cursing his staff for incompetent swine.
"He's a cheery old card," grunted Harry to Jack
As they slogged up to Arras with rifle and pack;
but he did for them both by his plan of attack.'

Dowding thought the Germans did things much better. He was not alone in this opinion. Fred Winterbotham who was shot down (in July 1917) and captured by the Germans said of them:

'It was impossible not to be be impressed by the logical and highly effective methods the German Air Force used, not only to preserve fuel and save the lives of as many pilots as possible, but also to achieve the same results as we did by our constant and often useless patrols, largely for morale purposes.' The British planes were: '...out of date... completely out-classed both in speed and gun power by the more modern German fighters.'

Dowding was commanding – and flying with - Number 9 Wing in 1916, carrying out Trenchard's tactics, which Dowding called:

'The wasteful and bloody policy of the Somme, whereby tiny formations of fighters were sent out day after day to be continually subjected to anti-aircraft fire, and to be attacked in superior numbers whenever the enemy chose to do so.'

Hugh Dowding set out to replace this lazy, wasteful and bloody policy by the use of forethought and planning. He was later to say: 'There is no greater pacifist in the country than myself.' As a slight aside, The British general Montgomery, while he would not have called himself a pacifist, learned much the same lesson from the bloody fields of the Somme.

Dowding's boss, Hugh Trenchard did not appreciate what he thought of as Dowding's timidity: and when the latter complained that his new pilots were poorly trained and therefore bound to suffer high losses, he was promoted and sent home. Back in England, Dowding complained anew about the low level of training new recruits received before being posted to the Western Front. 'Boom' Trenchard thought Dowding – 'dismal Jimmy' as he called him - lacked aggression and wanted to sack him but was argued out of doing so. During the years that followed the founding of the RAF, Trenchard (ennobled as Lord Trenchard), changed his mind about Dowding and promoted and supported him.

The historian AJP Taylor summed up Trenchard well:

'..like Haig, his hero, Trenchard was an extremely resolute and dogged commander, whose weapons did not come up to (his) expectations and whose plans did not correspond to the facts.'

Fortunately for the Royal Air Force (in which I had the honour to serve myself), 'Stuffy' was a rather different man than 'Boom'. Fortunately for all of mankind, in fact.

Dowding's spade work

During Dowding's time as Air Member for Supply and Research (1930-1936) aircraft design was developing rapidly, as was the fear of war with Germany. Although without scientific or technical training, he displayed a great capacity for understanding technical matters. During the first war, he had said 'People talk very lightly about casualties. They'll say "We only lost four pilots today." I feel as if I had lost four sons.' Dowding wasn't going to lose any sons if he could help it: and the way to protect them was to give them the best equipment that science could offer and train them thoroughly in its use.

Dowding invited tenders from two aircraft manufacturers for new fighters. These were to become the Spitfire and Hurricane. Both aircraft were powered by the Rolls Royce Merlin engine. Take a bow the designers of these three; Mitchell, Camm and Lovesey. Take a bow, too, Squadron Leader Ralph Sorley; for it was he, who, as head of Dowding's Operational Requirements research section, specified that the new fighter aircraft should be armed with eight machine guns (before that, RAF fighter planes had a maximum of four).

Dowding was a 'hands-on' commander, testing the machine guns himself. He even had to win an argument that the windscreens of his fighters be made of bulletproof glass. When he was told by technical experts that strengthened windshields were too heavy to be fitted into Hurricanes and Spitfires, he replied: "If a Chicago gangster can have bulletproof glass in his motor car, why not my pilots in their aeroplanes?" 'Stuffy' got his bulletproof glass.

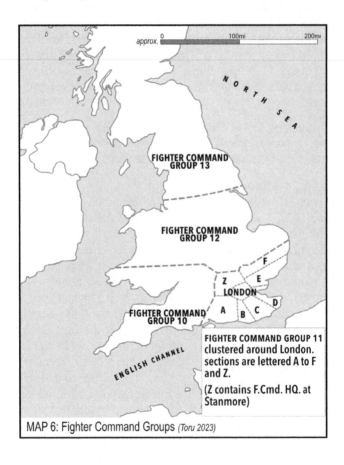

approx. 0   100mi   200mi

NORTH SEA

FIGHTER COMMAND GROUP 13

FIGHTER COMMAND GROUP 12

F
Z E
LONDON
D
A B C
FIGHTER COMMAND GROUP 10

ENGLISH CHANNEL

FIGHTER COMMAND GROUP 11 clustered around London. sections are lettered A to F and Z.

(Z contains F.Cmd. HQ. at Stanmore)

MAP 6: Fighter Command Groups *(Toru 2023)*

Most Fighter Command airfields had grass runways. Dowding would have liked to address this, too, but Fighter Command was the Cinderella of the RAF. The final rearmament plan before the war (scheme M) allocated £175,000,000 for bombers but only £45,000,000 for fighters.

Then, of course, there was radar. We have seen how the Bawdsey radar research station had set up Chain Home – the aerial sites around the coast that tracked incoming aircraft. This, as Dowding stated in 1937, led to a need within the RAF for:

'...operation rooms at all commands and stations with tables on which courses of all aircraft, hostile and friendly could be tracked.'

The main (underground) Operations Block was at Fighter Command HQ at Bentley Priory, buried in a 42' deep hole. Here it was that Geoffrey Roberts and Edward Fennessy installed the first Filter Room in 1938. Here reports from the various radar stations were collated with input from the Royal Observer Corps and the RAF 'Y' listening services. These gave estimated numbers of aircraft, their positions and, crucially, whether they were friendly (IFF - Identification Friend or Foe - was yet another of the radar and radio devices to be developed at Bawdsey and improved by input from the RAF).

Then the information was passed to the Central Operations Room, next door, and from there to Group headquarters and station operation rooms. RAF Fighter Command's coverage of Britain was divided into several 'Groups.' Tactically (being nearest the continent), the most important of these was 11 Group, covering the south eastern approaches to London. Its headquarters was at Uxbridge, a few miles from Fighter Command HQ. Each Group was divided into several Sectors, which handled operations for one or more airfields. For instance, 11 Group was split into Sectors A through F running anticlockwise from the south-west (Sussex, above the Isle of Wight) to north-east, along with Sector Z to the northwest (Northolt). Sector C, perhaps the busiest, was controlled from RAF Biggin Hill, in Kent.

The radar coverage of Britain was improved in November 1939 by the Chain Low aerials, which could detect low-level incoming aircraft: and which could be swung round to see inland. In the beginning these were rotated by a cyclist on a modified bike frame pedalling like mad. A joke of the era 'was that one could always identify one of the WAAF operators by her bulging calf muscles and unusually slim figure.' (Motorised controls for CHL were introduced in April 1941.)

This network of air defence was, and is, called The Dowding System. With it, and his weapons and pilots and ground crews, Hugh Dowding was to face the German Air Force – the Luftwaffe - when war broke out.

Churchill squanders Fighter Command in France: May 1940

By the outbreak of war, Dowding had built up Fighter Command to a point where he was confident that he could beat the Luftwaffe over the British Isles. That, as we have seen, was because he had been planning for this moment for many years. For all of those years of preparations, his plan was nearly brought to nothing – and that by none other than Winston Churchill.

When Heinz Guderian's German tank army poured into France, his blitzkrieg (lightning war) quickly defeated the French and British army divisions in his way. Partly this was because of poor allied equipment, partly it was because of poor allied generals – but mostly it was because of the idiocy of the French reliance on the fixed fortifications of the Maginot Line, which was supposed to stop any German advance. As these fortifications did not continue to the sea, they were easily bypassed by the Germans through the forests of the Ardennes. It is a measure of the quality of the French high command that they thought the Ardennes impassable to tanks.

The attack came on the 10th of May 1940. On the same day – though not for that reason - Chamberlain stepped down as Prime Minister of Britain and Winston Churchill stepped in. A baptism of fire. Churchill's made his 'Blood, toil, sweat and tears' speech, his first to Parliament as Prime Minister, three days later, on the 13th of May 1940. It is perhaps the most famous speech in the English language. In that speech he stated his war aim:

'Victory. Victory at all costs, victory in spite of all terror, victory, however long and hard the road may be; for without victory, there is no survival.'

That was as the French armies and the British Expeditionary forces in northern France were being routed by the Germans and were falling back towards the coast.

In the three weeks between the German breakthrough and the evacuation from Dunkirk, Churchill, who read and understood French very well and spoke it fairly fluently (in his own inimitable way), visited France six times. He loved France and would do almost anything to aid her against the German advance. Unfortunately, as he ordered more and more RAF squadrons to France to try and avoid military collapse, his sympathy went beyond the bounds of military sense. Dowding strenuously opposed this. Protecting and attacking ground forces at the limit of their range was not a job Fighter Command aircraft were designed or equipped for. If his carefully husbanded squadrons were lost over France, England would have insufficient defences.

On the 15th of May, Dowding demanded and was granted an audience with Churchill and Lord Beaverbrook (who was in charge of aircraft repair facilities) and Sir Cyril Newall (Chief of the Air Staff) to outline his fears. The next day he wrote one of the most important letters in the history of mankind; stating his fears. The key points were:

'I must point out that within the last few days the equivalent of 10 Squadrons have been sent to France, that the Hurricane Squadrons remaining in this country are seriously depleted, and that the more Squadrons which are sent to France the higher will be the wastage and the more insistent the demands for reinforcements... I would remind the Air Council that the last estimate which they made as to the force necessary to defend this country was 52 Squadrons, and my strength has now been reduced to the equivalent of 36 Squadrons *...if the Home Defence Force is drained away in desperate attempts to remedy the situation in France, defeat in France will involve*

73

the final, complete and irremediable defeat of this country.' (My italics.).

In spite of this, Churchill ordered ten more squadrons to France. Dowding now had 26 squadrons in Britain. Finally, on the 19th May, Churchill ordered that no more fighter squadrons be sent to France and the RAF flew their remaining fighters home. The return of the surviving aircraft, in Dowding's words, 'converted a desperate into a serious situation.'

Although no further squadrons were sent to be based in France, the RAF still needed to provide cover for the evacuation of British and French troops from Dunkirk. These planes flew from airfields in Kent. The air officer in charge of the operation was Air Commodore Keith Park: a popular and inspirational leader who flew his own Hurricane and constantly visited his airfields during the battle. The quality of the man can be seen in that his Hurricane is said to have been the last RAF aircraft over the invasion beaches.

On the 27th of May 1940, the Chiefs of Staff were asked by Churchill whether they thought Britain could continue to fight Germany. They replied that if Fighter Command could remain 'in being' they, with the help of the Royal Navy, could prevent an invasion. If not, no.

During the nine days of fighting during the evacuation of Dunkirk, from May the 26th to June the 4th, Fighter Command flew 2,739 sorties and lost 99 aircraft, mostly Spitfires and Hurricanes.

Dowding appeared before Cabinet a second time, on the 3rd of June to tell them that he was now down to 500 fighters (equivalent to about 30 full squadrons), including some needing repairs and servicing and if the Luftwaffe were to attack England now, he could not guarantee air superiority for more than 48 hours. In three weeks Fighter Command had lost over 430 planes over France and almost as many pilots.

And what of the French air force in all this? One might think the defence of France was primarily their concern. With about two and a half thousand aircraft, one would have expected them to have made a dent in the German advance. Individual pilots fought with bravery and success. Between them the Armée de l'Air and the RAF accounted for 1,428 German aircraft destroyed before the French surrender. But the French air force pilots were fighting more than the Germans. Apart from the obvious speed and power of the German advance, their planes were outmoded and often in the wrong places. The French actually had more serviceable aircraft at the end of the battle than at the beginning.

The worst enemy that the French armed forces faced were the failures of their own leaders. Firstly there was the ludicrous fact that the Maginot Line did not go all the way to the sea and could be (and was) bypassed. Secondly, both MI6 and the French air force had spotted the enormous build-up of German armour in the Ardennes and had, days before the attack, informed the French army HQ of the fact; but no action had been taken. The supreme commander of the French army was Maurice Gamelin.

As an aside, Winterbotham, in *The Ultra Secret* hints at worse faults in Gamelin than breath-taking incompetence; 'To the intelligent onlooker, it appeared that he was deliberately allowing the Germans a quick victory.' Gamelin's countrymen thought so too. The Vichy government tried him for treason. Gamelin refused to testify and was imprisoned.

When the French surrendered, they made the threat to Britain even more desperate by releasing 400 Luftwaffe pilots who had been shot down (by the British and French air forces) and captured in France. Churchill and Spears had repeatedly asked the French cabinet to send these captives to England but the French government had not complied.

The Battle of Britain

The Battle of Britain is reckoned to have started on July the 10th, 1940. The first part of the battle, while the Germans completed the moves of their bomber and fighter fleets to (mainly) French airfields, was exploratory, mostly over the channel – on British convoys. Losses here were more or less equal, a worrying statistic for the greatly outnumbered RAF. Across the water, landing barges for the invasion were towed from Dutch and German ports and rivers and assembled at

Boulogne, Dunkirk, Dieppe and a dozen other French and Belgian ports.

By mid-July, the Germans had around 900 serviceable fighters (Messerschmitt BF109s and BF110s) and around 900 serviceable bombers in the battle area. RAF Fighter Command had just over 500 serviceable Hurricanes and Spitfires. So, in terms of numbers, the RAF was at a very great disadvantage: with just over half of the 900 fighters Dowding had calculated were needed to defend the British Isles.

Dowding put Keith Park, who had overseen the RAF at Dunkirk, in charge of 11 Group, covering London's approaches from the south and east. This may have upset the commander of 12 Group, Trafford Leigh-Mallory, who was, from the point of view of experience in the role of Group commander, the more obvious choice to command the key 11 Group.

By early August the Germans were ready to strike the knock-out blow. Fred Winterbotham, the man who had spied on Germany pre-war and was now in charge of communications between Hut 3 at Bletchley Park and the air force and army, had had a direct teleprinter line installed to a soundproof room 'down the hole' - as the operations block at Bentley Priory was called. Air Commander Keith Park was on the distribution list, too. Hermann Goering's signals to his staff were being decoded at Bletchley Park (German-speaking WAAF officers had been drafted in to assist). This high level information told Dowding what to expect. The warning knell was Goering's message on the 8th of August to all units. 'within a short period you will wipe the British Air Force from the sky.' Dowding, Park and Churchill got the message before many of the intended recipients.

The pilots of the Battle of Britain on both sides were brave men. That is more than just a commonplace and obvious remark, it is a warning, if it were needed, that an evil regime, too, can inspire bravery – even heroism - in its troops. The warning is one that each of us, and especially soldiers, should heed. Military discipline or no, it is not enough to believe without question what we are told. Indeed, at the end of the war, at the Nuremburg Trials, many men who claimed to have 'only followed orders' would go to the gallows.

The world saw no weakness in the German war machine – only a juggernaut which rolled over country after country, with attacks spear-headed by the terrifying scream of the vertically-diving Stuka bomber. However, the Luftwaffe had disadvantages too. Some were down to geography. They were fighting a long way from home, mainly at the other side of a sea, the English Channel. German airmen who bailed out rarely made it back. Then there were Dowding's defences, built up with the money from various defence reviews.

The Spitfire

The Spitfire, the most effective fighter on the British side, was at least equal to and in some respects outclassed the main German fighter, the BF109, while both the Spitfire and Hurricane outclassed the BF110. 'Johnnie' Johnson, the fighter ace, brimmed with enthusiasm for the Spitfire: 'Stick forward, centralise the controls and she comes out like the thoroughbred she is – I could hug her!' The Hurricane shot down rather more German planes than the Spitfire, although, as there were twice as many of them, and as they were directed mainly at bombers while Spitfires went for their fighter escorts, the comparison is a bit unfair. The Rolls Royce Merlin engine, which powered both, was superb: arguably the best piston engine of World War Two.

The first heavy waves of German bomber attacks were on the airfields and the south coast ports - Dover, Portsmouth and Southampton.

Ominously, the Luftwaffe also struck at the Achilles' heel of Fighter Command, the radar stations. I mentioned in the previous chapter that the Germans had overflown the English east coast with an airship, listening for radio emissions from the radar masts. Although they had not detected any such, Major General Wolfgang Martini, head of the Luftwaffe's Signals group, didn't believe that the British could have been putting up masts all along their coasts for no reason. He badgered Field Marshall Goering, the head of the Luftwaffe, into attacking the radar sites. On the 12th of August 1940 – the glorious twelfth, the start of the grouse shooting season on the northern moors – he managed to get some resources diverted away from the main German thrust of battle. This time it would be the grouse that attacked the beaters. They went for the sites at Dunkirk (in Kent), Dover, Rye, and Pevensey; and they sent 16 Stukas against Ventnor station, on the Isle of Wight. They did minor damage to the first four of these stations but they knocked Ventnor out for weeks. There was now a hole in the radar chain.

The next day Goering summoned Martini to his luxurious estate at Carrinhall and told him to stop wasting his time; he didn't have the resources to waste on sideshows. 'If he had continued' said Edward Fennessy, the man in charge of networking the sites together;

'Fighter Command would have been blind. He would have wiped Fighter Command out as an effective unit, Their failure to demolish the masts meant that that day he lost the Battle of Britain.'

'That day' was August the 13th 1940, the day the Germans called *Adler Tag* (Eagle Day). This was the day the RAF was scheduled to be wiped out. The assault was by the main part of the German bomber and fighter fleets – virtually the whole weight of both sides of the Luftwaffe – and was designed to destroy, and was met by, RAF Fighter Command.

Dowding and Park's tactic was to employ their aircraft in squadron size (approximately 16 aircraft) so as to be always able to quickly challenge the Luftwaffe's incursions. It all hinged on the radar stations, the aircraft and the men who flew them.

While Sir Hugh Dowding controlled the Battle from day to day, it was Keith Park who controlled it hour by hour. Dowding chose well. 'Johnnie' Johnson said of Park: 'He was the only man who could have lost the war in a day or even an afternoon'. Dowding said much the same thing.

Information from Bletchley Park's Hut 3 to Fighter Command helped. As Ronald Lewin wrote in *Ultra goes to war:*

'Whenever Bletchley could provide in advance deciphered German orders for a complicated series of attacks, stretching over many hours, Dowding was able to plan and orchestrate his response with ample foreknowledge.'

More importantly for the immediate battles was the Filter Room at Bentley Priory. Into it flowed information from all of the radar stations (except, temporarily, Ventnor). This was co-ordinated with Observer Corps sightings and 'Y' service intercepts of German pilot's chatter. Maybe those pilots were merely humming the catchy hit of the moment *Wir fahren gegen Engeland* (we sail against England, also available as a board game), maybe they would let slip their destination.

The best operatives on the tracking tables were women – mostly air force WAAFs. Eileen Younghusband, in her key book, *One woman's war*, who served at Bentley Priory (near to, and often referred to as, Stanmore):

'It was found that male Filterers, mostly well over thirty years of age were far too slow during periods of intense activity and they had to be removed from the table. The women were all between the ages of nineteen and twenty-four ...all personnel involved had to have quick reactions, mathematical ability and have lasting energy. The women chosen ranged from psychology and science students, young actresses, county debutantes, grammar school high flyers to daughters of famous people - novelists, painters, musicians and vicars. But they were without exception dedicated to their work.'

These were the graduates of 'Q Central', RAF Leighton Buzzard, that we met in the last chapter. Bentley Priory/

Stanmore was the most important filter room of them all (there were seven in total). Only the best were sent there.

Not surprisingly, the young airman often saw more in these young women than their operational efficiency. And on the squadrons the pilots were often the same age as the plotters. Dowding had ordained that: 'only exceptionally should officers over 26 years of age be posted to command Fighter Squadrons.'

A common refrain is echoed by 'Johnnie' Johnson: 'The majority were blondes and some were quite beautiful. It couldn't be just coincidence, I reflected, that the most glamorous WAAF plotters seemed to find their way to the operations rooms at Fighter Command and the groups.'

Fred Winterbotham was rather taken with one of the plotters at Bentley Priory, Petrea Trant: 'On one occasion I noticed a lovely girl who was working harder than most. She looked up and I saw a pair of laughing brown eyes. She became my wife.'

Romance, of course, was very much an aside. Mostly it was long hours and strain. I will touch on some of the deeper problems when I write about Bomber Command.

The radar family was so new that it was growing even as the battle progressed. From 54 stations in July to 76 in September. The radar data was crucial. 'Without signals' Park said, 'The only thing I commanded was my desk at Uxbridge.'

The Dowding system which controlled the (smaller) RAF forces survived *Adler Tag* as it was to survive all of the other hammer blows meted out by the Luftwaffe armadas. The German pilots were unnerved by it. Luftwaffe veteran Hans-Ekkehard Bob said later:

'Once I experienced a Spitfire formation all of a sudden coming up from behind and wondered how that was even possible. Having no visibility whatsoever, neither from above nor from below, how was it possible that an enemy formation was able to get into a firing position from behind?'

In the battle of attrition which went on through August and early September, the RAF had other advantages that came good. A major one was the organisation that Lord Beaverbrook ran.

Beaverbrook, a Canadian newspaper magnate, had been appointed by Churchill to shake up aircraft production. He had finally got the woefully-mismanaged Castle Bromwich factory producing Spitfires. (This newly built factory had been funded by Lord Swinton, whom we have already met, and instigated by Wilfrid Freeman, whom we will meet later). Britain was now producing 500 single seat fighters (Hurricanes and Spitfires) a month, Germany just 140 (Messerschmitt BF109s).

Beaverbrook was also in charge of the Civilian Repair Organisation. Managed from Magdalen College, Oxford, this was a vast and complex organisation that picked up and patched up crashed RAF aircraft. One Hurricane that flew in the battle had been shot down three times. Beaverbrook and Dowding got on extremely well professionally. They also had a huge respect for each other. Beaverbrook would phone Dowding each day to ask what more he could do. When Dowding said his pilots were 'sons to me', it was more than warm words. Both he and Beaverbrook had sons who were pilots in Fighter Command, fighting in the battle – Dowding's being his only son. Both boys survived. Peter Gossage, the son of Park's predecessor at the helm of 11 group, did not. He flew a Hurricane covering the Dunkirk evacuation. He spun into the ground, aged 20. The RAF was family. The war was not to treat the family well. Of the 1,095 officer cadets who passed through RAF Cranwell in 1939, over half (555) died in the war.

Providing pilots was a greater problem than replacing aircraft. Only 200 pilots were coming out of training a month to replace those shot down – and those were 'green' – lucky to survive their first battle with an experienced enemy. To plug this gap – although he was a little late in doing so – Dowding called in Polish and Czech pilots. Most of the nearly 3,000 pilots who flew for Fighter Command were from Britain, the empire and commonwealth, plus a few Irish and Americans, but about a tenth were from mainland Europe: 141 Polish, 86 Czech, 29 Belgian and 13 Free French (although it is an unfortunate truth that after the fall of France, far more French pilots flew against the RAF – in Iraq and Africa and against Gibraltar – than for it).

It was a war of allies – and the Poles and Czechs especially fought with a skill, intensity and hatred of the enemy above the norm. The RAF had inherited the aces – many of whom had already survived battle against the Luftwaffe - from these unfortunate countries. Men of the quality of Josef František, who the Germans had chased round Europe. He had flown for the air forces of Czechoslovakia, Poland and France before joining the RAF. He had 17 confirmed victories in a period of 4 weeks in September 1940. A nonconformist, the RAF found it best to let him patrol alone, a role in which he was highly successful. He was killed in a crash in October 1940 in the final week of the Battle of Britain.

'Johnnie' Johnson was of the opinion that 'A mixed unit was happier and more efficient than one comprised of pilots of a single nationality. The Canadian fighter pilots had a reputation for toughness.'

Dowding marshalled his forces well. When the Germans launched raids from Norway and Denmark, thinking that Dowding's defence of the south must have left the north defenceless, the northern squadrons were ready and defeated the attacks. The Luftwaffe lost about a fifth of their aircraft and never repeated the attempt.

10 Group to the west and 12 Group to the north of the pivotal 11 group, were reserved for the protection of 11 group airfields and to be called in as needed. Dowding rotated his squadrons between Groups as they became reduced to half strength (9 operational aircraft). Outnumbered by the German air fleets and often flying several sorties a day that happened quickly. Some squadrons lasted a week, the maximum was six weeks, as day after day they were scrambled into the air during the long summer months of the battle. Thus Dowding moved formations from airfield to airfield – out of relatively safe sectors and into the cauldron of Kent and Sussex, resting tired squadrons.

With this level of attrition came mounting tiredness and, in some, crippling fear. 'Johnnie' Johnson says:

'We all knew the meaning of fear, and felt it according to our temperament and training. I never knew a pilot who fell outside this category: our simple duty was to control this fear and prevent its natural transition to panic. We knew fear and lived and fought with it. Once you let it give way to panic, you were finished.'

Bletchley Park's knowledge of Goering's signals was excellent. Goering's insight into the RAF, on the other hand, was poor. His 'knowledge' was duly picked up and passed on by Bletchley Park. Within a week of his main attacks, he 'knew' that the RAF was down to 300 aircraft. In fact they had more than double that. And so his calculations continued. By the end of the battle, those of the Luftwaffe who survived would joke that they were off to tackle 'the last 50 fighters.'

Also, courtesy of decoded Luftwaffe signals, Fred Winterbotham – and hence Dowding, Park, Churchill and Beaverbrook - learned that German aircraft replacements were no longer coming through and they had no comparable repair facilities to the Beaverbrook ones. The German air force was down to half its former strength. 'This was vital information. It showed that despite the appalling position of the RAF, the Luftwaffe was crippled; their morale too was suffering.' Bletchley's information was more precious than gold. There must be no hint of its existence except to those who had to know. Winterbotham says: 'I watched Dowding and Keith Park handle the Ultra with supreme care, never hinting that the top secret alerts, which were given to the key sector aerodrome commanders, had come from intercepted signals.'

Then Goering changed his tactics. For two weeks his Luftwaffe targeted British airfields and aircraft factories almost exclusively. Now the production lines at Castle Bromwich became critical, as the main Spitfire (Supermarine) factory at Southampton was heavily bombed. This was the worst moment for the RAF: and if the attacks had continued for another fortnight, in Winterbotham's opinion, they might well have lost the battle. Winterbotham says of the attacks on the sector airfields 'Some of the little operations rooms, such as that of Biggin Hill where I had watched the battles earlier on, had been hit and many of the girls had been killed, yet within hours an emergency room was again operational.' In this period Fighter Command lost 200 more Spitfires and Hurricanes than it received. Of a total complement of around 1,000 pilots, 231 had been killed, wounded or were missing. Six of the seven sector airfields were badly damaged and so were five forward airfields. The tide had turned. The RAF were losing the battle.

Target London; the first London Blitz

Then Hermann Goering changed his tactics yet again. RAF Bomber Command had begun to bomb Berlin (in retaliation, it was said, for Luftwaffe 'overshoot' bombing of London), causing Hitler to relax his veto on attacking the British capital. So Goering attacked London, the richest, biggest and fattest target in the world, reasoning that his adversary could not afford to defend this with 'penny packets'. The whole of the now (as he believed) vastly depleted Fighter Command would have to protect the capital and so he could finish it off at a stroke.

On September the 7th 1940, Bletchley Park (Ultra) picked up an order from Goering for a 300 bomber raid on the London docks with a massive fighter cover. Invasion Alert Number 1 (Imminent invasion expected) was issued by the Air Ministry and troops and Home Guards were brought up to immediate readiness. As Winterbotham later wrote: 'Thanks to Ultra, Goering's signal was in the hand of the Prime Minister and Dowding within minutes of its dispatch.' The East End was hit in the afternoon by 300 bombers and 600 fighters.

Dowding, however, was not down to his last few aircraft. He now called on 12 Group to the north. As ever, the Luftwaffe was astounded. Whatever airfield they came from on the vast 200 mile long sweep from Normandy to Belgium, however they approached their target and whatever their target was, the RAF were there waiting for them, often above them.

By chance, on that very same day, an article in *The Observer*, by its editor, James Garvin said:

'The next seven days may decide the future of the entire world. There has never been a more critical week in world history. The perils of any Nazi attempt to invade Britain at once are manifold. But it is now or never for them. If they flinch we win.'

Garvin was a perceptive man. The Nazis did flinch: that very night Goering tried a new tactic, sending his bombers in after dark. A night attack followed the day attack. The night blitz –

the second battle – had begun. The two would overlap, and London was now to go through hell for eight months, but this was the start of a major change. With growing and unsustainable day time fighter losses, the Luftwaffe would soon switch practically the whole of their bomber offensive on London and the ports to the night. But not quite yet…

On September the 15th the Luftwaffe launched a major day attack as around 100 German bombers protected by 400 fighters fought with nearly 200 spitfires and Hurricanes over the streets of London. Portland and Southampton were also hit. The Germans lost 56 aircraft that day, to the RAF's 27. Fourteen of the RAF pilots survived.

The RAF still had over 600 fighters, while the Luftwaffe now had only about half of that number. They had bombers, but they could no longer defend them. Dowding had confounded the experts. The bomber would not 'always get through' – in the day anyway. The RAF had blunted the Luftwaffe.

In the daylight battles alone, between June and October 1940, the Luftwaffe had lost 1733 aircraft (the RAF had lost 915), in addition to thousands of airmen. They were too weak to continue the day fight. They would intensify their night attacks and all but cease the day battle.

On the seventeenth of September, Bletchley Park intercepted a signal from the German General Staff to the officer in charge of loading transport aircraft in Belgium and Holland. These were the planes earmarked to ferry German troops to England when the RAF had been cleared from the skies. The loading equipment was to be dismantled. Operation Sealion, Hitler's plan to occupy Britain, was put on hold. Winterbotham was called from Bletchley to Churchill's war room, buried beneath the streets of London, near to parliament and Westminster Abbey, to explain this to the military commanders. After the conference, he went up to the surface with Churchill. An air raid was in progress, but Churchill brushed past the phalanx of military commanders who urged him to caution, round the blast wall and out onto Horse Guards Road. In Winterbotham's stirring prose:

'Just across the other side of St James's Park, Carlton House Terrace was ablaze: the boom of bombs exploding to the south, the crack and rattle of the AA guns and exploding shells, the red-white glow of the fires silhouetting the tall black trunks of the great trees in the park. It was a moment in history to remember, and above the noise came the angry voice of Winston Churchill: "By God, we will get the bastards for this."

'There was,' says Winterbotham, 'an unconfirmed rumour that the admirals were prepared to guard Nelson's Column in Trafalgar Square in case the statue on top should be replaced by one of Dowding.'

The RAF – or rather Dowding's Fighter Command - had chewed up the Luftwaffe and spat it out in pieces. The last victory had been denied Hitler. He would throw the dice again. Daylight was no good for him – could he beat Britain into submission at night? Unfortunately for the Luftwaffe, Bowen at Bawdsey had thought of that too and Dowding had incorporated his defence – airborne radar – into his constantly-refined battle plan. Vincent Orange tells how:

'Almost every evening from September onward, Dowding would be driven to Kenley or Redhill to observe experiments with airborne radar. He would return to Uxbridge to talk with Park, his driver picking his way through streets littered with masonry and assorted wreckage, every ravaged house a reminder of the shortcomings of the air defences. Back at Bentley Priory, where he often worked far into the night, naked electric bulbs showed a neglected building, bare, damp, dirty and freezing cold. A WAAF plotter met him leaving the building one night, his face grey with fatigue, but he did not fail to hold the door open, and his hand went up to his cap when he said good night.'

The reason why the Luftwaffe could not be defeated at night was simply that the brand-new science, airborne radar controlled interception, was not yet good enough. And the night attacks were terrible. London was bombed for 57 consecutive nights from 7th September 1940. Large areas of the British capital, as well as many other cities such as Southampton, Portsmouth, Bristol, Swansea, Liverpool and Hull were laid waste by incendiary and high explosive bombs. Tens of thousands of men, women and children died. Hundreds of thousands of homes were destroyed. The people fled the cities. Children were billeted with strangers all across the country. This was no precision attack on the RAF, or industry – the accuracy of night navigation forbade that – it was indiscriminate bombing of the type already used by the Luftwaffe on Guernica, Rotterdam and Warsaw (the Nazis would call this 'terror bombing' when the RAF repaid the compliment).

The RAF would finally win that battle too – partly by using the Beaufighter aeroplane, which was fast enough to catch the raiders, partly by better ground control of the intercepting aircraft, partly by the pilots getting better with practice, partly by advances in the radar used. The victory of the second, night, battle came in May 1941 and is worth a book in itself: and it has it, in Roderick Chisholm's *Cover of darkness*. Chisholm flew night fighters, felt fear and fatigue and the unreality of fighting in God's beautiful heavens to kill his fellow man; and saw his brothers fall to their death. The book is well worth reading.

Battle of Britain – the significance

There are some key British battles. The Roman conquest. The Battle of Hastings. The defeat of the Spanish invasion by the fireships of Drake. The breaking of Napoleon's armies at Waterloo. The defeat of the French fleet at Trafalgar. All fade into insignificance against the Battle of Britain: for this battle quite simply saved the civilised world.

If the RAF had failed in 1940, then any ships of the Royal Navy operating in the English Channel would have been sunk by bombing. With no Royal Navy, Hitler's army, supplemented by his parachute divisions, would have taken Britain.

The first wave of the landing was to have been eleven infantry and two airborne divisions, each of around 16,000 men. The second wave was to be eight tank and motorised divisions. The third wave was to have been six more infantry divisions. The special forces – the Brandenburg Regiment, blooded in Poland where they had already left a trail of death, were to arrive with the first wave.

The death squads (the *Einsaztsgruppen*; the troops who set up the mobile gas chambers and shooting grounds in Poland, the Ukraine and Russia that killed an estimated two million people) would follow. Their first task – after killing the underground resistance – would have been to murder Jews, gypsies and the mentally subnormal. Concentration camps, sterilisations, gassings and all the other methods of Hitler's madmen would have followed in due course. The consequence for Britain were quite clear. *The Orders concerning the Organisation and Function of Military Government in England*, dated the 9th of September 1940, ordained that:

'The able-bodied male population between the ages of seventeen and forty-five will …be interned and dispatched to the continent with the minimum of delay.' Indeed that is precisely what did happen to all of the mainland-born males in the Channel Islands (the only part of Britain to be occupied by the Nazis). The fate of the women was not described in the invasion plan.

The ships of the Royal Navy, the most powerful on Earth (those that did not manage to flee or scuttle themselves), would have been taken by the Germans.

With Britain out of the way, Hitler would have struck the Soviet Union earlier and harder. Without 'general winter' and support from the West, there is little doubt Russia would have fallen. Stalingrad would probably have succumbed without note, just like Kiev. The Russian 'unter mensch' (sub-humans), as the Nazis termed them, would have been slaughtered en masse, as they were in all Nazi-occupied eastern areas.

In my first chapter, I mentioned a Gallup poll carried out in the United States in May 1940. The question in that poll, you may recall, was whether America would be the next Nazi target after Britain fell. Two in three Americans believed that would be the case. They were almost certainly correct. What would have been the result?

It is an easily confirmed (though little generally known) historical fact that at the beginning of the Second World War the British led the world in atomic research. Having been the first to split the atom, they had already begun the world's first atomic weapon research programme (under the Maud Committee).

If Britain had fallen and the Nazis had got hold of that research, the first atom bomb could have been German. The Germans were the world leaders in rocketry. If the Nazi bomb had been placed on a German rocket, there is a strong possibility that the first atom bombs would not have been on Japan but on New York and Washington. I will return to atomics and German rocketry later in this book.

The Second World war was the first war in man's bloody history where the prize was the entire world. RAF Fighter Command – The Few - had won the greatest victory in the history of their – and arguably any - country. And 'The One' who had led them was Hugh Dowding. His first biographer, Basil Collier said of him:

'It is scarcely an exaggeration to say that, but for Dowding, there would have been no Hurricane, no Spitfire, no radar chain, no escape for the Royal Air Force from the fate that had overwhelmed its counterparts in European countries, no avoidance of irremediable disaster.'

He might have added that to win the battle Dowding had not only had to beat the Luftwaffe; he had to out-argue Churchill too.

The appreciation of his fellows

The admirals guarding Nelson's column needn't have bothered. Dowding wasn't lauded, or even thanked. He was given the push. He was already a marked man. He had been due to end his three year contract as head of Fighter Command in June 1939, at the age of 57. Then, in dribs and drabs, sometimes with only a day's notice, it was extended a further five times. This was incompetence, contempt and malevolence of a high order in the Air Ministry. The further work – and strain – it put on Dowding **while he was running the Battle of Britain** is painful to imagine. As soon as he, and Park, had won that battle the Air Ministry got rid of them.

According to Vincent Orange there was:

'..an easily understandable desire to see the back of Dowding. He was notoriously intolerant of the slackness normal in the comfortable pre-war Whitehall world in which he had served for six years. He was abstemious and unsmiling even on social occasions. He was damnably eloquent on paper (see his letter) and an untiring critic in meetings, a man who had actually read all the papers.'

Efficient. Not sufficiently respectful. Outshining his peers. Worst of all, he had gone against holy writ. In breaking the Luftwaffe's bombers he had disproved the 'Trenchard doctrine' that 'the bomber will always get through.' Being right was Stuffy's unpardonable sin. Dowding must go: but how?

Big Wing: Leigh-Mallory and Bader

One of Dowding's main critics was Sir Trafford Leigh-Mallory, the commander of Twelve Group, based in the Midlands (12 Group HQ was at Duxford, in Cambridgeshire). He was the man, it will be recalled, whom Dowding had bypassed when he appointed Keith Park to the running of Eleven Group (the protectors of the channel approaches and London) - the most important of his commands. Dowding had had to rebuke Leigh-Mallory on more than one occasion. If one looks at the evidence in detail (and my account is, of course, a précis), it's hard to say why Dowding hadn't sacked him during the Battle of Britain.

One of the worst of Leigh-Mallory's errors was to circulate the views of Wing Commander Douglas Bader and his poorly thought-out and widely discredited – indeed plain wrong – 'Big Wing' theory. The theory was that squadrons should gather together and attack incoming aircraft en masse. The main fault (although not the only one) of 'Big Wing' was that so much time was taken up by multiple squadrons forming up that the Luftwaffe was given time to bomb their target and head for home. It was tried by Park and that's what happened. There are plenty of accounts of fighter pilots thoughts on the matter. A typical, but especially important one, is that of 'Johnnie' Johnson. Johnson was the Allied fighter pilot who shot down the most Luftwaffe planes (34) during the war. He was admiring of Bader's courage (he flew with him) but not of 'Big Wing':

'Time is one of the most important factors in air fighting... (a) profound tactical error would have been committed had Park sent off nothing less than a Balbo (Big Wing) ...as advocated by the proponents of the large formations.'

That Leigh-Mallory touted this odd theory says little for his abilities. But there are quite a few other faults in his judgement. For example, Vincent Orange relates how in 1938 he had asked Dowding for 29 of the then 41 fighter squadrons for his area (north of London), leaving 12 squadrons for the defence of London and none for the rest of the country. Astonishing. Leigh-Mallory (as Johnnie Johnson wrote in an appreciation of him after his death) 'Did not pretend to know about fighter tactics.' Possibly that is why Dowding had not selected him as the commander of 11 Group.

Leigh-Mallory's liking for 'Big Wing' was not only a product of his ignorance of fighter tactics; he had fallen under the spell of the high-priest of the Big Wing theory, Douglas Bader. Bader was - to put it politely - a force of nature who few could resist. As Johnson – and many others - said: 'nobody argued with Bader.' The tin-legged hero, icon of the RAF, always got his way with those he commanded and often with his more impressionable superiors, including the genial Leigh-Mallory: even ringing him up in bed to complain that he wasn't getting enough action. But, Bader, and indeed Leigh-Mallory, were but pawns in the game to get rid of Dowding and his protégé, Keith Park.

The machinations and the characters who conspired to bring down Dowding are a subject in their own right: and are covered in the books by Jack Dixon and Vincent Orange which I list in the bibliography. Of those in power, only Beaverbrook and Churchill supported him. Winston Churchill did not think a lot of the air staff. As far back as 1935, he had written: 'I wonder whether the existing brain power of the Royal Air Force is at all adequate to its staff work, or to the study of the decisive strategic problems involved.' Evidently not. Dowding, however, obviously was. While that might make his lesser-talented compatriots mob him, it also caused Churchill to stand by him.

Churchill, one would have thought, would have been ample support. And so for a time he was. In July 1940 Winston wrote to the Secretary of State for Air (Sir Archibald Sinclair):

'I was very much taken aback the other night when you told me that you had considered removing Sir Hugh Dowding at the expiration of his present appointment …he is one of the best men you have got and I say this having been in contact with him for about two years. I have greatly admired the whole of his work in Fighter Command, especially in resisting ..the immense pressure to dissipate the fighter strength during the great French battle. In fact, he has my full confidence.'

Quite. This shows not only Churchill's good sense but also his ability to learn by his mistakes. That all-too-rare quality was one of Churchill's greatest strengths, as it was one of Dowding's. Dowding had seen how the German air force outperformed the RFC in the first war and moulded Fighter Command so it could not do so again. The Trenchard camp - and Trenchard was very much still alive and working in the background – were broadly of the opinion that having beaten the Germans once, there was obviously nothing to be learned from them.

But Churchill eventually did go along with Dowding's dismissal. In early November 1940, Dowding was rung up by Sir Archibald Sinclair and told that; "the Air Ministry has no further work for you." He was asked to clear his desk within twenty-four hours. Shortly after this, Keith Park was removed too and told that his services were not required any more.

'To my dying day' said Park in 1968, 'I shall feel bitter at the base intrigue which was used to remove Dowding and myself as soon as we won the battle.' Leigh-Mallory replaced Keith Park. Hugh Dowding was replaced by Sholto-Douglas (a Trenchard-doctrine airman).

Airbrush

But the Air Ministry not only wanted rid of Dowding and Park: they wanted their names removed from history, too. They (the Air Ministry) published an account, *The Battle of Britain August-October 1940*, shortly afterwards. Not surprisingly the nation which had seen themselves delivered from catastrophe were eager to know to whom they owed their salvation: and how. They knew what had been at play – as the article in *The Observer* I quoted earlier is witness. The neat little A5 booklet sold heavily: 300,000 on the first day, and several millions in all. In its 32 pages it gives good descriptions of the rival aircraft. Radar gets no mention – although there are strong hints that something other than the Observer Corps was at work: 'It is not easy to describe (the detection methods) without giving away state secrets.' Only two individuals who were then living are named, one on each side. The German is Hermann Goering, head of the Luftwaffe. The Briton is Winston Churchill. The Air Ministry were as adept with the airbrush as with the knife.

To his credit, Churchill objected to this, calling it an 'offence'. He wrote at once to castigate the Minister for Air (Sinclair) saying that it was;

'As If the admiralty had told the tale of Trafalgar and left Lord Nelson out of it. ....The jealousies and cliquism which have led to the committing of this offence are a discredit to the Air Ministry. ....It grieves me very much that you should associate yourself with such behaviour.'

Sinclair waffled but bent to the storm. A revised edition naming Dowding and Park was issued.

In fact Churchill, evidently troubled about what he'd acquiesced to, went further. In 1943 he procured a peerage for Dowding, who became Baron Dowding of Bentley Priory. Why Churchill agreed to the dismissal of Dowding has always disturbed me. That he should have been party to such a base act was foreign to what I believed the man to have been: so had I been wrong about Churchill? I was much relieved, then, in my research for this book, to find illumination in a book by David Reynolds called *In Command of History – Churchill fighting and writing the second world war.* Mr Reynolds has done his homework. He has explored early drafts of Churchill's works, including *Their Finest Hour*: One of those drafts explains that he had reluctantly yielded to Air Ministry pressure and 'I was wrong not to insist on my view.' Churchill was indeed mistaken.

Interviewed by Russian journalists in 1945, Field Marshal Gerd von Rundstedt, the most senior surviving German commander, was asked which battle of the war he regarded as the most decisive. They expected him stay Stalingrad. Instead he answered 'the Battle of Britain: here the German armies learned for the first time that they could be beaten and they didn't like it.'

Dowding was, in the words of 'Bomber' Harris, who we will meet later: 'The only commander who won one of the decisive battles of history and got *sacked* for his pains.'

Dowding's last public appearance was in 1969, at the London premiere of the excellent film 'The Battle of Britain'.

Sadly crippled by arthritis and confined to a wheelchair, he was given a standing ovation by the audience of 350, many of them 'Dowding's chicks' – former pilots. The Queen smiles and bows to receive 'Stuffy's' salute. Perfect. But I get ahead of myself.

Queen Elizabeth II receives
'Stuffy's' salute

Dowding's victory was to spark off the most amazing sequel; the Arrival by parachute of Hitler's number two, Rudolf Hess to try and end the war between Germany and Britain. And that is where Winston Churchill, to whom I devote my next chapter, comes to the forefront of the picture.

5: Winston Churchill – the guardian of the flame

Success is not final, failure is not fatal. It is the courage to continue that counts. *Winston Churchill*

Churchill

In the first chapter of this book, I stated my belief that without Hugh Sinclair, Hugh Dowding and Winston Churchill the free world would have been enslaved in World War Two. Sinclair's part – indeed his life – was finished before battle was joined. Dowding's battle was won by 1941.

Churchill is different. His trademarks - the 'V' sign, the cigars, the bellicose growl, the baby face - are so powerful in themselves that they hide his deeper qualities. Churchill was a historical colossus. Like Napoleon, Alexander, Caesar, here was a man around whom the world turned, changed and was rearranged. His role in global events pervades this book and beyond. He planned and mastered the alliances which preserved freedom and defeated the powers of fascism. He shaped the future of Europe, America and the world. It was through him that the British Empire ended and America succeeded to world power.

Hitler was perfectly aware of the threat that Churchill posed to him. In January 1939 the head of the British section of the German war ministry's intelligence department, Count Gerhard von Schwerin, risked his life by travelling secretly to London. The goal of his visit was to do everything that he could to avoid war between Germany and Britain. To this end, he spoke to the Foreign Office and security services. He suggested to them, among other measures, that Churchill: 'The only Englishman Hitler is afraid of' should be brought into the Cabinet. The powers that be in London brushed aside his suggestions as 'damned cheek.'

Why was Hitler afraid of Churchill? The Fuhrer was well aware - having lived through it - that Germany's defeat in the first war was primarily due to the British navy and the French and British armies. He, like Churchill, expected air warfare to be key in the rerun. Churchill was the most experienced and determined of all his enemies in air, land and sea warfare.

In one way, the two were alike. Both were leaders of great power, giants among men. But these giants were as different as chalk and cheese. Hitler believed himself to be the messenger of the gods, if not a god himself. If his followers fell, then they were not worthy to live. Hypnotic, ranting, spewing hatred and lies, he fouled his own nation and stamped down many others. If he had not been stopped, he would have broken the world. Churchill had a more ironic conception of his place on earth. "We are all worms," he said, "but I believe that I am a glow worm."

Churchill had the innate assurance (but surprisingly little of the arrogance) of the English upper classes. He was from the top drawer, both socially and intellectually. He was born, in 1874, in a mansion with a rather German name, Blenheim Palace, near Oxford, which belonged to his grandfather. It had been in the family for a good while, having been given to John Churchill, the First Duke of Marlborough, as a reward for destroying the armies of the French Sun King, Louis, in the seventeenth century. Stopping European dictators was in the blood.

Winston Churchill was the son of an English aristocrat and an American heiress, Jennie Jerome. His parents married at a time when a good number of rich Americans were marrying into the English upper classes. A great deal of money made in the United States flooded into what was still seen by many Americans as the mother country; often giving relief to that frequently threadbare if (sometimes) respectable institution, the English aristocracy. Churchill's Anglo-American roots were a subject that he set great store by; as was the wider story of Britain, her empire and the world.

Winston Churchill's writing skills were of the highest order – he was to win the Nobel prize for literature. He first came to the general public's notice in a series of books he wrote from the frontline of a couple of Britain's many imperial wars in Africa. What really 'made' him was *The Boer War* – which included his stirring account of his capture by and escape from

97

the Boers in South Africa. It was not only the subject of his stirring patriotic tales that entranced his readers – a good part of the country – but his skill in telling them.

In 1908 he married 'Clemmie' - Clementine Hozier – his beloved lifetime-companion.

When Churchill entered politics, Britain was the most powerful and richest country on Earth. He was certainly the most influential and important figure in twentieth century British history. Each of his political appointments was of importance both in itself and in the finished man. It is useful to know something of them if one wishes to know how Europe, and indeed the world, turned out as it has. This may be political history but, like most things to do with Winston, the story is far from dry.

Churchill was the political boss (the First Lord) of the Royal Navy from 1911 to 1915. The First Lord of the Admiralty – what a majestic, salty, shell-to-the-ear title that is. If you roll it on your lips; you can almost hear the tide surging up the Thames and splashing against the river wall of the House of Lords. The Royal Navy (The Andrew to its men) was by far the most powerful fleet on earth and a world unto itself. Winston was a boss such as the navy had never seen; a driving stickler for detail. As he recounted in *The World Crisis*, his six volume history of the First World War:

'I laboured continually to check and correct the opinions with which I had arrived at the Admiralty by the expert information which on every subject was now at my disposal.'

This shows that he was a hard worker and highlights another key Churchillian quality. He had the humility - or perhaps the self-confidence – to listen and learn. As he himself said; 'I am always ready to learn although I do not always like being taught.'

In this role, Churchill immediately sought the advice – tutorship might be a better word - of the 69 year old Admiral Jackie Fisher. Fisher, who has been called the second most important leader of the Royal Navy (after Horatio Nelson), had revolutionised the navy, driving improvements in the range, accuracy and rate of fire of naval gunnery and backing the use of the torpedo. He pushed through submarine development and the replacement of coal with oil for fuel. He introduced daily baked bread on board ships, whereas when he entered the service it was customary to eat hard biscuits, frequently infested with weevils.

Churchill was intensely interested in technical developments. One of these was flying. He drove-through the foundation of naval aviation and, characteristically, came out from behind his desk and insisted on being taught to fly himself. This was in 1911. The Wright brothers had made the first powered flight just 8 years earlier and aircraft were a mass of wires and canvas with little shelter. He flew over 140 times under instruction, although (sensible) family pressure meant that he never took his certificate or flew solo. An early pilot (who would later become an Air Commodore), Charles Samson, wrote of him:

'Without his help and driving power, the Royal Naval Air Service would not have reached the state of advancement it had done in 1914. *One of these days, the nation will understand what a great administrator he is.'*

I have italicised the final words of the quote as I believe that they are fundamental in understanding Winston Spencer Churchill's effectiveness and I have never seen them stated more clearly and succinctly.

Churchill instigated a Naval College, at Portsmouth, to bring academic rigour and discussion to naval strategy. Of the chaotic standard of war planning he said: 'The views of one First Sea Lord may be utterly at variance with another, as many reached office without any study of the history of war... the result has been an entire absence of continuity in Admiralty policy, with consequent financial waste.' Churchill encouraged officers to study history and to think about strategy and tactics. History was a key part of Churchill's education. In his words: 'Study history, study history. In history lies all the secrets of statecraft.

British naval intelligence was the best in the world – and intelligence was a subject that fascinated Churchill. As First

Lord of the Admiralty, he was deeply involved with Room 40: the place in the Old Admiralty buildings in London's Whitehall where naval intelligence from German radio intercepts was coordinated. It was set up in 1914 and was later to become (under Admiral 'Quex' Sinclair), the Government Code and Cypher School, which in turn was to become Bletchley Park.

The First Lord's use of English was masterful and he had no time for poorly written correspondence from his juniors. That these juniors were sometimes admirals did not deter him, which didn't always help his popularity. Generals, admirals and air marshals were to complain for half a century that Winston interfered too much. He could and would browbeat men. Take the recollection of Admiral Hall, the Director of Naval Intelligence:

'Once, I remember I was sent for by Mr Churchill very late at night (another of WSC's habits). He wished to discuss some point or other with me – at once. To be candid, I have not the slightest recollection what it was: I only know that his views and mine were diametrically opposed. We argued at some length. I knew I was right, but Mr Churchill was determined to bring me round to his point of view, and he continued his argument in the most brilliant fashion. It was long after midnight and I was dreadfully tired, but nothing seemed to tire the First Lord. He continued to talk, and I distinctly recall the odd feeling that although it was against my will, I should in a very short while be agreeing with everything that he said. But a bit of me still rebelled, and recalling the incident of the broken shard in Kipling's 'Kim', I began to mutter to myself "my name is Hall, my name is Hall."

Suddenly he broke off to look frowningly at me. "What's that you're muttering to yourself?" he demanded.

"I'm saying," I told him, "that my name is Hall, because if I listened to you any longer I shall be convinced that it is Brown."

"Then you don't agree with what I've been saying?" He was laughing heartily.

"First Lord," said I, "I don't agree with one word of it, but I can't argue with you, I've not had the training."

So the matter dropped and I went to bed.'

So, Churchill's ability to listen was at times conditional on the strength of character of his opponent. Often enough, Churchill bent the man to his will – and that could lead to disaster as it did, arguably, when he launched the Dardanelles campaign, and lost Jackie Fisher's support (and his job) because of it – or, much later, when he sent the warships HMS *Prince of Wales* and *Repulse* to their destruction off Singapore. The difference between Churchill and other iron-willed war leaders was that, if argued with convincingly and determinedly enough, there was a good chance he would laugh and give way. Had Hall been facing Hitler he would have been retired. Had he been facing Stalin he and his family would probably have died.

As the leader of the navy, Churchill drove through increases of pay to the lower ranks – and significantly improved the possibility of promotion of talented seamen to officers. An example of this also demonstrates how widely he did his research. Here is an extract from a minute from him in which he overrode the Promotion Board over the granting of cadetships:

'I have seen the three candidates. Considering that these three boys were 5th, 8th and 17th in the educational competitive examination …I see no reason why they should have been described as unfit for the naval service. It is quite true that one... has a slight cockney accent, and that the other two are the sons of a Chief Petty Officer and an engineer in the merchant service; but the whole intention of competitive examination is to open the career to ability, irrespective of class and fortune... cadetships are to be given in the three cases I have mentioned.'

This shows not only the fiercely reactionary class divide in the Royal Navy (and everywhere else in Britain and its empire) - but Churchill's determination to put the competence of the navy first. Winston as a socialist? The miners of Tonypandy might not agree with that – but that's another story: and one that is worth pursuing, for his story is so long and interesting, that it rewards attention in many areas – not just his influence on the outcomes of World Wars One and Two; and the transfer of world power to the USA.

Perhaps the greatest influences he had on the fleet that entered the First World War was on ships' armaments – commissioning ships with 15" guns. This meant that later, at the Battle of Jutland, the Royal Navy avoided what could have been a very significant defeat, which would have given the German fleet free rein in the Atlantic. Jutland might have been a British victory (instead of a draw) had the signals intelligence provided by Room 40 been properly used, a lesson that WSC doubtless learned. To quote Vice-Admiral Sir Peter Gretton in his excellent book, *Former Naval Person*:

> 'In matters of technical advance, the First Lord was always in the van, always supporting the pioneer, always sweeping away the obstruction of the unimaginative. It is frightening to picture the plight of the Navy in 1914 if his drive and enthusiasm had not invariably supported progress.'

Or, as Lord Kitchener put it when he bad formal farewell to the First Lord in 1915:

> 'There is one thing at least they can never take away from you. When the (First World) war came, you had the fleet ready.'

Churchill resigned over the mismanaged Dardanelles Offensive, which he had initiated. He spent some months in France as an officer in the trenches (which is where, as I recounted in chapter one, he nearly shot Sir Edward Spears, or himself, with his prototype automatic pistol).

Purely on his record in commanding the Royal Navy, Hitler would have been justified in fearing Churchill. But there was more.

Winston Churchill was appointed Minister of Munitions in 1917 and continued in the post until 1919. In this role, he improved weapon production. He was also the driving force for the introduction of the world's first tank. In any other man's life, this would have been extraordinary: in Churchill's, it is little more than a footnote. He backed the amalgamation of the Royal Naval Air Service (RNAS) which he had done so much to nurture, with the Royal Flying Corps (RFC) to make the Royal Air Force (RAF). The RAF, the first separate air force in the world, was founded on April the 1st 1918 (many in the service have at times remarked that the date was apt).

The British diaspora to the four corners of the world was a subject close to Churchill's heart; as can be seen by his great work *A history of the English speaking people*, a four volume history of Britain and its former colonies and possessions throughout the world which he wrote in 1917.

Churchill was the Secretary of State for War from 1919 until 1921. He was the Secretary of State for Air during the same period and for a couple of months longer. In this dual role he successfully fought to keep the Royal Air Force from being absorbed into the army.

Churchill was, as I have noted, obsessed with weapons. He put the then new field of air power above all others, saying: 'For good or ill, air mastery is today the supreme expression of military power and fleets and armies, however vital and important, must accept a subordinate rank.'

The First Sea Lord (the military head of the navy) at the time, Admiral Beatty, wrote of Churchill: 'it takes a good deal out of me when dealing with a man of his calibre and a very quick brain. A false step, remark, or even gesture is immediately fastened on so I have to keep my wits about me.'

It was at this time that Franklin D. Roosevelt met Churchill for the first time. It was at a dinner at Gray's Inn, in London. Roosevelt was then the Assistant Secretary of the United States Navy. In later years, Churchill couldn't recollect the meeting, but Roosevelt could. He later told the American Ambassador to Britain, Joseph Kennedy, that Churchill had acted "like a stinker" to him at the gathering and was: "one of the few men that had been rude to him". As it was to turn out, Winston might have been well advised to be a little more polite.

During his time as Secretary of State for the Colonies (1921-1922), Churchill was mostly concerned with Ireland and the Middle East. His hard-line attitude to Ireland – which won partial independence against Britain through an armed uprising during this period - seems to have been tempered by a letter from his wife, Clementine which said in part:

'Do, my darling, use your influence now for some sort of moderation or at any rate justice in Ireland. Put yourself in the place of the Irish – if you were their leader, you would not be cowed by severity and certainly not by reprisals which fall like the rain from heaven upon the just and the unjust.'

Clemmie was a great and wise counsel to her husband. As well as a degree of moderation, Churchill was to learn much from her – and from Ireland, where a small body of men and women embedded in the community, and with its support, fought against and forced peace from the much stronger British forces. Like many of his lessons, he would turn it to good use in the coming war against Hitler.

For five years, from 1924 to 1929, Churchill served as Chancellor of the Exchequer, a post second only to that of Prime Minister. At the time, Great Britain's was the largest economy in the world, the centre of a global empire on which 'the sun never set.'

As Britain's paymaster, Churchill grew increasingly concerned that the American Republican Party's extremely tough stance over First World War debt and reparations was severely damaging global trade. He was also worried that the United States' insistence on building a large fleet would imperil the primacy of the Royal Navy.

The fact that America had not spent its national fortune on the fighting in Europe between 1914 and 1918 wasn't the only reason America was overtaking (or had overtaken) Britain as the wealthiest country in the world. Her appeal for workers to colonise her lands had taken millions of people across the Atlantic and provided a committed workforce which, along with new factories and new production ideas, would revolutionise the speed of industrial production. New York had overtaken London as the most populous city on earth.

As Chancellor, Churchill was the man holding the purse strings of what had been the richest country in the world. Seeing global financial domination slipping across the Atlantic was bound to rankle. In September 1928, after a private dinner at Chartwell, Churchill's country house in Kent, the Conservative politician James Wedderburn noted that the Chancellor had: 'talked very freely about the U.S.A. He thinks they are arrogant, fundamentally hostile to us, and that they wish to dominate world politics.':

'Poor old England,' Churchill wrote to his wife Clementine, after Herbert Hoover's election victory (in November 1928), 'she is being slowly but surely forced into the shade. Why can't they let us alone? They have exacted every penny owing from Europe, surely they might leave us to manage our own affairs.'

Clementine wrote back saying that he ought to become Foreign Secretary; 'But I am afraid your known hostility to America might stand in the way. You would have to try and understand and master America and make her like you.'

As usual, Clemmie talked a great deal of sense. As was often the case, Churchill listened to her. And anyway, further visits to America (he had first visited the country in 1895) softened his attitude. As is often the case, familiarity bred understanding rather than contempt; 'No people respond more spontaneously to fair play,' he was to tell a colleague a decade later. 'If you treat Americans well they always want to treat you better.'

Churchill had a habit of changing political parties which won him few friends. He spent most of the 1930s 'in the political wilderness'. He used some of the time in writing. He wrote an excellent book *Marlborough* on his ancestor John Churchill, the first Duke of Marlborough – perhaps the greatest general England ever produced. He also finished his six volumes about the first war. The books did not minimise his own central position in that conflict, prompting Sir Arthur Balfour's quip: 'Winston has written an enormous book about himself and called it *The World Crisis*.'

Churchill was still a Member of Parliament and, with the increase of Germany's military power and the rise of the Nazis, an increasingly vocal one. His contacts with Desmond Morton of the SIS gave him direct (although unofficial) access to British intelligence. Profiting from knowing what the enemy was up to had always been a great interest for Winston. His ancestor Marlborough had said: 'no war can be conducted successfully without early and good intelligence.'

Christopher Andrew in *Her Majesty's Secret Service* says of Churchill: 'No British statesman in modern times has more passionately believed in the value of secret intelligence. None has been more determined to put it to good use.'

Churchill's thirst for information could hardly have been more different than that of Field Marshall Haig, who had commanded the British armies in the first war. Desmond Morton – who was Haig's private secretary in that war - says of him, (Haig) 'He hated being told any new information, however irrefutable, which militated against his preconceived ideas and beliefs.' As I mentioned in the previous chapter, Haig was nicknamed 'The Butcher' for the two million casualties which the British army suffered during the first war. Like many men who had survived that war, Churchill was keen to avoid casualties.

On the outbreak of the Second World War, in 1939, Churchill once again became the First Lord of the Admiralty. There is a tale – which it would be nice to believe – that a signal was flashed round the fleet – 'Winston's back.' Franklin Roosevelt, by now the American President, wrote to Churchill the next day, expressing his delight that Churchill was in charge of the Royal Navy again and suggesting that they start a correspondence on naval and wider matters.

Hitler, who was as avid a reader of European history as Churchill, was quite right to be afraid of him.

Churchill became Prime Minister on May the 10th 1940, the day that the Germans launched their blitzkrieg in the west. I have talked already of his unsuccessful attempts to make France fight on – and his unwise commitment of the RAF to continue that fight. He was facing almost as great a battle at home.

Churchill takes on the cabinet

His was a baptism of fire. Not only was he now Prime Minister, he was also the Minister of Defence – a new post. As such, he took close control of the three armed forces. As well as shuttling back and forth to France, he was rallying his people with the greatest calls to arms a nation had ever heard. On May the 13th he stood up in the House of Commons and growled:

"I have nothing to offer but blood, toil, tears and sweat ... You ask, what is our policy? I will say: it is to wage war, by sea, land and air, with all our might and with all the strength that God can give us; to wage war against a monstrous tyranny, never surpassed in the dark and lamentable catalogue of human crime. That is our policy. You ask, what is our aim? I can answer in one word: Victory. Victory at all costs —victory in spite of all terror — victory, however long and hard the road may be, for without victory there is no survival."

The days of appeasement were over. There could be no further retreat - but was it already too late?

Churchill had been Prime Minister for just one day when he was approached by the scientist, Henry Tizard, whose committee had driven the development of radar. Tizard wanted Churchill to give all of Britain's secrets – radar, atomic, armaments and intelligence, to America unconditionally, free of charge. What good were they to Britain if she should fall? Tizard argued that Britain needed American industrial capacity to manufacture and improve the weapons that Britain had developed. To this end, he had forged links with the United States, appointing a Nobel Prize winner (A. V. Hill) to contact American scientists in key industries.

This was no technology exchange. These were the frightening days of May 1940, when every sensible person beyond Britain's shores (and many inside them) thought she had lost. Britain was the world's leader in radar, atomics, communications and intelligence. This was an outright gift of the most advanced military technology in the world. Give Britain's secrets away for nothing? Churchill vetoed the scheme.

Three days later came Dowding's letter saying that if any more RAF planes were sent to France, Britain would not be able to defend her skies. As we know, Churchill stopped sending them.

As the rate of the French collapse accelerated, Churchill was faced with perhaps his greatest fight of all, his need to win over his five-man war cabinet to continue the fight. On one side of

107

the argument was Churchill, on the other Lord Halifax, the Foreign Secretary. Halifax was all for asking Italy to broker a peace agreement between the Nazis and Britain, whereby Britain would keep its empire. This was, of course, no new idea. It was the arrangement the Nazis had pressed for all along, as Delmer, Winterbotham and a host of others had been reporting for years. The German Foreign Minister, von Ribbentrop, had offered the very same deal directly to Churchill himself, in 1937. Churchill said no to Halifax, as he had to von Ribbentrop.

Lord Halifax, not unnaturally, thought there was no chance of beating Hitler and regarded Churchill as a fantasist. He said of him: 'It does drive one to despair when Winston works himself up into a passion of emotion when he ought to make his brain think and reason.' What to Halifax was 'reason' was appeasement: that slippery slope which had led the west closer and closer to the precipice; perhaps over the precipice. Churchill was of a different belief. What Halifax regarded as his (Churchill's) 'passion of emotion' was rather more than that. It was the stubborn adherence to a basic principle. Evil must not triumph if a glimmer of hope remained. In his own stirring words, as true in the everyday as in this fundamental crisis in man's history: 'Success is not final, failure is not fatal. It is the courage to continue that counts.'

Churchill won the fight in Cabinet; but how to get back from the precipice?

Then came the Dunkirk evacuation, and on the day of its completion (June the 4th 1940), one of Churchill's greatest speeches:

"Even though large tracts of Europe and many old and famous States have fallen or may fall into the grip of the Gestapo and all the odious apparatus of Nazi rule, we shall not flag or fail. We shall go on to the end, we shall fight in France, we shall fight on the seas and oceans, we shall fight with growing confidence and growing strength in the air, we shall defend our island, whatever the cost may be, we shall fight on the beaches, we shall fight on the landing grounds, we shall fight in the fields and in the streets, we shall fight in the hills; we shall never surrender, and even if, which I do not for a moment believe, this island or a large part of it were subjugated and starving, then our Empire beyond the seas, armed and guarded by the British Fleet, would carry on the struggle, until, in God's good time, the New World, with all its power and might, steps forth to the rescue and the liberation of the old."

The Labour MP Josiah Wedgwood said of this speech that it was: "worth 1,000 guns, and the speeches of 1,000 years."

The battle to enthuse his own government when just about all others thought the cause lost took it out of Churchill. He was sixty-five years old and it was at this time that those close to him saw how shattered and exhausted he actually was. As I've said in chapter one, Churchill's army representative in France was Major General Edward Spears. Spears, even more than Churchill, shuttled back and forth across the Channel. He remembers one night sitting with Churchill in a room overlooking Horse Guards, in London. Churchill was profoundly unhappy:

'The news was bad, agonising... the gods of Hitler's Germany had taken charge of heaven. Perhaps the old Norsemen were right in their belief that one day evil would prevail in the world.' Big Ben had just chimed. It was one o'clock in the morning. 'I did not take my eyes off the heavy hunched figure in black. The strong light under a green shade caused the pale face to look paler than usual. For the first time in my life I understood the agony of Gethsemane, what it meant to carry absolutely alone an immeasurable burden.'

The next day, Italy declared war on Britain and France. The eagle had made the kill, the jackal now felt safe to worry the corpse of France. Mussolini did not fear Britain. "These men are not made of the same stuff as Drake and the other magnificent men who made the Empire," he told his son in law, Ciano (who he would later have shot), "they are the tired sons of a long line of rich men."

On the 18th of June 1940 came Churchill's 'finest hour' speech:

"Hitler knows that he will have to break us in this island or lose the war... but if we fail, then the whole world,

109

including the United States, including all that we have
known and cared for, will sink into the abyss of a new dark
age made more sinister, and perhaps more protracted, by the
lights of perverted science. Let us therefore brace ourselves
to our duties, and so bear ourselves, that if the British
Empire and its Commonwealth last for a thousand years,
men will still say; 'This was their finest hour.'"

As can be seen, Churchill made constant reference to
America. Quite apart from the military situation, Britain was
broke. A couple of weeks earlier the Chiefs of Staff had
reported that 'without full economic and financial support we
do not think we could continue the war with any chance of
success.'

Clemmie's letter

On the 27th of June 1940, Winston Churchill was given a
letter from his wife. It read:

My Darling,

I hope you will forgive me if I tell you something that I
feel you ought to know.

One of the men in your entourage (a devoted friend) has
been to me & told me that there is a danger of your being
generally disliked by your colleagues and subordinates
because of your rough sarcastic & overbearing manner – it
seems your Private Secretaries have agreed to behave like
school boys & 'take what's coming to them' & then escape
out of your presence shrugging their shoulders. Higher up, if
an idea is suggested (say at a conference) you are supposed
to be so contemptuous that presently no ideas, good or bad,
will be forthcoming. I was astonished & upset because in all
these years I have been accustomed to all those who have
worked with & under you, loving you. I said this & I was
told 'No doubt it's the strain.'

My Darling Winston, I must confess that I have noticed a
deterioration in your manner; & you are not so kind as you
used to be.

It is for you to give the orders & if they are bungled –
except for the King, the Archbishop of Canterbury & the
Speaker - you can sack anyone and everyone. Therefore with

power you must combine urbanity, kindness and if possible Olympic calm... I cannot bear that those who serve the country and yourself would not love you as well as admire and respect you. Besides you won't get the best results by irritability and rudeness. They will breed either dislike or a slave mentality (rebellion in war being out of the question).

Please forgive your loving devoted and watchful,

Clemmie

I wrote this at Chequers last Sunday, tore it up, but here it is now.

Churchill was to write: 'My most brilliant success was to be able to persuade my wife to marry me.' Clemmie's letter certainly supports that statement. That he listened to her reflects well on Winston himself, of course. Arguably, it also goes some way to explaining how he steered his country through the war. The European dictators were men who cared little for the happiness or opinions of their families. If Eva wrote to Adolf after Stalingrad, the letter does not survive. Hitler's first lover committed suicide and he had his brother in law shot. Mussolini had his son in law shot. If these men were so disastrous in their own lives – or so selfish as not to care – what chance did their countries have?

Two days after Clemmie's letter, Churchill authorised Henry Tizard to assemble Britain's military secrets and take them to America as an unconditional gift. Maybe they would persuade the President to help. Even if not, they would give Roosevelt the means to save America, should Britain fall: 'Victory at all costs, for without it there is no survival.' This was as true for America as it was for Britain. I will come back to the Tizard Mission in a couple of pages.

The Luftwaffe intensified their attacks on British shipping in the English Channel as Hitler strove to clear a way for Operation Sealion, his planned seaborne landings in England. The Battle of Britain – Dowding's battle - had begun.

Hitler's first peace offer

In the south of England, troops and civilians prepared for the invasion at fever pitch. Beaches were covered with barbed wire and mined. Piers were blown up. Concrete blockhouses – 'pill boxes' - were built overlooking landing places. 'Stop lines' – defensive barriers – were dug, built, wired and manned at major geographical obstacles; such as along the banks of the River Thames. Groups of men were trained to operate secretly, and expendably, behind advancing German lines.

Barely a week into that battle, Hitler made a radio broadcast to Britain in which he offered peace. Sefton Delmer, the reporter from Berlin who we met in chapter one, replied to it. Delmer, after arriving aboard the *Madura*, had been invited to broadcast on the BBC's German service. He had never yet spoken on the radio but he was the senior German speaker on the spot in the BBC when Hitler made his broadcast. It was on Friday July the nineteenth, 1940. Delmer recorded Hitler's words:

"'It almost causes me pain," I heard him piously announce, "to think that I should have been selected by providence to deal the final blow to the edifice... Mr Churchill ought for once to believe me when I prophesy that a great empire will be destroyed which I have no intention to even harm... I appeal to common sense... I can see no reason why this war must go on.'"

Tom Delmer was on the air for his first broadcast within the hour – and he took it on himself to reply:

'My colleagues at the B.B.C. had approved of what I had to say. That was enough authority for me. '"Herr Hitler", I said in my smoothest and most deferential German, "you have on occasion in the past consulted me as to the mood of the British public. So permit me to render your excellency this little service once again tonight. Let me tell you what we in Britain think of this appeal of yours to what you are pleased to call our reason and common sense. Herr Fuhrer and Reichkanzler, we hurl it right back at you, right in your evil smelling teeth.'"

His speech was neither diplomatic nor elegant. It caused waves in parliament, but Churchill did little more than chuckle at being beaten to the draw. In the circumstances, he felt that it was fair comment. The rebuttal caused disbelief and consternation in Berlin. Hitler's riposte was, as we have seen in the previous chapter, swift and savage. The attacks were switched from shipping to the mainland of England, and soon to London, the seat of British power and, of course, one of the places from which Churchill ran the war.

Chequers, Ditchley and American influence

Winston had, in fact, three main command posts: His 'war rooms' deep beneath Whitehall in London, Chequers in Buckinghamshire and (for a time) Ditchley, in Oxfordshire. Chequers is a fairy-tale Elizabethan manor set in the beech woods of the Chiltern hills, near Princes Risborough, about thirty five miles north west of central London. It's about thirty miles from Blenheim, Churchill's birthplace.

The Chequers estate had been purchased in 1912 by Ruth and Faith Moore. The Moore sisters were heiresses to the fortune of their father, a New York banker. Ruth and her husband, Sir Arthur Lee, gifted the house to the nation in 1917, to be used as the official residence for the serving Prime Minister of Britain. The story of Chequers is in a way a straw in the wind of the way that the old country – Britain – was being bypassed in wealth by her offspring, America. Many country houses were being brought up by rich Americans, just as many British noble families were joining their fortunes with those who actually had fortunes. If the Lee sisters had not bought Chequers it would have passed to 'a Philadelphia show girl'. Churchill first visited the Buckinghamshire mansion in 1921, long before he became Prime Minister. He wrote to Clemmie:

'You would like to see this place – Perhaps you will some day! It is just the kind of house you admire – a panelled museum full of history, full of treasures – but insufficiently warmed – Anyhow a wonderful possession.'

The third of Churchill's command posts was at Ditchley in Oxfordshire – about the same distance further west from Chequers as Chequers is from London. Ditchley was owned by Nancy and Ronald Tree. They too were Americans. They lent Ditchley – unpaid – to Churchill mainly at weekends 'when the moon was bright' - a time when Chequers was deemed unsafe

113

due to probable visits from the Luftwaffe (though they never actually came).

Many of the most important meetings of the war took place at Chequers and Ditchley. Whether in London, Buckinghamshire or Oxfordshire, the meetings at Churchill's court generally started late at night and continued into the small hours. Winston usually had a brandy at his side – his consumption of alcohol was great – and a cigar (often unlit). These were his essential tools. He famously quipped that "I have taken more out of alcohol than alcohol has taken out of me." Goebbels was fond of castigating his drinking habits – but many of those closer (and more sympathetic) to him remarked that booze seemed to invigorate rather than deaden him.

Courting America

As the German armies stood on the Channel coast and the Luftwaffe was swooping for another easy kill, Churchill was feverishly courting American help. On June the 28th 1940, the day after Clemmie's letter, he telegrammed the British ambassador in Washington stressing the position:

'We have really not had help worth speaking of from the United States so far. We know (the) President is our best friend but it is no use trying to dance attendance upon Republican and Democratic Conventions. What really matters is whether Hitler is master of Britain in three months or not. I think not.'

Winston Churchill was not expecting American troops. Apart from the fact that many of her citizens had German and Italian roots, the American armed forces were unprepared for war. Her armies and air force were small – far smaller than Britain's and Germany's – and how was she expected to get them 'across the pond'? If she did, piecemeal, would they not immediately be overwhelmed by the Germans? Besides, the majority of the American public wanted nothing to do with the war. President Roosevelt was campaigning for a third term of office saying that he would not send American troops to Europe.

What Churchill needed more of was weapons – and primarily destroyers to protect the convoys which were already

Anti-war protest NYC, July 1941

carrying fuel and food across the Atlantic. He wrote to Roosevelt, stressing the urgency of Britain's need for these ships. For Roosevelt providing major weapons was, as Churchill had acknowledged, a political danger. Nevertheless, he sanctioned the release of fifty destroyers in exchange for long leases on British possessions in America (Britain, as I've said, was already running out of cash to pay for her purchases).

The destroyers were old, mothballed World War One craft - six months later only nine of them were still serviceable (none had been sunk). Nonetheless fifty destroyers were fifty destroyers. This was, as Churchill said: "a decidedly un-neutral act." America was sliding towards war.

The Tizard mission – Britannia hands over her trident

The Tizard Mission arrived in America a couple of days after Roosevelt released the destroyers. Churchill had, as I've said, authorised Professor Henry Tizard to hand over all of Britain's military secrets. The importance of this act is hard to exaggerate. The gift of Britain's superior weapons technology to America was to tilt the balance of military power decisively from Britain to the USA – and indeed would finally lead to the end of the war. The infrastructure that America built up to exploit it would lead to America becoming the world's foremost industrial nation. It was the Romans who first depicted Britain as Britannia; a young woman carrying a shield and a trident. The maiden had with time inherited the mantle of Rome. Now she was handing over her trident to the New World.

The gift was fourfold. Most immediately important was the cavity magnetron which I've mentioned in my chapter about radar. This would be described by an American historian as 'the most valuable cargo ever to come to our shores'. It would soon be a deciding factor in the Battle of the Atlantic. Radar

115

improvements in general, made possible by British developments, would also be one of the key weapons in American fleet actions in the Pacific. The radar representative was E G 'Taffy' Bowen – the key figure in the development of air radar.

Also in the free gift was Sir Frank Whittle's blueprint for the jet engine. Although this was in advance of American designs and would be key in America's later development of jets, no American jets saw combat in the war, and British jets were late into battle. The Germans took the lead here.

Then there was the proximity fuse – which I will write about later.

The fourth major British secret that Tizard bought with him was the research which would lead to the atomic bomb. The flowering of nuclear physics which led to the bomb is one of the most remarkable (if double-edged) advances of man's science. It grew from the researches and experiments of Rutherford, Cockcroft, Walton, the Curies, Einstein, Bohr and many others. Essentially its original genesis was in Germany in the late nineteenth century (where many of the British scientists had studied).

By the outbreak of the Second World War, Britain was the world leader in atomic development; centred round work in the English universities of Cambridge, Manchester, Birmingham, Oxford and Liverpool. The most important of these centres was the Cavendish Laboratory at Cambridge – under Lord Rutherford 'the father of nuclear physics'. It was at Cambridge that in 'the year of miracles' (1932) James Chadwick first discovered the neutron. Later in that same year and also at the Cavendish, John Cockcroft had, with Ernest Walton, carried out the first controlled splitting of the atom. Cockcroft was one of the delegates in the Tizard mission.

Cockcroft carried with him a treatise by Rudolf Peierls and Otto Fritsch – two Hungarian Jewish scientists who had fled to England and were working at Birmingham University. This treatise proved the possibility of the atom bomb. Peierls and Fritsch had deduced that the quantity of Uranium-235 needed to make a bomb - 'only a pound or two' – was much smaller than previously believed. Until now, the possibility of the release of
116

an enormous amount of energy by the splitting of the atom was generally discounted among physicists. As late as 1934, Rutherford, Einstein and Bohr had all said they did not believe it to be possible. The Peierls/Fritsch report, along with instructions in the engineering and physics needed to do it, made the development of the bomb a practical possibility.

The findings of Tube Alloys, as the British nuclear research project was code named, were to be handed over in total to America. Britain had not the resources to continue the research. Eighty percent of its physicists were working on radar. America would do the work, bear the cost and reap any post-war financial benefit that might accrue. To help them they had the pick of the Jewish scientists – such as Rudolf Peierls and Otto Fritsch - that had fled Nazi persecution to Britain and America, as well as the Italian, Enrico Fermi, who had fled to America because his wife was Jewish. Britain, for its part, would henceforth take a secondary role in atomic development. It would, however, disrupt the production of heavy water - a key component in the process – by sabotage at the Norsk-Hydro works in Norway. This, it was hoped, would deny the Nazis any chance of the bomb.

The tilt of wealth and power from Britain to America had been going on for years. Now the USA was given the chance to be first in military science too. It was an opportunity that Uncle Sam would grasp with both hands.

This was, as I've said, an outright gift, not an exchange. The one scientific development that America had that promised to be useful to Britain - the Norden bombsight – was not given to Britain. That the bombsight did not live up to its developer's claims does not detract from the pettiness of the denial.

FDR's 3rd term. Lend-Lease

Roosevelt won his third term as president in early November 1940. The campaign had been difficult, his opponents having campaigned on the 'keep out of Europe' ticket. Roosevelt had pretended to be in agreement: "Let no man or woman thoughtlessly or falsely talk of the American people sending its armies to European lands." He had, however, introduced conscription in the USA and put his armed forces on a war footing.

Britain was losing ships and needed more. The cost of the ships and the supplies they carried were crippling the country financially. British gold reserves were being shipped from London to Canada and then to America in the largest movement of physical wealth in history. In a letter to Roosevelt on the 8th of December 1940, Churchill asked that America, if it would not put troops on the ground to preserve the freedom of the world, would at least put its hand in its pocket:

'Last of all, I come to the question of finance. The more rapid and abundant the flow of munitions and ships which you are able to send us, the sooner will our dollar credits be exhausted. They are already, as you know, very heavily drawn upon by the payments we have made to date... The moment approaches when we shall no longer be able to pay for supplies... I believe that you will agree that it would be wrong in principle and mutually disadvantageous in effect if, at the height of this struggle, Great Britain was divested of all its saleable assets so that after the victory was won with our blood, civilization saved and the time gained for the United States to be fully armed against all eventualities, we should stand stripped to the bone.'

Roosevelt took the point. In fact Britain was already bankrupt in all but name. It would take her 60 years to pay off her war debt to America. In a step closer to war, the American president introduced the Lend-Lease Act. This effectively wrote off the price of American aid. America was now the Allies' paymaster, supplying food, fuel and weapons for free, becoming, in the president's fine phrase: 'the arsenal of democracy.' What was not used by the allies was to be returned to the USA at the end of the war (in the event it would be mostly written off). This was another pivotal moment in America's ascent to primary world power. He who pays the piper calls the tune.

Canada, too, provided a similar, though much smaller, deal. It too, was supplying food, weapons and ships – and men. The

Canadian air force and navy were already fully committed to the struggle for liberty.

Peace offer 2 – Rudolph Hess, May 10/11 1941

The final Nazi appeal to Britain to stop fighting them came on the tenth of May 1941, in a twist so dramatic as to defy credibility, the Deputy Fuhrer of the Third Reich, Rudolph Hess, attempted to personally make peace with the enemy that his country could not conquer. He flew his plane, a Messerschmitt BF110, across the North Sea, parachuted out and landed in a field in Renfrewshire, Scotland. He sprained his ankle when he landed. The farmer, David McLean, who was ploughing at the time, helped him to his home and McLean's mum made Hess a cup of tea. After that, his welcome wasn't always as pleasant.

The flight seems to have been made by Hess in the belief that he could make contact with a Scottish aristocrat who would take him to the King whom he would persuade to remove Churchill. An odd reading of Britain's (admittedly unwritten) constitution. Hess was not a fool though. Fred Winterbotham, 'our man in the Reich', who had known him from 1934 onwards said of him: 'I found (in him) a certain depth of character and intelligence which was missing in other Nazi leaders.' There is a very credible theory that he had been lured to Britain by the British Secret Intelligence Service.

Hess parachuted into Scotland on the last night of the first London Blitz. The Germans had lost both the day and night phases of the Battle of Britain. Hess was their final card. If you can't beat them, join them: or at least stop fighting them.

Sefton Delmer, in his book, *Black Boomerang*, tells what happened next. When Hess was interrogated by Lord Beaverbrook (who had met both Hess and Hitler several times previously), the Deputy Fuhrer told him that the object of his flight had been to make peace with Britain "on any terms", providing that Britain would then join Germany in attacking Russia. "I am convinced," he summed up, "that world domination awaits the Soviet Union in the future, if her power is not broken now."

119

Here it was writ large. Britain must choose a side in the great battle of the world, fascism against communism. Every country in continental Europe was either under one of these ideologies or existing under sufferance. The third way, democracy, was dead everywhere - what was the point of trying to resurrect a corpse? Hess came bearing the old familiar offer. If Britain supported Germany – or at least left her alone to do what she wanted - she would return the compliment. The empire would be safe.

Churchill had been Prime Minister for one year to the day when Hess landed. France had fallen. Hugh Dowding and Keith Park had won the Battle of Britain; but how Churchill – fine rhetoric or not - could win against Germany remained a mystery. Britain's convoys were under greater and greater threat. The clever mathematicians and engineers at Bletchley Park were only on the first steps of their long mind-journey to crack the German codes. How could they possibly make sense of the dots and dashes in the ether which carried Germany's orders to her submarines and armies? If they did not, Britain would probably starve. America, although she was supplying fuel, food and some arms, was no nearer declaring war on Germany.

What of this second offer of peace, then? Why not just leave the Europeans to their fate. As for fighting Russia – make encouraging noises, perhaps, but don't send the troops.

It can't have been easy for Churchill, this second temptation. By now, he knew that continuation of the war would come at a huge price for his country. If Britain did continue her lone fight to free Europe, it would be with the full knowledge that the wounds she would take would mean the end of world leadership for the 'Island race'. If she fought and lost, the world would be Thor's. If she fought and won, it could only be by surrendering the guardianship of the flame – democracy, freedom, call it what you will - to America.

Hess held out an olive branch. This fight could end now – why should it continue? What was the point in it for Britain? Hers was a sacrifice that no nation had ever been asked to make before: her own future – perhaps her very life - for the salvation of her neighbours. Was the flame worth this?

Churchill had won his struggle with the Cabinet; and he had won the support of his people. The decision was his alone. He chose the honourable course. His people would fight. They would die or diminish – but they would not bend to evil. Maybe it wasn't all on quite such an elevated plane in Winston's head. Maybe he chewed on those words he had growled as he watched Carlton House Terrace crumble and blaze under German bombs: "We'll get the bastards for this."

Winston Spencer Churchill. Whatever his motives for making this decision that would shape the world, one can be quite certain that they were powered by his integrity, courage and humanity. And his formidable intelligence. For these were the glow of the glow worm: these the fuel of the flame. That was why Hitler feared him and his country loved him.

This was his finest hour… so far.

12th June 1941 – The Declaration of St James's Palace

London in spring 1941. The second largest city in the world had suffered weeks of attacks from the world's largest air force. Great swathes of the city lay in ruins and thousands were dead or in hospital. The children had gone, led away by their teachers in heart breaking, heart-broken crocodiles, clutching their little cardboard suitcases: gone to live with surrogate parents in the countryside. The statue of Richard the Lionheart outside the Houses of Parliament stood before the breached great window, his sword bent but defiant.

Richard the Lionheart statue with bent sword

Here, at this hour, in this place, the fate of Europe stood in the balance. This had happened once before. In the first pages of Europe's history, the tribes in the dark forests beyond the Rhine had become a people by snuffing out the invading legions of

121

the Roman general, Varus. Centuries later they had crossed the great river and over-run the enemy empire – Rome - itself. They had carried with them the Dark Ages which had lasted half a millennium. Now the threat had come again. Only Britain, the seat of the empire which counted itself the heir to Rome, remained.

Through the whole of recorded history and before, Europe had been a battleground. As tribes became nations, wars had become even bloodier and increasingly frequent. In the twentieth century, in the space of thirty years, the continent had twice torn herself apart. If things did not change, its future would be as its past: misery and conflict. It was time – beyond time – for the leaders of the nations to end the bloodshed and find a way to live in peace. If there was a perfect time and place for man to grow up, it was here, now, in London, the embattled keep of an embattled kingdom, the last bastion in Europe. Here, in exile, were the legitimate governments of eight European countries.

The rulers of the defeated lands took counsel in the city's oldest palace, St James, and pledged their broken swords to victory. They pondered, too, a question that the leaders of mankind must answer if man is to survive:

'Would we win only to live in dread of yet another war? Should we not define some purpose more creative than military victory? Is it not possible to shape a better life for all countries and peoples and cut the causes of war at their roots?'

Britain and her Dominions (Canada, Australia, New Zealand and South Africa) endorsed a two-fold pledge: to defeat the Axis powers and to develop a peace force to stop rogue nations from seizing powers in the future. The leaders of the eight exiled elected governments of Europe (Belgium, Czechoslovakia, Greece, Luxembourg, the Netherlands, Norway, Poland and Yugoslavia) signed. So did a representative of General de Gaulle's *France Libre* (I explain a little more about *France Libre* in the appendix at the end of this chapter).

They pledged that:

'The only true basis of enduring peace is the willing cooperation of free peoples in a world in which, relieved of the menace of aggression, all may enjoy economic and social security; It is our intention to work together, and with other free peoples, both in war and peace, to this end.'

This was the Declaration of Saint James's Palace: the foundation stone of what would soon become the United Nations. Needless to say, perhaps, the chief architect of that institution would be Winston Churchill.

***

Churchill was the greatest orator of modern times; but on one occasion, and in one of his greatest speeches at that, I think he missed a trick. It was in that speech when he told his fellow countrymen that all he could offer them were 'blood, sweat, toil and tears'. It is my belief that he should have included brains in that list; for, in my opinion, it was brains that were the real decider of who would win the war.

One of those amazing brains was, of course, Churchill himself; but there were many others working in the Intelligence Zone – on radar, atomics, computing, intelligence and an old favourite of Winston's, weapons. We will look at his 'private' weapons factory in the next chapter.

Appendix: Vichy France and France Libre during WW2

Alongside the eight unarguably legitimate allied governments in exile in London in 1940 was de Gaulle's *France Libre*: one of whose enemies was the French government ruling from Vichy, in mainland France. Because of this rupture in their camp, France spoke with two voices; *France Libre* wanted liberation from the Nazis while Vichy France seemed quite content to be a vassal country.

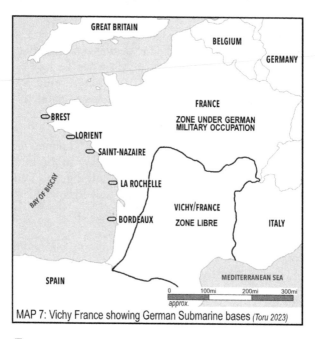

MAP 7: Vichy France showing German Submarine bases *(Toru 2023)*

Vichy France

The French collaborationist government at Vichy, led by Marshall Phillipe Pétain, considered itself to be the legitimate government of France. Legally it is difficult to argue with the claim as, after surrendering to the Germans, the then French government had voted overwhelmingly (569 to 80) to dissolve itself and hand its power to Pétain (an elderly general who had won fame in the First World War). But this was not power over the whole of France; but rather the leavings from the victor's table. In the surrender agreement, the Germans gave a small part of France to Italy and kept two regions (departments), Alsace and Lorraine for itself. The rest it split in two. The Nazis ruled the northern and coastal areas directly, the rest they allowed the French to rule themselves. Pétain – essentially a dictator - ruled his bit of France from the town of Vichy. This area was called by the French the *Zone Libre* – the free zone. It is more widely known as Vichy France, or simply Vichy. Vichy also ruled over France's colonies, many of them in North Africa.

America recognised Pétain's Vichy until November 1942; their ambassador to the country being Admiral William Leahy. Leahy's brief was to gain the confidence of Pétain and persuade him away from helping Nazi Germany, above all keeping what was left of the French fleet out of German hands.

Unlike America, Britain recognised de Gaulle's *France Libre*, based in London, as France's legitimate government.

De Gaulle's France Libre

At the start of the war Charles de Gaulle was a Colonel in the French army. When Hitler's armies invaded in 1940, he led an armoured division which counter attacked one of the German spearheads. His attack was repulsed, but as recognition of his martial spirit, he was promoted and appointed Undersecretary of War. Refusing to accept the defeat of France, he was rescued from France on an RAF plane sent by Churchill. As a refugee in London, he tried to rally his countrymen to his cause.

As I've said, the French government had meanwhile surrendered and were collaborating with Germany under Pétain (Vichy). De Gaulle was tried in his absence by a French military court 'for treason and desertion to a foreign country.' He was found guilty, stripped of his rank and sentenced to death. His property was confiscated.

De Gaulle's attempts to raise support from the French army in England were not a great success. It might be thought that in the 110,000 French soldiers rescued from Dunkirk by the Royal Navy, he would have had a ready-made army. However, by the time that France surrendered, most of these had already gone home with the intent – initially – of continuing the fight. By the time de Gaulle began his recruitment there were perhaps 12,000 French soldiers and sailors still in Britain.

De Gaulle recruited between two and three thousand soldiers in 1940. This included a couple of cohesive units; a battalion of the Chasseurs Alpines and another from the French Foreign Legion. His attempts to recruit individual soldiers from the holding camps for French troops in Britain were, however, disappointing. Typical was his visit to the White City camp in London in the summer of 1940, when of the 1,600 or so troops there, only 152 signed up with *France Libre*. Another 34 volunteered for the British army and 35 for the Royal Navy (the pay was better in the British armed forces). The rest went back to France.

Added to this *France Libre* had a couple of thousand sailors (4,500 by the end of 1941), some of whom were fishermen and some military. It also recruited about 300 French airmen.

De Gaulle's attempts were frustrated by French officers, who often forbade their men from joining him and sometimes even threatened them. They told their men that Vichy, the legal government of France, was not at war with Germany and therefore to fight for de Gaulle against Germany would be treachery. To add to the dissuasion, delegates from some of the Vichy French consulates in Britain toured the camps where French troops were held and advised them that Britain had little chance of survival, and it would therefore be very unwise for them to join de Gaulle. It would go badly for them when Britain fell; and what about their families in France? Much better to return home, they urged; things were not too bad there now – just different.

In the words of Lord David Astor, a prominent English supporter of de Gaulle:

'The most surprising aspect of the relations between de Gaulle and other people was the attitude of the French. We were constantly being surprised by the ill-will of those who could have been called intellectuals, of almost all the politicians and of many soldiers. This distrust that he aroused among the most outstanding members of the French community in London could not fail to strike us. In our country (Britain) it was not with the British but chiefly with the French that he had trouble. And the reason these quarrels did not become more public is the pressure brought to bear by the British to restore calm.'

Apart from being pressured by their own superiors, the vast majority of the French troops believed that Britain would soon be invaded. Only the bravest of the brave and those who (like de Gaulle) believed that the honour and future of their country was worth risking their lives for, volunteered to join France Libre. The fact that Britain's Royal Navy had recently shelled and destroyed a French naval force at Oran also dissuaded many potential recruits.

Oran

The decision to neutralise the French navy, made by Churchill, was a logical one. The German forces already had all the tanks, aircraft, guns and factories of France; Churchill was terrified that they would soon have France's navy too. Had that happened, Britain would probably have lost the war. This prompted the British Prime Minister to order his navy to recruit or at least neutralise the French fleet. Consequently the Royal Navy confronted two portions of that fleet (at the same time and on the same day) and gave each of them the same four options:

Join the British fleet

or disarm your ships

or sail to French or American ports outside the war zone for the duration of the war

or we will sink you.

One part of the fleet voted to disarm and spent the rest of the war quietly in port (Alexandria, in Egypt), the other rejected the first three options and was sunk. 1307 French sailors died under the guns of the Royal Navy.

In the grim logic of war, the sinking of the ships (at Oran, in Algeria) was a necessary act. De Gaulle certainly regarded it as such. However, 1307 French sailors had been killed by the British, a fact that Goebbels and Pétain's Vichy government made much of; and which certainly did not help de Gaulle's recruitment drive.

The great majority of French servicemen in Britain returned to France via Spain, North Africa or America (some in chartered neutral boats, some in British ships, some as best they could).

In proportion to the 5,000,000 enlisted French men at the start of the war, the number who joined de Gaulle was derisory. Compare, for example, the 4,500 French sailors under his command at the end of 1941 with the 27,000 Norwegians who manned the British convoys. A small number of French pilots served with the Royal Air Force; 13 are on the Battle of Britain roll of honour compared with 28 Belgians, 145 Poles and 88 Czechs.

I do not mention the small numbers of Frenchmen who joined *France Libre* in order to criticise France as a nation, nor do I believe that it indicates a lack of bravery in the French – as later chapters on the resistance will attest. I mention it because I think it worthy of acknowledgement. Maybe it's the Englishman in me.

The reluctance to join de Gaulle also shows how a nation in shock will instinctively cling to its leaders, rightly or wrongly. Unfortunately France had suffered a double defeat – a military one and a betrayal by its leaders. It would learn of its betrayal quickly and many of its best citizens would pay with their lives – in the resistance – to help to recover the freedom and *honneur* of their country.

On the plus side, de Gaulle's forces were truly the cream of their nation. The obstacles that Vichy France placed in the way of its men escaping to fight the Germans form part of *No drums no trumpets*, one of the greatest war stories of all time. In it Alec le Vernoy tells how he escaped to Gibraltar (twice), fought with the SAS destroying German armour, ended up in a concentration camp and escaped to join the resistance. This is, in my opinion, one of the ten greatest action books to come out of the war. If you want to know the extremes of human courage, I recommend you read it.

The attitude of Vichy France was that If any foreign power landed troops on her territories, they would be invaders who would be shot. This would not help to motivate Britain and America to supply men to 'liberate' French territory.

Even if you are well versed in the history of the Second World War, the contents of this appendix will probably be new to you. Winston Churchill, looking to the future, kept the lid on the mini civil-war between the French in England. He also took the rough with the smooth. These are hardly unique character traits, it is true; but they are important to note, for it was the sum of Churchill's traits which made of him the greatest statesman of his century. It is ironic, then (and I will talk a little of this later) how he was repaid by General Charles de Gaulle.

6: Churchill's Toyshop

Britannia waives the rules

In the days of Britain's Empire, her troops were commanded from the War Office in London's Whitehall. This labyrinthine palace sprawls across seven floors, housing over 1,000 offices. From here Britain ran the army which ruled a third of the Earth. Here, in 1938, Lieutenant-Colonel J.F.C. ('Joe') Holland founded a new section called Military Intelligence Research (MIR), whose purpose was the waging of 'irregular warfare' – sabotage.

In the early part of the war Holland's full-time staff consisted of two officers and their two secretaries, four men sharing an office on an upper floor. The two officers were Major Millis Jefferis and Lieutenant-Colonel Colin Gubbins. They looked after different aspects of sabotage. Gubbins was in charge of finding people to carry out attacks behind enemy lines. Jefferis' job was to furnish weapons for these irregulars (or terrorists as their enemies preferred to call them). Sometimes the weapons came off the shelf, sometimes they needed to be designed and made.

The two sections would shortly split. Colin Gubbins would go off to head up a new organisation the Special Operations Executive - SOE. That deserves – and will get – a chapter in its own right. In the current chapter I shall tell you what became of Major Jefferis' side of the office; and how it grew into what its detractors called 'Winston Churchill's toyshop'.

Major Millis Jefferis, who was born in 1899, was a military engineer of genius who had cut his teeth building seemingly impossible bridges to defeat the warrior tribes of Northwest India. A key part of making those bridges possible was, of course, making sure that they could take the load and stress they would be subjected to. These calculations were carried out by Jefferis, whose personal passion for advanced algebra was nourished by a two year secondment to Cambridge University for its further study. Millis was a 'one off'. The study of calculus at what was arguably the world's foremost mathematical institution was not part of the normal career path for a soldier in the British army.

Major Jefferis' first appointee, and soon to become his deputy, was Stuart Macrae, whom Jefferis contacted in June 1939 to enquire about the availability of some powerful American magnets. Macrae had written an article about these magnets in the magazine, *Armchair Science*, of which he was the editor. Macrae (who had designed weapons for the British army during the first war) was intrigued and very interested by the enquiry. He suggested that they meet to discuss what the magnets were needed for. After checking Macrae's security clearance, Millis Jefferis invited him for a chat at the Arts Theatre Club in Soho. The pair managed to 'nab a window seat' there'. Macrae was impressed by Major Jefferis:

"With a leathery looking face, a barrel-like torso and arms that reached almost to the floor, he looked a bit like a gorilla... he had a brain like lightning."

Jefferis' interest in magnets was not theoretical. He wanted them so that he could stick explosive mines to metal. These would be used by Gubbins' underwater saboteurs to sink Axis shipping. The two discussed the matter and the talk widened as Jefferis described the various other weapons that he was working a sixteen hour day to invent and produce for MIR. That there were gaps in weapon development for 'irregular warfare' is not surprising. Sabotage, in the absence of an army that could challenge Germany, was a tactic born of desperation.

Weapon development was right up Macrae's street. It fascinated him scientifically and he was intensely patriotic. He not only offered advice on the mines, he volunteered to make them himself – moreover he wanted no payment, only his expenses. Money, as it was to turn out, was never to become an issue. It came from a secret service fund – which did not, officially, exist.

With Jefferis' 'bag of gold' at his disposal, Macrae went looking for workshop facilities where he could develop the magnetic mine. He found them in the premises of an old acquaintance, Captain C.V. Clarke, MC, of Bedford. 'Nobby' Clarke had won his Military Cross in the first war and was now a manufacturer of trailers and caravans – including the one and only double-decker caravan in the land. He and Macrae devised the prototype anti-shipping mine. The field trials were carried out in Bedford public baths (closed to the public for these occasions). They soon worked out the dimensions, construction and filling for their magnetically attached mine which they christened 'The Limpet'.

Then they had to come up with a suitable water soluble pellet to form a fuse which would delay detonation until the diver had left the scene. Differences in water temperature and salinity changed the speed of dissolution of their first pellets: but finally they found the answer by requisitioning a sweet – an aniseed ball - from one of Clarke's children. Then they toured Bedford and bought every aniseed ball that they could find - thus depriving the town's children of the sweet (eventually they got them straight from Barratt, the manufacturers).

Having cleaned out the sweet shops, they next turned their attentions to Bedford's chemists and barbers, buying up the entire stock of men's contraceptives (to keep damp away from the aniseed balls until the required moment), thus, in Macrae's words: 'enhancing our already dubious reputation in Bedford.'

All this was done in 1939, before war broke out. The first few hundred Limpets were made in Bedford. By the end of the war over half a million of them would flow from their production lines: and they would sink hundreds of thousands of tons of enemy shipping (and several British ships too, Italian naval divers having got hold of some).

Stuart Macrae was still carrying out his day job - editing magazines - but not for much longer. Major Jefferis decided that he needed him full time, so had him commissioned into the army. He joined Jefferis in London where they worked together on more weapons, initially on a timing switch; and pressure switches actuated by pulling (as in trip wires) and pushing (as in derailing a train). Soon, Macrae, too, was working sixteen hours a day. Sometimes he worked all night. In his words:

'If only Millis (Jefferis) had lived in Roman times I am sure he could have become a Chief Flogger on one of those oar-powered galleons.'

By the start of the war, MIR was turning out no less than 11 separate devices - the main ones being the limpet and pressure switches. Macrae, as well as weapon design, was sub-contracting manufacture to various small engineering workshops in London, including the musical instrument makers, Boosey and Hawkes. These precision engineers were often in ramshackle premises in places such as Park Royal and Clerkenwell, London being then a much more workaday place than it is now.

Their activities were soon to come to the notice of a very martially minded man in a very high place.

Churchill and Lindemann

When Winston Churchill took over the Admiralty at the outbreak of war, he took with him as scientific advisor an old friend, Professor Frederick Lindemann. One of Churchill's many interests was, of course, weapons. He quickly came up with a plan to disrupt German shipping on the river Rhine by dropping mines into the river. He asked Lindemann to source the mines. The Professor did not have much luck with the weapons development departments of the three armed forces: nothing suitable was available off the shelf and new weapons would take time to design. Churchill would have to take his place in the queue. He might have to wait months, years maybe. That was not good enough for Churchill, who asked Lindemann to find an alternative producer. The Professor ran Major Millis Jefferis to ground at the War Office and invited him to meet Churchill. The latter explained that he wanted mines that could be put in the river from the French side, or dropped into it by aircraft. It took just five minutes to discuss and agree the specification. Jefferis promised that he would come up with a weapon design 'in a week or two'. He was as good as his word, delivering a prototype exactly 14 days later.

Jefferis and Macrae developed the mines very quickly, testing them out both in the Thames and at Walton-on-Thames reservoir. Churchill arranged several late-night meetings (his 'midnight follies') at which Jefferis and Macrae demonstrated to the Cabinet – one by one – the device. Finally, Churchill took his own special train from Charing Cross (Clemmie waved them off) with Lindemann, Jefferis and Macrae and the group went to France to explain the mining plan to their allies. They were courteously received but the French would not agree to the plan. Churchill pressed the French 'very hard,' but, as he later wrote:

'The President of the Republic himself had intervened and (said) that no aggressive action must be taken which might only draw reprisals upon France. This idea of not irritating the enemy did not commend itself to me.'

Unfortunately, not attacking their enemy did not save France from German irritation, as the latter made clear in their own good time. Only after they had defeated Poland and rearranged their troops in a logical manner did they invade France. That was also the day when Churchill left the Admiralty to become Prime Minister. One of the first things he did on taking that office was to create for himself a new post, as Minister of Defence. There wasn't much to the MoD to begin with: it had no departments or personnel, except for a secretary or two. It was merely Churchill's mechanism for running the war. It stood above the Admiralty, War Office and Air Ministry. He chaired its meetings and the military and political leaders of the three armed forces were his committee.

The bomb makers are bombed out of London

During this time, Jefferis's organisation at the War Office – now renamed MIR(c) – continued developing armaments. They were working on quite a range of weapons. As well as the old favourites – the Limpet, an aerial mine and pressure switches - they were also moving into 'mainstream' arms production to plug a very serious gap. Britain was in imminent danger of invasion: and had practically no effective anti-tank weapons. The standard anti-tank gun was the Boyes rifle which, as many accounts tell, was completely ineffective against German armour, even at short range. In the words of Stuart Macrae:

'Against German tanks it was no more than its name suggested.' There are many accounts of British gunners in France firing at Panzer tanks from close range only to see the shell bounce off. A dangerous occupation and one which hastened the retreat to Dunkirk.

So MIR(c) were in the process of developing the Sticky Bomb – a device that when thrown would stick to armour and burn through it. They were also working on a mortar – the Blacker Bombard. They developed these weapons at breakneck speed, demonstrating them to Churchill and the top brass at Princes Risborough, near Chequers, the Prime Minister's country retreat.

By a mixture of trickery, intelligence and knowing how to work the system, Macrae (the organisational brains of the new establishment), had requisitioned a property in Portland Place, close to the headquarters of the BBC, producing weapons in the cellars. London, in late 1940, was not a great place to be as the Luftwaffe tested the theory that the 'bomber will always get through.' Initially they seemed to be right. As I've mentioned previously, the London Night Blitz started on September 7th 1940 and continued for 76 consecutive nights. Macrae recounts:

'Hours of working time were lost through various members of our small staff arriving late in the morning and having to leave early if they hoped to get home. Soon we were unable to get ahead with anything at all …our store at Hendon was completely destroyed by incendiary bombs and we lost almost our entire stock of devices… only a few weeks later, 35 Portland Place was itself hit and we were put completely out of action.'

Macrae wanted to move to the country, preferably somewhere near Churchill at Chequers. To this end, he sought out and requisitioned 'The Firs', a property in Whitchurch, in Buckinghamshire. This 'empire building' did not go unnoticed. Powerful forces in the establishment thought that MIR(c) was getting above itself. Weapon production – especially mainstream weapon production – was no work for amateurs. Some wanted to merge the section into existing establishments. Another suggestion was that the organisation should go over to the Special Operations Executive (SOE) – the sabotage organisation that Jefferis's erstwhile office companion, Colin Gubbins was now in charge of. SOE, the product of the amalgamation of three different parent organisations (as I will tell in due course), had several research establishments. As Macrae told it:

'No doubt any one of them would have been happy to absorb us and we would have lived happily ever after at one of the comfortable country mansions they had managed to acquire. But we did not want to be absorbed. Our value lay in our independence.'

To avoid his section being taken over, Stuart Macrae enlisted the support of Professor Lindemann, Churchill's chief scientific adviser. He could not have approached a more powerful or more sympathetic intermediary. Lindemann backed him to the hilt. Frederick Lindemann, by now one of the most powerful men in Britain, would influence the war in several ways. As such, I would like to talk about him in a bit more detail before returning to the story of Churchill's Toyshop.

Professor Frederick Lindemann

Professor Frederick Lindemann had been perhaps Churchill's strongest supporter during Winston's 'years in the wilderness'. In the visitors book at Chartwell, Churchill's house in Kent, Lindemann's is the most frequent signature, with eighty-six visits.

Lindemann was born – much to his later annoyance – in Germany. His mother (like Churchill's) was American. His father, German by birth, later took British nationality. The Lindemann family was aristocratic and extremely wealthy. Frederick was schooled in Britain and, from the age of 16, studied physics in Berlin. He spoke English, French and German fluently. The study of physics was growing rapidly and Germany was the world leader in the subject - support for 'Newton's science' coming from the very top. Kaiser Wilhelm himself said:

'Mathematics and physical science have shown mankind how we may force the door of God's stupendous workshop.'

Major discoveries were being made, fundamental theories posited and proved. In physics this was the great awakening - a time of giants. All knew and learned from the others' work – many of them were friends.

In 1900, Max Planck – a German – published his Quantum Theory which dealt with how energy acts at an atomic level. Other scientists would quickly build on his theory to discover more about the atom. Another German, Albert Einstein, developed the theoretical physical view of the world. Practical experimentation of their theories was worked on by Ernest Rutherford in Manchester, England.

Rutherford was born in New Zealand of British parents. Einstein's ancestry was Jewish. Lindemann was a mixture of German, French, American and English. Marie Curie was French, of Polish parents. Those national labels are, of course, transitory. What matters most if mankind is to to live in happiness – perhaps to survive at all - is not ancestry or nationalism or even intelligence, but a regard for others. A basic truth which the world had, in the twentieth century, still to learn. Perhaps it never will.

Lindemann, at the University of Berlin, worked under Professor Walther Ernst – a top rank physicist - who was doing research into low temperature physics. After returning to England, Lindemann spent the First World War developing aircraft for the British air force at the Royal Aircraft factory in Farnborough. He was a brave man who risked his life to come up with a solution for an until-then uncontrollable aerial spin which had taken many pilots to their deaths. It was noted at Farnborough that he had an 'inbred terror of being seen as a figure of fun.' In that class and race ridden age, his foreign name and the fact that he had studied in Berlin and spoke with a German accent made him stand out. According to his biographer:

> 'The workshop staff at Farnborough firmly believed that he was a German and that he was never allowed enough fuel to carry him across the Channel.'

Lindemann was known as "Baron Berlin" to his many detractors because of his German name and haughty aristocratic manner. He affected not to care: but he never forgot or forgave a slight, real or imaginary.

After the first war, he was offered and took the Chair of Experimental Philosophy (physics) at Oxford University. For this post, he was sponsored by (among others) the greatest experimental physicist of his age, Ernest Rutherford, who was in charge of the Cavendish Laboratory at Cambridge. Under Rutherford's leadership the Cavendish would be the cradle and nursery for the development of nuclear physics; which is why he is known as the Father of Nuclear Physics.

Lindemann wanted to make the Clarendon Laboratory at Oxford the equal of the Cavendish at Cambridge. He had a long way to go. The Clarendon was badly off in equipment, money and direction. He solicited funds from many sources. He also courted the upper classes: the further up the better. A fellow don quipped: "Why is Lindemann like a coastal steamer?" To which the answer was: "because he goes from peer to peer."

He first met Winston Churchill in 1921, at the country seat of the Duke of Westminster. Although Churchill was distant at first, a close relationship grew up between the two men over the following years. Churchill was intensely interested in Lindemann's vision of how to improve Oxford's – indeed Britain's - scientific knowledge. He was also impressed by Lindemann's ability to sum up complex scientific arguments on a single sheet of paper. Both men were intensely patriotic and increasingly concerned about events in Germany. Churchill referred to Lindemann as 'The Prof' and would make him Lord Cherwell later in the war.

Professor Lindemann was increasingly hands-off in the day-to-day running of the Clarendon Laboratory – although he kept up the flow of money and recruited talented staff. His vision became more political; as his biographer says:

> 'Lindemann was convinced that science would dominate the fate of the civilised world. He regarded the (German) expulsion of so many excellent brains, even a genius like Einstein, not only as a foul misdeed, but as an indescribable stupidity of the Nazi regime, and he decided to make good use of the error by collecting a group of eminent men in his laboratory.'

Lindemann knew most of the top physicists in Europe, many of whom were Jewish. Albert Einstein, who had renounced his German citizenship in 1933, because of Nazi persecution of Jews, was a friend of his. Einstein was a frequent visitor to Oxford, staying with Lindemann at Christ Church College, where the latter had his rooms. Although Professor Einstein spoke no English, the students and dons of Oxford were entranced by this genial, open, humane, genius.

Albert Einstein at Oxford with Frederick Lindemann.
(Lindemann had arranged the doctorate Einstein is receiving.)

After his visit to Oxford in 1931, Einstein (in exchange for brief periods of residence each year more or less at his convenience) was elected a 'research student' (i.e. a fellow) of Christ Church College. This paid an annual stipend of £400 and was to have continued until 1937. The arrangement had been proposed by Lindemann, probably in the hope that Einstein would settle in Oxford. In the event, Albert Einstein returned only twice more (he finally went to Princeton, in America).

As the Nazis turned on them, Lindemann gave help to a number of Jewish scientists. With money provided by Britain's then leading and richest company, Imperial Chemical Industries (ICI) he placed them in Oxford University, where he concentrated on low temperature and nuclear physics. Lindemann was a lifesaver – literally - to the 'Jewish' professors. I use speech marks as many of those whom the Nazis regarded as Jews thought of themselves as German. At least two of 'Lindemann's Jews' held the Iron Cross won when fighting for their country - Germany - in the First World War. Others thought of themselves as without state, race or religion: simply members of the eternal swirl of humanity. Nazi racial theories were foul, idiotic crimes against humanity, but I will drop the inverted commas from now on; the Nazis made no bones about who they regarded as Jews.

After Hitler came to power, the Jews in Germany came more and more frequently under open attack. Their businesses were smashed and boycotted, they were evicted from their jobs and they were assaulted and sometimes murdered in the streets and in their homes. Their places of worship were ransacked and burned. In academia, too, Jews were targeted, with physics being described as 'a Jewish science.' Those with sufficient foresight and funds fled Germany. Others killed themselves. All across Germany, the Nazis took 'action against the un-German spirit' by making pyres of books. As the German Jewish philosopher Heine had remarked a century earlier: 'Those who burn books will burn people.' In less than ten years, the Nazis would do exactly that to 6,000,000 Jewish men, women and children.

Book burning in Berlin, May 1933

One of the physicists who Lindemann found a post for at Oxford was a 25 year old Hungarian Jew who taught at Breslau university. A new and better life started for Nicholas Kurti on his arrival in England in 1933:

'I had my first cup of English tea. And believe it or not, that tea in Paddington Station was probably better than any tea I ever had before. I don't know whether this would be true today. I remember I caught the 8.10 train to Oxford. I didn't see anything of Oxford that Saturday evening because it was dark. And next morning it was one of those beautiful autumn days which I think you only find in England. It had been raining I think during the night, and in the morning, the sun was shining. Round about half-past nine or ten, Mendelssohn (his host) said, "I will show you Oxford," I got on the pillion seat of his motor-bicycle and he drove me round. Well, on Sunday morning, even today Oxford is fairly empty, but in those days it was completely so. There was hardly a soul on the street, and there we were going through wonderful streets lined by wonderful buildings, with the green lawns and so on.

And after this quarter hour's ride, I suddenly said to myself, "Well, why don't I stay and spend the rest of my life in England and in Oxford?" — an idea which never occurred to me before, Although I loved Paris, I never thought of settling in Paris, or settling in France. I didn't like Berlin very much although it was intellectually very exciting and stimulating, but I never, never thought, even before the Nazis came to power, that I would want to live and settle in Germany. And that first visit to Oxford immediately gave me the idea, here, this is the country, this is the place I want to stay in. Now I don't know if the same thing would have happened if my first visit in England had been, shall we say, to Leeds or even to Sheffield, but Oxford was wonderful, and that is where I stayed for the rest of my life.'

Nicholas Kurti did indeed settle in Oxford; to Germany's loss and England's gain.

The rescue of many Jewish scientists and the introduction of modern physics to Oxford University are admirable achievements by Frederick Lindemann. He was not, himself, a physicist of the stature of Einstein, Rutherford, Curie, Bohr, Cockcroft or the other greats. Nor did he claim to be - saying of himself that: "I can understand and criticise anything, but I have

141

not got the creative power to do it myself." As far as his work in developing physics at Oxford was concerned, that lack was of no moment. He employed greater technicians than himself, and acted mostly as a fundraiser and figurehead.

However, in his role as chief scientist to Winston Churchill, Lindemann too often allowed his faults to dictate his actions. Those faults were, an inability to compromise, a belief that he was an expert, regardless of the subject, and a very thin skin. He regarded any disagreement with his statements as a personal attack on himself, regardless of whether he was right or wrong. He was a bitterly sarcastic man who, as his biographer wrote, would use falsehoods to win arguments. Rarely did he deign to discuss a matter, except with those in power over him. He was also a terrible snob. It is, perhaps, no coincidence that the author of his biography *The Prof in Two Worlds* was the Earl of Birkenhead.

As this book goes on, I will occasionally refer to some of the consequences of Frederick Lindemann's character on British war policy. Someone once collared Churchill on the subject of the unreasonableness of his chief scientific advisor. Winston was unrepentant. "Love me, love my dog," he growled. "If you don't love my dog, you can't love me." This remark warrants a red cross in the demerit column of the Churchill ledger. As anyone who has been bitten can testify, careless owners should not be allowed to keep animals which draw blood. In Churchill's defence, though, he did have quite a lot on his plate.

To return to weapon development at MIR(c). Stuart Macrae's ambition was to keep his section from being swallowed by an organisation which would slow it down. Macrae was what the Americans call 'a cute operator.' He succeeded by suggesting to Lindemann that he, 'The Prof', should take charge of the section. Lindemann agreed that, yes, he was the right man and took the idea to Churchill. By that time, he was probably convinced that it had been his idea all along. Churchill was sympathetic. He was, for obvious reasons (including the Boyes rifle fiasco I have mentioned earlier), not satisfied with many aspects of weapon production. He forthwith instructed General Ismay, his military advisor:

'Report to me on the position of Major Jefferis. By whom is he employed? Who is he under? I regard this officer as a singularly capable and forceful man who should be brought forward to a higher position. He ought certainly to be promoted Lieutenant-Colonel as it will give him more authority.'

As Churchill would later write:

'It was no time to proceed by ordinary channels. In order

Millis Jefferis has the preferable role in this experiment at Whitchurch

to secure quick action, I decided to keep under my own hand, as Minister of Defence, the experimental establishment at Whitchurch.'

The experimental establishment at Whitchurch was The Firs, the property that Macrae had requisitioned in the country. Whitchurch is to the north of Aylesbury about halfway between Chequers and Bletchley Park. Officially it was called MD1, the first and for years the only department of the Ministry of Defence. Its detractors called it Winston Churchill's Toyshop. Lindemann was the boss, but he ruled with a very light hand and rarely, if ever, dictated policy. The onsite supremo was the newly promoted Lieutenant-Colonel Millis Jefferis, a weapons' designer of genius who was not in the slightest interested in administration. The man who looked after that was Stuart Macrae.

Move to the Firs – October 1940

The Second World War sometimes resembles alphabet soup. MIR(c), which had now become MD1, had close links with the Special Operations Executive – SOE – of which Colin Gubbins was now in charge. Macrae was helped in setting up The Firs by Commander Langley, his opposite number in weapon development at SOE, who had set up Aston House in Hertfordshire. That was an interesting place too, as I'll explain a little later in the book.

Jefferis and Macrae were often at Chequers, giving demonstrations of their weapons to Churchill, Lindemann, service chiefs and the great and the good. On one occasion, the demonstrators nearly ran over the amiable King Haakon, the exiled king of Norway, with a remotely controlled device.

The not-quite so affectionately regarded Charles de Gaulle was at another demonstration - of a mortar: 'The missile very nearly wiped out General de Gaulle and unkind people suggested that the P.M. had in some way bribed Norman (Angier, who had built the mortar) to have a go at him....' (Churchill once famously said that the biggest cross he had to bear during the war was the cross of Lorraine – i.e. the Free French leader). Churchill was so taken with the mortar that he authorised an interim payment of £4,000 to develop it.

At yet another demonstration at Chequers, Churchill got a bit cross:

'This was the firing of a charge of very considerable size under a tank and there was every probability of shrapnel whizzing about, so I asked the P.M. kindly to step inside the splinter-proof shelter we had put there for his protection. But he perched himself on a little mound nearby and said, "No, I'll watch from here. Go ahead with the firing."

I argued with him and he got quite cross: "Get on with it," he said, "I'll take the responsibility." I had to tell him that the responsibility was mine not his and that if he refused to enter the shelter, I refused to explode the mine. Reluctantly, he gave way but he cheered up at once when the bang was over, because it had been an impressive one and lumps of metal had flown about.'

Part of MD1's remit was to evaluate suggestions made by individual citizens:

'There were lots of perpetual motion experts offering us free power, the old favourite of having a battery to drive a motor to drive a dynamo which would then charge the battery being an idea which we could bank on receiving almost every day.'

Death rays were another common theme. Not all of MD1's own designs were a success. One such was a special fluid Jefferis had come up with: a few drops of this put into a petrol tank was meant to wreck a car's engine within a few days. In practice the fluid enhanced the car's performance (sugar in the petrol tank didn't do it any harm either).

Sticky Bomb

Of more importance, orders were coming in from all three services for Limpet Mines and time and pressure switches.

And then there was the Sticky Bomb.

If the British were to 'fight them on the beaches and in the streets,' what were they going to fight with? Most of the guns and armour had been left in France and Molotov Cocktails were as ineffective against tanks as the Boyes rifle. Hence the Sticky Bomb. The specification for this was for a bomb or grenade which would stick and spread its explosive against a tank. This would then go bang and blow a hole. The requirement was simple – but its solution was not; 'if you have a vast toffee apple, you cannot carry it about in the nude (as it were) without it sticking to you.' After much experimentation, the answer was found to be to hold the explosive in a glass flask. A metal cover protected this. The operating instructions were not complex: Open the cover.

Smash the glass holding the charge against the item to be blown up. Leave.

The authorities however, were not happy. This was dangerous! One aspect that they especially objected to was the glass cover: it must be made 4 times thicker. However, this would have made it virtually unbreakable. Macrae took the matter up with the Prime Minister. Churchill got cross and wrote a note which read: 'Sticky Bomb. Make one million. WSC.'

The bomb was, in fact, so highly regarded that the army took it as well as the Home Guard. Hundreds of thousands were manufactured. It was never used in anger and was later supplanted by the PIAT mortar. However, its trials demonstrated that it would have been an effective weapon. Had the Germans managed to arrive in England and it was available, there is no doubt that it would have been used:

> 'We had the picture in mind that devoted soldiers or civilians would run up close to a tank and even thrust the bomb on it, even though the explosion cost them their lives …many would have done it.'

Against the relatively few tanks which could have been landed, it might well have been decisive.

The design of bombs, mortars, mines and other assorted explosive devices was just one part of Macrae's job at The Firs. As the demands from SOE and the regular forces grew ever greater, he was supervising the building of workshops – a factory – behind the main house: but it was impossible to get builders through the official channels. When he tried, he had trouble with the man from the ministry:

> 'The retired dyed-in-the-wool Colonel (who was in charge of authorising the building work) was not standing for any nonsense from upstarts like me, whether backed by the Prime Minister or not. I must submit my applications in writing and they would be dealt with in due course. If he approved them, then they would be submitted to the Office of Works who would prepare plans and estimates which would then come back to him so that he could apply for Treasury approval for the expenditure. To talk about starting

this work right away was complete and utter nonsense. I'd be lucky if it was started in three months.'

The same thing happened when Macrae tried to get an allocation of vehicles to bring in supplies and take away the devices that The Firs was turning out in quantity. Macrae went to see Professor Lindemann, who spoke to Churchill. In Macrae's words:

'It was not until this stage that General 'Pug' Ismay came into it. The P.M. said to the Prof. "See Pug about it," and that was that. Pug was a marvellous fellow with an absolute gift for inducing people to do what they were most reluctant to do without upsetting them or hurting their feelings.'

This was high praise from one consummate man-manager of another.

As they needed a large stores and transport centre, MD1 started their own works department – which grew to thirty hands - and a carpenters shop. To raise money, they asked the SOE section whom they were supplying (Aston House, a few miles over the border into Hertfordshire) for payments for the limpet mines that they were sending them from Whitchurch. The money was duly handed over, cash, no receipt necessary.

Professor Lindemann was fairly hands-off: calling once or twice a week to monitor progress, but always ready to cut red tape if necessary. Although well aware of the Professor's social incompetence: 'It would be difficult to find anyone who succeeded in making himself more unpopular than he did, everyone who disagreed with him was a fool,' Macrae knew how to handle Lindemann's crusty ways. Indeed he quite liked him (Macrae could manage most people).

The internal politics continued as various departments tried to take control of the Firs (principally Lord Beaverbrook's Ministry of Supply). Millis Jefferis wasn't interested in administration, he just wanted to design weapons and would have happily handed The Firs over. Macrae says of him that: 'like all brilliant scientists, mathematicians and so forth, he readily convinced himself that, with a brain such as his, he could solve problems of administration quite easily without having to put too much thought into it.' Lindemann (and

Macrae) thought differently. They believed that MD1 would fall apart unless Macrae ran it. Consequently Jefferis carried on as chief designer and titular head, while Macrae (as well as designing weapons), carried on with the day to day running of the place. He was a busy man.

The armed forces used Whitchurch as Churchill and Lindemann intended - to develop weapons quickly. In Macrae's words:

'The Royal Navy invaded us in a big way, but the Royal Air Force were close runners up. We could now claim to be by royal appointment sole suppliers of nasty booby traps to the British Army and Allies, if any.'

Jefferis was the inventive brain of the organisation. His development of weapons was founded on the use of calculus of a high order, such as is needed for the calculation of trajectories, the explosion of gases, the penetrating power of metal, timing and the other abstruse knowledge needed for the design of weapons. His habit of walking round with his pockets stuffed full of detonators, small batteries and pieces of wire impressed some and terrified others.

The unit was now producing the pull, pressure and release switches, as well as the Limpet Mine and Sticky Bombs in very large numbers. The speed with which the organising ability of Macrae got the Firs into production is impressive. Three months after getting the property, MD1 were loading trucks all night to get supplies to Bombay, Australia and the Middle East. Macrae set up design units for the intricate and detailed work needed to manufacture aero switches (fixed on aircraft and calibrated to explode a charge at a specified height), as well as new generations of Limpets, timers, grenades and the like.

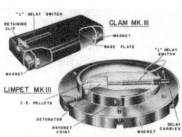

The Clam and the Limpet

A pocket version of The Limpet – The Clam – was developed. These went in vast numbers to saboteurs and regular services 'to stick onto something they wanted to blow up'. The Russians alone were given nearly a million of them and were 'constantly clamouring for more.' They probably went to the vast partisan armies of Belarus and the Ukraine which inflicted catastrophic disruption and casualties on the German army.

The nature of the breakneck weapon development was at times unorthodox. Although much of the production was done at factories remote from The Firs, the many trial devices used at Whitchurch and Chequers needed high explosive. If the weapons were sent off to an ordnance factory, this could take up to a month:

> 'Among the staff, we had a professional hairdresser named Mr Bridle who, like all hairdressers, had made his business pay not by cutting hair but by mixing up concoctions, putting them into bottles and selling them to their customers.'

Mr Bridle was sent to the army's ordnance factory, given a quick course in the mixing of high and low intensity explosives and, on his return, The Firs had an explosives department. An army brigadier got to hear of this and ordered the explosives department (the summer house) to close. Macrae went to see Lindemann and then the brigadier: 'To the latter, I delivered a very tactful message from The Prof which I had invented in place of the forceful one he had given to me.' The message was to the effect that desperate times call for desperate remedies. Macrae sugared the pill by asking the brigadier to authorise the building of a proper facility:

> 'A year later, I was able to show him around our nice, new high-explosive and incendiary filling sheds, which complied with all the safety regulations and looked most impressive.'

Captain Stuart Macrae spent a lot of time going up and down the country to liaise with production factories. He did not like the fact that an officer of his rank was only allowed to travel third class when travelling by rail, as this meant that he had to share a sleeper compartment with three others (he tells us that he snored badly and did not want to be a nuisance). This inspired him to study Army Regulations, where, conveniently,

149

he found that if an officer was carrying explosives, he must travel first class:

'From then onwards, I made it a rule to have a couple of sticks of gelignite in my suitcase whenever I had to travel by rail – which I was then able to do in the utmost luxury.'

Sleepy Whitchurch – a village of perhaps a thousand people - hardly knew what had hit it when MD1 took over The Firs. The premises were surrounded with barbed wire and had a detachment of military police on duty – day and night. Explosives trials started early and ended late – once a missile left the premises, sailed across the road and wrecked the telephone lines which carried the traffic for nearby RAF Wing.

Workshops and barracks were built, as was a canteen and a theatre for plays and films (the villagers were welcome at these entertainments). In two years the 3 man section had become a

Piat Mortar

fully equipped research and development centre with a staff of 250.

Millis Jefferis developed the successor to the Sticky Bomb - the PIAT (projector infantry anti-tank) – a hand held anti-tank gun which was the most effective Allied anti-tank weapon of the war – not excepting, in Macrae's knowledgeable opinion, even the American Bazooka. The PIAT projectile used a hollow charge – that is a shell with a cone in the nose pointing inwards towards the body with the explosive behind it. This was a principle discovered in Germany in 1792.

A report from Matthew Halton (A Canadian reporter with the CBC) from Normandy on June 19th 1944 says:

'...German tanks rushed back and forth across our slit trench, spraying the Canadians with fire and steel. In reply the Canadians stalked those huge tanks with PIAT (Projector Infantry Anti-Tank) mortars. You know the PIAT mortar? If you fire it from fifteen to twenty feet, you are likely to be caught in the blast. The Canadians were crawling to within five or ten feet, and from that distance the mortar bombs went through the German armour. The Jerries inside got the blast. Twenty-nine Panther and Tiger tanks were burnt out. Some job!'

The PIAT weighed 60 pounds. Macrae says that it earned 'five or six' Victoria Crosses during the war. He also said that in his opinion you deserved a VC if you used one, such was the blast. It was: 'a two man job, one for the gun, one for the shells – though some supermen did the whole job by themselves.'

Macrae's organisation and Jefferis's design genius allowed MD1 to become: 'The finest special weapons development department in the world ...the Americans envied us and freely admitted that they could not rival us here.'

MD1 also designed and produced several guns, bombs and rockets using hollow charges – which would 'drill a nice hole through 2 inches of armour plate or a yard of concrete. Larger sizes would penetrate any concrete pillbox and that was what they were wanted for.'

As ever in this book, I have space only to tell only part of this extraordinary story. If I have whetted your appetite, I heartily recommend that you read Stuart Macrae's book *Winston Churchill's Toyshop*. Macrae, who met Churchill many times, said of him:

'The amount of information he could store away in that great head of his was fantastic. In discussion, he could without effort remember the location of almost every important ship of the fleet and could do the same where army divisions were concerned.'

On the subject of his speeches, he says:

'I was on many occasions one of a dozen or so officers who would be summoned to Chequers at the weekend because he was preparing one of his speeches and proposed to make some reference to the departments we represented or their work ...seldom did a correction have to be made, but if it were made, it would be accepted without question.'

Macrae, too, emphasises the collegiate way that Churchill worked, gathering experts on the subject he was interested in and questioning and listening to them. Macrae says of him that he was 'the greatest man I ever knew.'

MD1 was to make a critical contribution to the war at sea. This came about because Commander Charles Goodeve (the unorthodox head of the Admiralty's special weapons department) had heard of Whitchurch's facilities and asked Lindemann if he could use them. He was welcomed and quickly seconded several naval staff to The Firs. Between them, Jefferis and the navy developed an anti-submarine system called the Hedgehog which would sound the death knell for many an Axis submarine.

Ian Fleming and Nevil Shute were two naval officers who were deeply involved in this work. Fleming wasn't known for his devoutness but he did like a drink. He may have walked a mile up the road to the pub at Oving, with its sweeping views over the Vale of Aylesbury. Being a man with an inquisitive mind, he may then have climbed the few steps into the churchyard next door to the pub. If so, he couldn't have failed to see the fine, leaning eighteenth century gravestone which was (and is) closest to the church porch. This beautiful spot is where one James Bond has his long home.

The Hedgehog

Be that as it may, the primary weapons that were developed by, and with, the Royal Navy at

Whitchurch were the Hedgehog, and its successor, the Squid.

The Hedgehog was a mortar which fired a battery of 24 contact fused bombs (which looked like firework rockets). The array was fired in an arc ahead of the attacking ship after the target submarine had been 'pinged' by underwater sound pulses sent out by the ship (ASDIC/SONAR).

Previously submarines had been 'bombed' by depth charges which were dropped from the rear and sides of the attacking ship. These exploded at pre-set depths, setting off shock waves. Apart from being inherently inaccurate, such explosions greatly disturbed the water, causing ASDIC to lose contact with its prey. Hedgehog, on the other hand, exploded on impact with the submarine, with infinitely more damaging effect. Moreover, if the projectiles didn't hit the target they didn't go off, so that the attacking ship could change course and maintain contact while still 'seeing' the U-boat as it manoeuvred.

U-boats often escaped from depth charge attacks, but not so often from Hedgehog. A Hedgehog attack was ten times more likely to sink a submarine than a depth charge attack. It was used by both the Royal Navy and The United States Navy and was to account for 37 U-boat's in the Atlantic and several Japanese ones in the Pacific (in 1944 the USS *England* sank 6 Japanese submarines in 12 days with the Hedgehog).

Not surprisingly, the archetypal schoolboy, Churchill, lover of all things that went bang, adored the Hedgehog. A target was drawn out in the shape of a submarine in a field behind Whitchurch and Winston went along to see:

'The P.M. was delighted when he came to Whitchurch to see the Hedgehog demonstrated. He kept on demanding a repeat performance until we ran out of rounds.'

Macrae said that he saw another side of Churchill at weapon demonstrations:

'He would be like a small boy on holiday. Commander Thompson (his bodyguard) would be in attendance carrying a Sten gun and when there was any lull in the proceedings, Winston would lower himself to the ground and bang away with this thing at the nearest target.'

*Commander Thompson (rear) has seen
it all before*

By the end of the war MD1 had produced 26 new weapons ranging from small booby traps to heavy artillery, aircraft bombs to naval mines.

Mary and Stuart Macrae were lodging in the village of Whitchurch, within walking distance of The Firs. Mary had found a job locally. Her journey to work was along narrow, winding and often muddy roads which wandered uphill and down vale and were overhung everywhere by great and ancient trees. Sometimes the bus that picked her up had to wait behind a herd of cows which were being taken for milking. As the bus threaded through the next couple of villages, it would stop and others would get on. Half an hour later they would arrive at their workplace, Bletchley Park; which is also where we are going next.

7: Bletchley unbombed

Bletchley Park is famed worldwide as the place where Colossus, the world's first electronic digital computer, was switched into life: the birthplace of the information age. The children and grandchild of that moment are today's computers and the internet. If Arnold Schwarzenegger's *terminator* had wanted to try to smother the modern world at birth, he would have been well advised to impersonate the ticket inspector at Bletchley station sometime in the late nineteen thirties and push Turing, Welchman and Newman under the down train to Euston.

Bletchley Park was (with the sole possible exception of the atom bomb) the major weapon of World War Two: the brain of the allied war effort. I will return to the place again and again throughout the book. I will not write (except in a very general way and where I find it unavoidable) about the technical aspects of code breaking. Many 'bits and bytes' accounts of Bletchley Park have been written, and by far more competent hands than mine. I do not intend to add another. This chapter is a brief look at Bletchley Park in the first couple of years of the war. It is about some exceptional people and how their actions and interactions affected the world.

I shall use the abbreviation 'BP' for Bletchley Park in the rest of this book.

Bletchley Park – safe haven for the secret service
In 1937, the head of SIS, Quex Sinclair told one of his staff (Alistair Denniston, the head of GC & CS; the Government Code and Cypher School), that he was now 'convinced of the inevitability of war'. As we know from the first chapter, Quex – with the aid of Fred Winterbotham amongst others - had convinced the government too. A large amount of public funds

had been given to his secret service. He needed the money both to rapidly extend SIS and to move a good part of it away from London to a safe area.

Quex bought BP in 1938, purchasing it in his own name (though not apparently with his own money; after his death his sister transferred ownership to the government for ten shillings). As I mentioned earlier, there were several reasons why he had chosen BP as his war HQ. The estate is next to the railway station in the small town from which it takes its name. Bletchley station was – and is – a stop on the south to north line between England's largest cities, London and Birmingham. It was also a stop on the east to west line between Cambridge and Oxford. Britain's telephone cable backbone ran up Watling street, less than a mile away. A signals school had operated there (in Fenny Stratford), in the first war; making this one of the oldest communications networks in the world.

Quex Sinclair began to relocate many of his staff out of London in August 1939. While his headquarters staff (including himself) stayed in the capital, he relocated both GC & CS (his code breakers) and most of his communications engineers. And there was a third SIS section at BP. In 1938 Sinclair had set up Section D (D for destruction) with a Major Grand in charge. Grand was given the task of doing things which the government did not want to acknowledge. His selling point to potential recruits was unusual to say the least: "I can't tell you what sort of job it would be. All I can say is that if you join us, you mustn't be afraid of forgery… or murder." Section D was later to become part of Churchill's dirty tricks department – the Special Operations Executive (SOE) – as I will explain later.

Apart from the cryptographers of GC & CS, and SIS's communications staff and saboteurs, many clerks and ancillary staff also arrived at Bletchley Park in the first days of the war.

The Government Code and Cypher School –
the GC &CS

The department of SIS which dealt with code breaking, the Government Code and Cypher School had been set up in 1919. GC & CS were the cryptographers who are today synonymous with Bletchley Park. Those code breakers had, at the outbreak of the war, a very tough nut to crack: finding out what their enemies were saying to each other. The main method Germany (and, later, to a much lesser extent, Italy) used for secret communications was the Enigma machine.

Sinclair had already instructed the head of GC & CS, Alastair Denniston, to begin recruiting staff to break the Enigma codes and so read the minds of the enemy. GC & CS were looking for 'men of the professor type' from the universities, principally Oxford and Cambridge. Denniston's most successful recruiters were Frank Adcock and Frank Birch, both of whom had taught history at Cambridge. Both were ex-members of the secret services who knew that their country was looking down the barrel of a gun (in WW1, Adcock had invented an antennae array which was later to be crucial in detecting U-boats).

Adcock and Birch were excellent recruiters who had many friends and contacts amongst their fellow teaching staff at Cambridge University. But things had moved on from their time. In the first war, decoding enemy messages had been the purview of historians and linguists. Not anymore; GC & CS realised that the invention of Enigma meant that mathematical skills were now the most important necessity in cryptography. Consequently, most of the top cryptographers of Bletchley Park, such as Turing, Welchman, Alexander, Tutte, Jeffreys, Babbage and Newman, were mathematicians from Cambridge University.

After recruitment, these staff were sent on short introductory courses. A couple of them began work immediately; but mostly they were told that they would be contacted for deployment to BP should war be declared.

The British secret service weren't operating completely in the dark in how to decipher the Enigma generated messages. Their most important source of help was their close cooperation with both the French and Polish intelligence services.

But what exactly was the Enigma machine?

Enigma

The German army, navy, air force, SS, police and various other agencies used Enigma machines to encrypt messages prior to transmitting them by radio. The machine was an electro-mechanical device which looked like a typewriter. It was mechanically operated, the pressing down of a letter causing physical movements in the machine and also an electric signal to pass through its internal wiring. The letter which was pressed on the keyboard was scrambled within the machine to result in another letter as the output. One oddity about the machine was that the letter which came out was never the same as the one that was typed in. That is to say, if you typed in an 'A' the letter you got out would be one of the other 25 letters, but never 'A.' That was the first tiny chink in its security.

The five available rotors, boxed up. Each rotor has 26 positions - A to Z

A 3 rotor (seen above the keyboard) Enigma.

The Enigma machine had a number of slots in the top of the machine into which rotors (wheels) could be placed. The army version of the Enigma had three such slots, the version used by the German submarine force had four. In the three fixed-wheel version, the three rotors were selected from five which were available to the operator. In the four position version, the choice was from eight.

Although each wheel was identical on the outside, each was wired differently inside. The order of the settings of these wheels were changed each day. The 3 wheels themselves have 17,576 (26 x 26 x 26) possible settings. When the internal wiring between them is added, the possibilities become over a million million... and that is without mentioning the plugboard - which multiplies the possibilities exponentially. It is an immensely complex mechanism – so complex that the Germans thought the code unbreakable. At first, GC & CS agreed. In the words of Gordon Welchman, Alan Turing's equal at BP, Enigma was: "unbreakable if properly used."

Cracking Enigma – French and Polish help

The German armed forces started to use Enigma in the 1920s. Shortly after that, the Deuxième Bureau – French intelligence – was approached by a worker in the German cypher office who had a large sexual appetite and a small wallet. He (Hans Schmidt) offered to sell the French a copy of the machine's manual, operating instructions, and the key settings covering a certain period. The French bought the information and shared it with British and Polish intelligence (Schmidt would pay for his treachery with his life in 1943). Even given this information, neither the Deuxième Bureau nor GC & CS could decipher Enigma coded messages. The Poles were more successful. They were dab hands at intelligence work - they had to be - Poland had been partitioned and shared out among its more powerful neighbours, notably Russia and Germany, more than once over the centuries. After the First World War, the Russians attempted invasion once again. The Russian troops were defeated because Polish code breakers read their communications and out-manoeuvred them.

When the French spymaster, Captain Gustave Bertrand, handed the Enigma information to Poland, a Polish mathematician, Marian Rejewski, who was already working on the same problem, put the intelligence to good use. He constructed a copy of the Enigma machine and devised a method of cracking the code, using a hand-operated machine and perforated coded sheets. He called the machine a "Bomba" (bomb) – which was, allegedly, the type of ice cream he happened to be eating when the solution came to him. With the Bomba and the coded (Zygalski) sheets the Poles succeeded in breaking into several of the German army Enigma codes. I won't describe how the Bomba and the sheets worked – they were quickly superseded by British improvements – but they were pivotal in the early development of Bletchley Park.

In 1939, Britain and France signed a treaty that bound them both, should the Nazis invade Poland, to declare war on Germany. Poland was, as we've seen, the country where the breaking of the German Enigma was the most advanced. Also in 1939, Polish intelligence invited their French and British counterparts to their country. For the second and final of these visits, Sinclair sent the head of GC & CS, Alistair Denniston, and his chief cryptographer, Dilly Knox. With them was Commander Sandwith, of the Royal Navy's listening services. Gustave Bertrand represented French intelligence. It was at this meeting that the Poles handed over the plans for the Bombas and, later, two Enigma machines.

GC & CS's chief cryptographer, Dilly Knox, did not comport himself well with regard to the Poles. His boss, Hugh Denniston, in a letter of apology to Bertrand wrote of him:

'He is a man of exceptional intelligence but he does not know the word co-operation. In Warsaw I had some deplorable experiences with him. He wants to do everything himself... he can't stand it when someone knows more than he does.'

Apparently he was miffed that the Poles had succeeded where he had failed. Shades of Professor Lindemann.

Quex Sinclair died in November 1939. After his death, SIS's new 'C' was Stewart Menzies, a suave old Etonian (heir to a whisky distillery). He had been Admiral Sinclair's deputy and was Quex's choice as his successor. Although he stayed in London, he was Bletchley Park's overall boss.

GC & CS – Denniston, Knox, Turing and Welchman

The work accommodation at BP was in the house itself and in a number of huts in the grounds. The huts were built by Captain Faulkener, the local builder from whom Quex had bought BP. They varied in size but generally had internal plasterboard walls and a central passageway with rooms off it. Hut 6, which was the first (and main) decoding hut, was about

60 feet long and 30 wide. The furniture consisted of tables and stacking chairs. There were no toilets in the huts.

In the main house itself was GC & CS's boss, Alastair Denniston, and Dilly Knox, its chief cryptographer. A number of newly enrolled mathematicians had arrived from Cambridge to help him – the most influential of whom would be Alan Turing and Gordon Welchman.

The BP staff were billeted with the local population; with or without their concurrence. The incomers could be sniffy about the small towns and villages in which they found themselves, especially Bletchley and Wolverton – traditional railway towns. According to (Lord) Asa Briggs, who worked at Bletchley:

"there was little mixing between railwaymen who played games like darts, shuffleboard, shove ha'penny and dominoes …pubs with obviously erudite customers were... the Cock and the Bull in two old stabling inns in Stoney Stratford. It was reputed that a few of their customers spoke classical Greek to each other over their beers."

Gordon Welchman, who would become head of Hut 6, was billeted in a pub – the Duncombe Arms at Great Brickhill. He liked it very well there. Alan Turing was billeted at another, the Crown in Shenley Brook End. These were unsettled and unsettling times. In 1940, fearing a German invasion, Turing converted his savings into two silver bars and buried them nearby but forgot exactly where and was never able to find them. As far as it is known, they are still undiscovered.

Air intelligence – enter Doctor Jones

Wing Commander Winterbotham, who had worked with Quex Sinclair and his successor Stewart Menzies for years, was in charge of air intelligence at SIS. He claims to have come up with the name 'Ultra' to describe BP's intelligence output. His first job at Bletchley was to arrange the collation of intelligence. That intelligence came from several sources - the decoders, agents on the ground, spy planes and radio listening services. Winterbotham set up a section for this work – in Hut 3. Hut 3 was originally staffed with officers from all three of the armed forces, RAF, army and Royal Navy (who ran Hut 3 would be a running sore in BP for a couple of years). Winterbotham also set up an organisation to securely pass information from 'his' Hut 3 to generals in the field. Presenting the information to Churchill in London would be a job for his boss – Stewart Menzies.

When the war began, Germany had the strongest army on Earth: and few, if any, could match her in science. Between the wars the three countries who won the most Nobel prizes for science were Germany, with 20, Britain, with 14, and the United States who had 10. SIS had few sources of information – spies – in Nazi Germany. Those it did have were not scientists. This was a major gap in intelligence. Britain needed to know what new weapons were being developed by the world's super power: in particular in the fields of radar, atomics, armaments and air warfare. The man tasked to find out was a twenty-eight year old Scientific Officer working at the Air Ministry, Doctor Reginald Jones.

Dr. Jones had been recruited during a meeting with Robert Watson-Watt and Henry Tizard at the Air Ministry (about a suspected German radar dish which had been spotted on the Baltic coast). He did not at first realise that his new job was with the secret service. His new boss was Wing Commander Winterbotham, who sent him to Bletchley to familiarise himself with the intelligence that Hut 3 held on Germany and to generally find out what BP was up to. Jones is another character who will return to my narrative later in the war. He would become the key figure in British aerial intelligence, mixing with service chiefs, major scientists and the political elite (from Churchill down).

Unlike most of his Oxbridge contemporaries, Reginald Jones was not from the upper classes. His father was a Sergeant in the Grenadier Guards. He started his schooling in London's Brixton:

'My contemporaries encompassing everything from barrow boy to millionaire scrap merchant and trade union peer... my main hobby was, as with many other schoolboys of my generation, the making of radio receiving sets. There has never been anything comparable in any other period of history to the impact of radio on the ordinary individual in the 1930s. It was the product of some the most imaginative developments that ever occurred in physics, and it was as near magic as anyone could conceive, in that with a few mainly home-made components simply connected together one could conjure speech and music out of the air.'

By hard work and sheer intelligence, Jones won a place at the University of Oxford, under Frederick Lindemann who, as we know, was building up the physics department there. Reginald ('Reg') Jones, says that Lindemann 'led him up the (academic) garden path' by making assumptions that were incorrect and says that Lindemann was guilty of 'characteristic overstatements.' However, he was at one with 'The Prof' in his patriotism and rejection of pacifism. While Jones was at Oxford the notorious resolution of the Oxford Union that 'under no circumstances will this house fight for King and country,' took place. There is strong evidence that this helped Mussolini and Hitler to believe that the British establishment was rotten and that British territories were ripe for the picking.

After the carnage of the first war, pacifism was the norm in society in Britain, France and America. And there was a respect in the west for the strongman, dictator or not. Hitler was Time magazine's man of the year in 1938. Stalin got the award in 1939. Those who spoke out against dictators – Churchill included – were generally seen as war-mongers.

When he first arrived at Bletchley Park, Reg Jones was billeted seven miles away, at Winslow Hall. Also billeted there was Edward Travis, the deputy director of GC & CS. Travis's over-riding problem at the time, and a frequent subject of their evening discussions at Winslow Hall, was, of course, how to decipher Enigma traffic (Travis introduced Jones to Alan Turing. They, too, discussed the problem).

Although reading up old SIS files didn't tell Jones much about German scientific advances, Jones was not working entirely in the dark. In October 1939 the British naval attaché in Oslo received an anonymous letter offering secret German scientific and technical information and asking for one of the BBC news broadcasts in German to begin with the uncharacteristic phrase 'Hallo, hier ist London' if it was desired to take the offer up. The broadcast was made and in November

163

a packet of seven typed pages and a sealed box was delivered to the naval attaché. Winterbotham passed this to Jones, who decided that it was genuine, though the three service ministries regarded it as a "plant" and discarded their copies. The report covered German radar, torpedoes, shells and rockets. Jones said of it:

'In the few dull moments of the War, I used to look up the Oslo report to see what should be coming along next.'

Before returning to Doctor Jones, I would like to explain how Bletchley Park's processes evolved in those early days – and how that caused a few feathers to be ruffled…

Welchman improves Bletchley processes (Sept 39 – April 40)

The Cambridge mathematicians, and especially Turing and Welchman, were key figures in GC & CS' code breaking at Bletchley Park. Welchman would also be crucial in the outstandingly successful development and organisation of BP as a whole; but it wasn't all plain sailing for him at first. When he arrived at the park, at the outbreak of the war, he was side-lined – or at least that was his impression – by GC & CS's Chief Cryptographer, Dilly (Dilwyn) Knox. Welchman was not entirely impressed by Knox:

'Knox was neither an organisation man nor a technical man… Dilly seems to have disliked most of the men with whom he came in contact… I got the impression that he didn't like me.'

Welchman was 'turned out' by Knox who sent him to another building to study agents' call signs. But Welchman's genius was not to be smothered. In his 'outer darkness' he came up with an improvement to the Zygalski sheets which the Poles had pioneered. He might as well have saved his time; for Knox's section had, in fact, already discovered and were using the same method. When Welchman proffered his 'break through', Knox was neither abashed that he had not fully briefed his junior, nor impressed by the latter's enterprise. His reaction was unnuanced fury that Welchman had gone beyond his remit. Dilly, perhaps, sensed a challenger. If so, he was right.

Welchman was a polymath. As well as being a genius at cypher cracking, he looked at the physical structure of the German communications' organisation. He worked closely with army, navy and air force listening stations to record and find the source of the different emissions from the continent – traffic analysis. The Enigma operators changed their call signs – the identifiers of who they were – every day. Knowing where they were meant their units could be identified. He also chivvied for more staff – visiting Cambridge himself to recruit former colleagues such as Stuart Milner-Barry, who would in turn recruit Hugh Alexander.

Welchman, according to a colleague, could see through problems as he had the ability to think in 'abstract, multi-dimensional space.' In this he was like Turing, with whom he developed the methods for deciphering Enigma. Unlike Turing, he also saw what extra resources BP needed to decipher messages on an industrial scale: and made sure it got them. It was Welchman who, above all, made Bletchley Park the intelligence factory that it became. He has rightly been called the father of modern signals intelligence in both Britain and the United States. In the words of Stuart Milner-Barry:

'If Gordon Welchman had not been there, I doubt if Ultra would have played the part that it did in shortening the war.'

I mentioned earlier that Hut 6 was the first and largest decoding section at Bletchley Park. It was Welchman who was behind the creation of Hut 6 and was its first head. Welchman took his suggestions for the organisation of Bletchley Park not to Hugh Denniston, but to his deputy, Edward Travis - he who spent his evenings discussing Enigma with Doctor Reginald Jones. It was Travis who made the practical arrangements to make Welchman's ideas possible.

Intelligence failure – Norway April 8th 1940
Intelligence did not help Britain much when Norway and Denmark were invaded in April 1940. What little warning there was was duly passed to the Joint Intelligence Committee (who

co-ordinated intelligence from all sources) but not acted on. The swift and overpowering German strikes came, therefore, as a surprise to the British military.

A month later, on the 10th of May 1940, the Germans launched their attack in the west. On the same day, Chamberlain resigned and Churchill became Prime Minister. One of Churchill's first jobs was to make sure he was up to date with all that was known of the enemy's intelligence: which was precisely what Quex had set BP up to provide. Stewart Menzies, Quex's successor, personally delivered 'a small red box' daily to 10 Downing Street, containing an executive summary of relevant reports and intercepts obtained by Bletchley during the last 24 hours. The box was marked 'only to be opened by the Prime Minister in person.' Only Churchill and Menzies held keys for it.

May 1940 – Bletchley and Dunkirk

By this time Bletchley had improved on the original Polish methods and introduced its own, new, processes to supplement them. This had allowed them to break into four German army and five Luftwaffe methods of encrypting messages (ciphers). One of these BP called 'Red'. This was the cipher that was used between the German air force (Luftwaffe) and their army (the Wehrmacht) for co-operation. It was through messages using this cipher that the German army, if held up by British or French tanks or guns, could call in air support. That is to say that as soon as the tanks at the sharp end of the German advance met opposition they would call in Stuka dive bombers. This innovation in ground and air attack was key to the Nazi *Blitzkrieg* ('lightning war'). Later in the war the allies themselves would copy the method and call it 'Cab Rank' or 'Taxi Rank'. In 1940, however, this advance in warfare came as a very very nasty surprise to the Allies. The Blitzkrieg of the Panzer armies of Heinz Guderian and Erwin Rommel cut the French and British armies to pieces. The courage of the defending troops on the ground was not the issue. Superior German general-ship, techniques, training and tactics most certainly were.

The key man at BP in deciphering the Enigma messages, Gordon Welchman, had no illusions about the scale of the challenge:

'The Germans had done such a good job...the problems which we faced were unprecedented. Never before had radio signals and cryptography been employed on such a large scale to provide battlefield communications.'

His problem was about to get much, much, worse. On the day of the German attack on the west, the 10th of May 1940, the Germans changed their coding procedures in such a way that Bletchley could no longer read the messages. Hut 6 was working a

Panzer General Heinz Guderian's command car. Note Enigma

24 hour, 7 day week and, by feverish effort, Welchman's team managed to read the ciphers again within two weeks. They did this by identifying and exploiting sloppy operating procedures used by the Enigma operators. One method was the Herivel tip (named after John Herivel, a 21 year old maths graduate plucked from his doctorate studies at Cambridge). Herivel guessed that stressed Enigma operators might be lazy in choosing rotor settings on their machines and might base them on, for example, a setting which they had previously used. The other method BP used (to guess text settings) was what they termed 'sillies' (or cillis). This was again based on common procedural short cuts that the Enigma operators made. For those who are interested in learning more about these methods, I recommend reading Gordon Welchman's *Hut Six Story*.

Ultra had little, if any, bearing on the decision of Lord Gort (the leader of Britain's Expeditionary force) to evacuate his men from Dunkirk. Bletchley's man at Gort's headquarters was Henry Dryden. Dryden had been head-hunted from Cambridge University and had been called into the Military Section of Sinclair's GC and CS in London (under John Tiltman) several months before the war began. His degree was in French and German. When the GC and CS was moved to Bletchley Park, he was one of the first to work in Hut 3. He was posted to Gort's headquarters to decrypt Enigma messages a few days before the German attack. He looked, perhaps, a little conspicuous, in 'civvies'. On the day of the German break through, he was told to 'Burn that bloody suit and get into uniform.' He did his best, although officer's uniforms were hard to come by, so he still continued to wear coloured socks.

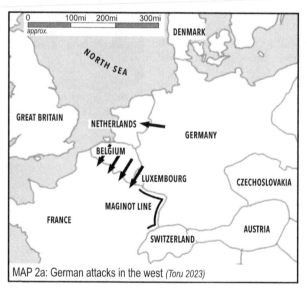

MAP 2a: German attacks in the west *(Toru 2023)*

When the Nazis launched their attack, Gort moved his British troops into Belgium to fight German Army Group B. However, even as they moved up, German Army Group A motored through the 'impassable' Ardennes forest, defeated the French at the Sedan crossing of the river Meuse and swung north west to cut off the British from the sea.

These were the key days when BP was locked out of the German army and air force Red code, and could not decipher the messages between the attacking armoured columns and their supporting aircraft. Back at Bletchley, Gordon Welchman says that while 'the flood of Hut 6 decodes could have had little if any effect on the course of the Battle Of France... they must have given early warning that the military situation was utterly hopeless.' Over at Gort's headquarters, BP's man in the frontline, Henry Dryden agrees that most of the messages he and his men were acting on were not Ultra but plain language conversations between the German tanks and Stuka dive bombers as they 'taxi-ranked' to break any opposition; but he confirms Welchman's sentiment that they gave Lord Gort 'an increasingly bleak operational picture.'

Bletchley did give Gort a decrypt of a signal from General von Brauchitsch at the German Army High Command which ordered German Army Group A to get behind Gort and keep his army from the coast; but Gort had already ordered his force to retreat by then.

The Luftwaffe to Wehrmacht 'Red' code was, as I've said, transmitted using the 3 rotor Enigma machines. The 4 wheel U-boat version was a much, much tougher nut to crack. Turing and 'Doc' Keen were heading up a team working on a mechanical device – which they would call the Bombe in deference to the Polish Bomba - to solve that problem. As part of the task, raiding groups were tasked with getting hold of Enigmas, rotors and code books from German ships. The first fruit of their labours would come with a successful 'pinch' from the Lofoten Islands in March 1941.

Reginald Jones - the first battle of the beams

The Axis messages that BP deciphered in Hut 6 did not always give the whole story. That's where Hut 3 – which translated decoded messages and married them with information from other sources – came in.

The diversity of different source material can be seen if one looks at R.V. Jones's first success. Jones, whom we last saw poring over the Oslo Report, had moved back to London after working on pooling intelligence in Hut 3. The return to the capital was not the wisest of moves, as Bletchley was bombed only once during the war and there were no casualties. London was to suffer 30,000 deaths from air attacks. However, Reg Jones was spending a lot of time at the Air Ministry and with Menzies and Winterbotham at SIS's headquarters, which remained in London. Jones had not been married very long and his wife, Vera, was six months pregnant. They had managed to get a rental on a flat on the top floor of a block on Richmond Common. The building stood in a commanding position with a magnificent sweep of a view from Kew Gardens round to Windsor Castle, ten miles distant. And it was cheap. Rents for London properties had fallen sharply when the bombings started.

Jones' input to the air war was crucial. Knowing British radar capabilities, he kept a weather eye open for what the Germans might be up to – and that turned out to be the X-Beam. His first hint of the device came from Trent Park in Cockfosters, in North London, in June 1940. Trent Park was yet another country house in the Intelligence Zone commandeered for the war effort. It was one of the places where captured German prisoners were held. The rooms on the site were bugged and the prisoners' conversations recorded. Jones was on the distribution list for a transcript of a conversation between two Luftwaffe prisoners discussing the 'X-Gerat'– the X apparatus. The transcript was from the chief interrogator at Trent Park, Flight Lieutenant Denys Felkin. Jones suspected that this might be a bomb aiming technique using crossing radio pulses. He asked Felkin to find out more. Felkin, by interrogating a captured bomber crew, found that the system did indeed consist of two intersecting beams – hence the 'X'.

Then came another hint. Papers found in a shot-down bomber referred to 'the *Knickebein* beam at 315 degrees' – due north west. Knickebein means crooked leg in German. This, again, suggested one of the transmission points for a pair of intersecting beams. Jones wondered if the X-Gerat and the Knickebein might be related. Shortly afterward Knickebein was mentioned again, in a Bletchley Park intercept which read:

'Knickebein, Kleve confirms 53 degrees 4 minutes north and 1 degree west.'

Jones asked Felkin at Trent Park to interrogate the prisoners further, to see if they would tell more. They wouldn't - but one of them was recorded as saying that no matter how hard the British looked for the 'equipment', they would never find it. Jones saw this as both a confirmation and a challenge. It prompted him to look closely at a detailed technical investigation which had been carried out on a German bomber - a Heinkel 111 - that had been shot down over the Firth of Forth. The RAF expert with whom he discussed the report told him that the only thing that struck him as odd about the aircraft's radio gear was that the blind landing device seemed unnecessarily sensitive.

Down at Trent Park, Denis Felkin struck lucky. A rare anti-Nazi Luftwaffe prisoner told him that Knickebein was an intersecting beam transmitted from two towers. He even sketched a tower.

I have summed the story up in a page or two – but its revelation was the fruit of many weeks work on Jones' part – and many enquiries. For example, he read (and filed) every single Luftwaffe decrypt from Bletchley – as well as poring over umpteen aerial reconnaissance photographs. The X-Beam was just one of his investigations and it was taking him a lot of time. He appealed to Professor Frederick Lindemann, who had taught him at Oxford and who was now Churchill's chief scientific advisor, for more resources. The prospect of the enemy bombing British cities accurately and at night was a terrifying one. Churchill himself signed off the request, scrawling on it: 'do this without fail.'

Another shot-down aircraft yielded papers which referred to a second station, in Bredstedt, in north Germany, near the border with Denmark. Again Jones spoke to Lindemann. This led him to be called into a very high level meeting which Lindemann had convened. The most senior of the air staff were present, as well as members of the Joint Intelligence Committee. Churchill was in the chair. Jones summarised his findings, which were that the Knickebein allowed German bombing of British targets by day or night regardless of weather conditions. The intersecting beams had an accuracy of within 400 yards of their aiming point. The beams that he had identified crossed at Derby, where the Rolls Royce works aero-engine plant was the chief manufacturer of the Merlin engine used in the Spitfire and Hurricane.

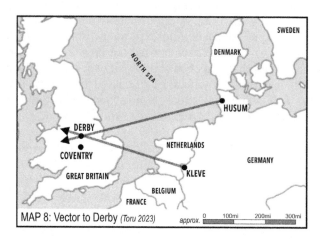

MAP 8: Vector to Derby *(Toru 2023)*

Churchill was aghast. He wrote of their meeting in *Their finest hour*:

> 'He (Jones) spoke in quiet tones, unrolling his chain of circumstantial evidence, the like of which for its convincing fascination was never surpassed by tales of Sherlock Holmes.'

Jones had never met Churchill before. He says of him: 'I had the feeling of being recharged by contact with a source of living power. Here was strength, resolution, humour, readiness to listen, to ask the searching question and, when convinced, to act.'

The two men were alike in many ways and would become friends.

Churchill accorded Jones whatever help he required to fight the beams. Accordingly Jones requested that the RAF fly monitoring flights on the frequencies he suggested. The flights found the beams – and the beams that pointed to Derby were jammed.

Jones still spent much time at Bletchley. On one November day, he went there to talk to Hut 6 about the use he made of their information. He had already spoken to Hut 3 – the interpreters - on the subject. His friend from Winslow Hall days, the deputy head of GC & CS, Edward Travis wanted him to give Hut 6 – who actually cracked the codes – some recognition too. They were feeling a bit left out; why should Hut 3 get all the credit? As Jones reported: 'There was some degree of feeling between the huts.'

Having assured Hut 6 that Churchill, Menzies and (some of) the top brass were fully aware of and extremely grateful for their work, he set off back to London. It was a memorable return trip down the arrow-straight Watling Street, on that November night. Much traffic was streaming north out of London to escape the anticipated nightly air raid and Jones was constantly dazzled by the lights of oncoming cars. And he was tired. On the outskirts of St Albans he ran into the back of a parked lorry, pitching himself and his passenger through the windscreen. He rang his wife, Vera, from the hospital – where he had gone to get stitched up - to tell her what was happening. He was lucky to catch her as an air raid was just beginning in London and she was about to go downstairs when she heard the telephone.

Jones returned to London by train the next morning, spent the day at the Air Ministry discussing the beams, and returned to his flat in Richmond as the night's air raid began. He and Vera sat down to dinner as the planes began releasing their bombs. The building began to sway and their soup to slop in the bowls:

'And then we heard a a noise that is unforgettable to anyone who has experienced it, sounding rather like ghosts in hollow chains rattling across the roof. Having once had an incendiary fall within three yards of me, I knew what it must be, and I went over to the back door of the flat, from which we used to admire the view across to Windsor Castle. The sight was fantastic – a panorama stretching far away to Kew Gardens, with all the domes, spires, and trees silhouetted in the pale blueish light from the ignited incendiaries which had been strewn everywhere.'

He shouted to Vera to come and look – she grabbed his arm and pulled him down the stairs, just as the flats were straddled by a stick of bombs. Some fell on the Earl Haig poppy factory opposite, killing several people, some in the tennis court of their block, a few feet from the flats. Then the lights went out. They spent the rest of the raid by candlelight in a neighbour's flat before, at 3am, stumbling back up the stairs to bed.

Not only had the electricity been cut; the water main was ruptured too – but Jones managed to coax the last of the rusty water from the ceiling tanks into their bath. The next day he was back at the Air Ministry, his head still swathed in bandages. The decrypts from Bletchley Park were on his desk. One revealed that the target for the previous night had been Richmond Park, a couple of hundred yards from his flat. Plainly Reg. Jones still had work to do with regard to anticipating the targets of the Luftwaffe.

When he got home, the bath was empty:

'I asked what had happened to it. Vera said, "Oh, it was full of dirty water, so I emptied it." For days we had to traipse for water down six flights of stairs and hundreds of yards to a stand pipe in the road. Life between us has never been quite the same since.'

From this, it will be seen that foiling the attack on Derby was only the start of what Jones called the Battle of the Beams. The Germans would refine and reposition their radar. Great and historic cities would be bombed - Coventry worst of all. The story is sobering in its scope: how could the two most technologically advanced nations in the world be so idiotic as to spend their resources in such a way? After the war R.V. Jones would write *Most Secret War* – the most important book about scientific intelligence to come out of the conflict. Jones writes with pace and humour – explaining difficult scientific subjects in an understandable way and introducing his reader to the great and the good – both in their greatness and their foibles. *Most Secret War* is a work of the highest quality both technically and in literary terms. I consider it a masterpiece. If you read no other book on the subject, I would recommend you read this.

Mavis Lever

Reginald Jones drew information from several sources in his 'Battle of the beams.' By contrast, the intelligence which led to the Battle of Matapan, which Winston Churchill called 'the greatest sea fight since Trafalgar,' came only from Bletchley decrypts. More specifically it came from 'Dilly's girls.'

Dilly Knox, it will be recalled, was, at the outbreak of the war, the Chief Cryptographer at BP. However, by May 1940, Menzies, BP's overall boss, had formalised the structure set up by Gordon Welchman. Welchman's Hut 6 decoded messages and then passed them to Hut 3 where they were translated and often amalgamated with information from other sources. Hut 3 then distributed them. (During 1940, the Royal Navy would set up its own, parallel, system: using Hut 8, with Turing in charge, and Hut 4.)

With Welchman in charge of the main decoding hut, Dilly Knox had been effectively side-lined. He was now running a research unit whose job it was to break previously uncracked Enigma variations. The unit was in The Cottage – behind the main house at Bletchley Park. Knox insisted on choosing his own team – and not liking men much (as Welchman had noticed) – he choose to staff it entirely with young women. In charge of 'Dilly's girls' was Margaret Rock, a graduate from the University of London. She had lost her father in the First World War when she was thirteen years old. Frank Rock, a surgeon, was one of 354 men who were drowned in January 1917 aboard HMS *Laurentic* when it hit a mine laid by a German U-boat in the freezing waters of Lough Swilly, in Ireland.

Margaret Rock was, according to Dilly Knox, 'one of the 5 finest minds in Bletchley.' Mavis Lever was the fifth woman to join Margaret's section. She was nineteen years old when she arrived at BP, in May 1940. She would quickly make her mark. Knox was to say of the pair of them: "give me a Rock and a Lever and I will move the universe."

Mavis Lilian Lever was the daughter of a postal worker and a seamstress and was born in Dulwich, in south-east London. She had curtailed her studies (in German) at University College London, to join Dilly Knox's section at Bletchley. Dilly's girls were largely self-taught as Knox, although (in the eyes of his 'girls'), a lovable man, was not a communicator. Knox's first words to her were: "Hallo, we're breaking machines. Have you got a pencil? Here, have a go." The 'girl in the green jumper' as Mavis remembers herself, recalls one of her first jobs at BP was cooking chips:

Mavis Lever

'May 1940 was perhaps the tensest month in Britain's history... after Dunkirk the trains taking exhausted soldiers up north all stopped at Bletchley on the way. A cry went out from the forces canteen for help. I remember the smell of my hair after I had cooked my 'finest hour' chips in between shifts all day. The fierce woman in charge had ordained that the young girls should be confined to the kitchen stove out of sight and that only the godly matrons would take out the tea and the chips to the troops in the trains. We thought that they would have preferred it the other way round: certainly we would have done.'

When not cooking chips or finding Dilly Knox's misplaced pipe or spectacles, 'Dilly's girls' were breaking codes: to begin with the Enigma settings used by the Italian navy. It was a slow process. Mavis Lever followed Dilly Knox's prescribed technique (called rodding) for months without success – and then tried her own variation. This produced the word 'personale' in one message: and from that she began 'to understand how the machine really worked.' Many years later, she wrote:

'I have recently read 'Turing's treatise on the Enigma... and feel sure that if I had seen it then I would have decided it was all too difficult. However, it seemed obvious enough that evening.'

She read the message and was promoted in the morning – which was a relief to her as she was only paid thirty-five bob (£1.75) a week and was spending two thirds of that on her billet.

That was the start. Getting deeper into the Italian naval Enigma was a long, long, process. A slack Italian operator gave a clue which allowed Lever to infer which letter he was typing. Mavis was alone in the Cottage at the time and sought the help of Keith Batey 'one of the clever Hut 6 mathematicians.' They would later marry.

On the 25th of March 1941, Mavis made yet another break, allowing her to decipher a message which read: 'today is X-3'. For the next 3 days 'Dilly's girls' teased out the Italian signals and hit the jackpot. They deciphered the battle plan of the Italian Admiral Iachino. The plan gave details of the attack force he was sending to intercept a British convoy sailing from Alexandria to reinforce the island of Crete. It included the course of the Italian main fleet.

The information was sent to Alexandria, in Egypt, to the Commander in Chief of the British Mediterranean fleet. Admiral Andrew Cunningham was grateful. He needed all the help that he could get.

The significance in terms of naval strategy

When Italy entered the war, it was with the idea of expanding its empire in Africa. To do so, Mussolini needed to expel the British and French from their African colonies. Accordingly he sent armies from the Italian colony in Libya to invade British-held Egypt. Although greatly outnumbered, the British armies quickly thrust the Italian forces back. Mussolini promptly appealed to Hitler for help. The Führer didn't let his friend down. He sent a German army – the Africa Corps – to Africa. This army was exceptional, even by German standards. Its leader was possibly the greatest general of the war – Erwin Rommel.

If Britain was to win the land war in Africa one essential was that she disrupted Axis supplies while defending her own. To do that, she had to control the Mediterranean. Which meant that she had to sink the Axis's ships.

The British navy was the most powerful in the world and dwarfed the Italian navy, with around three times as many surface ships. However, as well as operating in the Mediterranean, the Royal Navy was fighting the German fleet and submarines in the Atlantic. It was also patrolling the Pacific, in fear of Japanese aggression. As a result, British and Italian naval forces in the Mediterranean were more or less even in numbers. But sea power was by no means the only threat to the Royal Navy. In taking supplies through the Straits of Gibraltar to their island bases of Malta and Crete and to Egypt, the British navy was threatened not only by the Italian navy but by Italian and German aircraft flying from Sicily, Africa and Italy.

Admiral Andrew Cunningham, in Alexandria, to whom the Bletchley decrypt was sent, was, as I've said, the Commander in Chief of the Royal Navy's Mediterranean fleet. If Germany perhaps had the finest general of the war – Rommel – in North Africa, Britain had, arguably, in Cunningham. the Second World War's greatest admiral. Certainly Cunningham, a Scot, was Britain's best. His statue is in Trafalgar Square in London, near Nelson's column. They are fitting companions. Like Quex, Cunningham was a product of Stubbington school, he was 'a martinet with an intense spirit of attack.' Admiral Godfrey, the head of Naval Intelligence said of him: "like a giant Panda he had endearing qualities but he could bite."

He was a very brave man. Once, at Alexandria, he was on the deck of his flagship when a particularly vicious air raid blew a picket-boat lying nearby to pieces, showering the deck with metal. Admiral John Edlesten, who was with him, gathered a lot of still-warm fragments from the deck and remonstrated with Cunningham for not wearing a helmet. Cunningham was unrepentant. "Give those to me." He said. He then summoned the Officer of the Watch and asked him what the devil he meant by allowing the quarter-deck to be cluttered up with mess. Watching officers and men shook their heads in amused disbelief and the story spread quickly through the fleet. That was the boss all over. Morale was restored.

Lightening the mood and setting an example was, all too often, just about all Cunningham could do. His fleet had suffered great losses in men and ships: and he would lose many more. It wasn't all one way of course. Cunningham had already dealt the Italian navy a severe blow by launching a bombing attack from aircraft carriers at Taranto, in the heel of Italy (the lesson was studied closely by Japan, who would apply it at Pearl Harbour over a year later).

When he learned that the Italian navy was to be found off Crete, Cunningham boarded his flagship, HMS *Warspite* and set sail from Alexandria with his fleet.

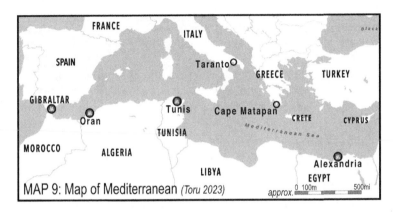

MAP 9: Map of Mediterranean *(Toru 2023)* approx.

The battle of Cape Matapan

His ships met the Italian fleet south of Cape Matapan on the afternoon of the 27th of March 1941. The forces were pretty evenly matched, but the day battle went in favour of the British. As night fell, Cunningham's Operational Staff Officer and his Master of the Fleet advised their commander to stop for the day. Cunningham, demurred ("You're a pack of yellow livered skunks.") and ordered that the battle be continued into the night. Prince Phillip was in charge of a searchlight unit during the operation. Cunningham's ships sank three heavy cruisers and two destroyers with the loss of 3,000 Italian sailors (1,000 of whom were picked up by the Royal Navy). The Royal Navy lost three men.

Cunningham's said of Matapan: 'It was hardly a battle... the lack of training of the Italian fleet for night action was unbelievable. They were really not fit to be allowed out after dark.'

This was a crucial battle in the war in the Mediterranean for it signalled the end of the Italian fleet as a major threat. The day after the battle Admiral Godfrey, head of naval intelligence,

179

rang Bletchley with the message: "Tell Dilly we have won a great victory in the Mediterranean and it is entirely due to him and his girls."

Admiral Cunningham visits BP

A few days later the admiral himself visited Bletchley Park. Dilly's girls had prepared as sumptuous a reception as their modest means allowed: somebody had been sent out to the nearest pub to BP, the Eight Belles, to buy a couple of bottles of sherry.

Cunningham was greatly interested in everything and charm itself to the 'girls' – although, on seeing so many young men in old sports jackets and shabby trousers, he couldn't curb his tongue, remarking: "what are all these velvet-arsed bastards doing here?".

'The cottage wall had just been whitewashed,' Mavis recalled. 'Someone (perhaps one of the velvet-arsed bastards) enticed the admiral to lean against it so he got whitewash on his lovely dark blue uniform. We tried not to giggle when he left.'

Dilly Knox was a very sick man. He died a year later, still working on naval Enigma even on his death bed. The poem that he penned on Matapan shows clearly the affection and respect that he had for his 'girls'. He called it 'An epitaph for Mussolini after Matapan':

'They have knelled your fall and ruin,
but your ears were far away,
English lassies rustling papers,
through the sodden Bletchley day.'

Actually Bletchley wasn't so much the ears of Allied intelligence as the brain. The ears were elsewhere, as I shall explain in the next chapter.

***

Apologia

I have called this chapter Bletchley unbombed. Partly I did so to stress the fact that Quex had got it right - Bletchley suffered only negligible damage, no disruption and no deaths from enemy action during the war. Mostly, though, I wanted to draw a dividing line between Bletchley in this first phase of the war and what was to come when the machine that Turing and Welchman were developing to break the German naval Enigma codes – the bombe – started to give results. While I apologise unreservedly for the toe-curling title, if that distinction sticks in your mind I hope that you will forgive me.

8: Sixth sense: Britannia's hidden hunters

Radio: the sixth sense

Deciphering and collating enemy messages at Bletchley Park was only part of the intelligence revolution that would be key to winning the war. The other essentials were capturing the coded messages in the first place, passing them to BP and then, after that intelligence factory had made sense of them, delivering the resultant briefs ('golden eggs' in Churchill's words) to those who could act on them. Having built at BP the most advanced information processing machine the world had ever seen, Britain set about building the world's most advanced communications network around it. The key to this was the mastery of radio – the 'sixth sense' of this chapter's heading.

'Sixth sense'? Am I being fanciful here? I think I can justify my claim. Mother nature grants almost all of her children five senses; sight, smell, hearing, touch and taste. And those clever children have teased from her another; the power to share their wisdom – and folly – across the very ether. In sending and receiving radio waves man has invented a companion that most of us now use every day and some of us are enslaved by. Cynics tell us that remote communication is now more important than conversation or the printed word: and sometimes it's hard to argue. People routinely sit in cafes chatting not with their families or their fellows at the next table but with others anywhere in the world.

We take the current state of affairs so much for granted that it is easy to forget how new this power actually is. At the outbreak of the Second World War, 'the wireless', as the physical radio equipment was then generally known, was scarcely forty years old. To the converted it was the key to the future; to the superstitious it was witchcraft.

Wireless communications – Marconi's world changer

Before I look in greater detail at the spiders' webs of aerials and transmitters that were at the heart of the Intelligence Zone, I would first like to go back a few short years to talk about the very birth of wireless communications – Marconi's use of radio waves to remove the need for wires for communication over distance.

Guglielmo Marconi's father was from an aristocratic Italian family, his mother was an Irish Jameson (her grandfather founded the famous whisky distillery). She made sure that her son was fluent in both Italian and English. Finding little interest or appreciation for his work in his own land, Marconi travelled to London in early 1896 – at the age of 21 – to seek a wider market. His formidable mother went with him.

Marconi gained the interest and support of William Preece, the Chief Electrical Engineer of the General Post Office – the GPO. London, the largest and richest city in the world and the heart of the empire on which the sun never set, was the biggest market for communications on the planet. There is a blue plaque on the British Telecom's centre (B.T. is essentially the privatised GPO) in London. It records that Marconi made the world's first public transmission of wireless signals from there (to another GPO building) on the 27th of July 1896.

Marconi's development of radio took place on the Isle of Wight and was nurtured by the Royal Navy. The great naval bases of Portsmouth and Southampton lie on the mainland (northern) side of the Solent strait. Radio was initially used as a means of keeping track of shipping in the strait – at that time probably the most crowded shipping lane on earth.

Marconi was treading the corridors of world power. The Royal Navy was the sinews (and, in its own opinion, the brains) of the mighty British Empire. Soon he was catapulted to the very top: in August 1898, he was summoned to Osborne House, Queen Victoria's residence on the island, to establish radio communication between the Queen and the Prince of Wales aboard the Royal Yacht. They exchanged 150 messages and the Queen was said to be "delighted".

From the navy and the laboratory – Marconi was awarded the Nobel prize for physics in 1909 – radio spread rapidly

183

within the military and then entered into civilian life. The British Broadcasting Company (the BBC) was formed in 1922 by a group of leading wireless manufacturers, including Marconi. The BBC began daily broadcasting in Marconi's

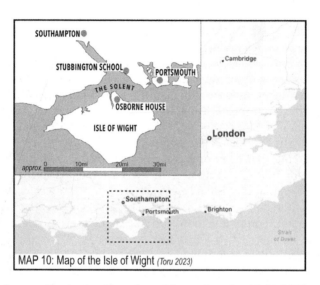

MAP 10: Map of the Isle of Wight *(Toru 2023)*

London studio, in the Strand, on November the 14th, 1922.

Young men especially were intoxicated, obsessed even, with capturing voices from the ether. The most common type of radio was the so–called cat's whisker detector, which consisted of a piece of crystalline mineral, usually galena (lead sulphide), with a fine wire touching its surface (the whisker). This is truly a thing of wonder as it uses only the received radio signal to produce sound, needing no external power. Commercial radio sets were expensive, so building one's own receiver was the only practical way for many to pick up radio broadcasts. Replacement crystals and whiskers were readily available.

The secret services joined the game a bit later. From the mid 1930's onwards, Quex Sinclair increased SIS's spending on monitoring enemy transmissions and, perhaps more importantly, started to coordinate such monitoring with work already being carried out by the armed services and the GPO. As Bletchley

Park grew, so did the network of receiving and transmitting stations which surrounded it.

To pluck information from the airwaves, process it and then pass it to Churchill and the allied military commanders was a process fraught with problems. First, the messages had to be received and transcribed, then passed on to Bletchley Park to be deciphered and dovetailed with existing information, then passed on to their final destinations. The input to Bletchley Park was passed from both civilian and military intercept sites and the size, scope and complexity of this operation is quite, quite, breath–taking. Between about 1936 and 1944 thousands of masts were put up in Britain, some in vast fields, some singly.

Additionally radar masts and direction finding stations on the coasts and elsewhere all passed tracking information inwards, towards Bletchley Park, the Admiralty in London and, also, as I've explained earlier, the RAF at Leighton Buzzard and Fighter Command at RAF Stanmore.

The Y stations and Huff-duff

The wireless intercept sites of the army, navy, air force and secret services were known as Y Stations – 'Y' being the pronunciation of 'WI' – wireless intercept. The Y station military listeners were often young women (their average age was about 20) from the armed forces – the WAAF, ATS and WRNS (Wrens).

They were taught Morse Code. Morse is a system whereby each letter in the alphabet (and each of the numbers 0 to 9) is represented by a mixture of 'dots' – a short transmission, and 'dashes' – a longer transmission. The most common letter 'e' has the simplest code – a single dot.

For the listeners, picking up and transcribing (mainly) Morse code – whether from Enigma or other sources – at high speed

185

was very wearing. They had to concentrate hard for long periods, isolating sometimes faint messages through a cacophony of other traffic and noises, on over–crowded radio bands. Added to this was the sometimes sloppy 'hand' of the sender, which could lead to the running together of letters (there is a pause between letters and a longer one between words). The listeners, writing even as they listened, had to be very good at their job.

In the Y stations, the radio waves were monitored day and night and individual listeners were assigned fixed frequencies to monitor and record. Intercept stations often led into larger sites which themselves fed into Bletchley. The largest sites were at Scarborough in Yorkshire (Royal Navy), Beaumanor Hall in

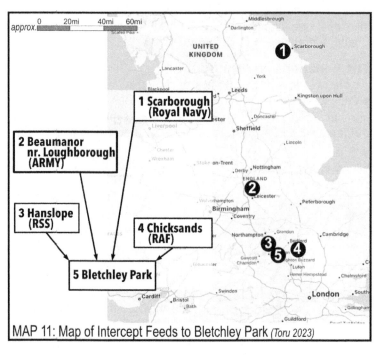

MAP 11: Map of Intercept Feeds to Bletchley Park *(Toru 2023)*

Leicestershire (the army), Hanslope in Buckinghamshire (secret service) and RAF Chicksands in Bedfordshire.

Apart from the main receiving sites, there were two main transmitting sites. These were controlled from Whaddon Hall (which I will talk about in greater detail in the next chapter) and Leighton Buzzard (which I've written about earlier).

The navy

The Royal Navy had around 30 Y stations. The main one, as I've said, was at Scarborough (on the Yorkshire coast) – which had, in 1942, about 65 receivers tuned into German naval traffic, mostly taking naval Enigma. Scarborough was an important place, 2,500 people were trained in Morse there during the war. The Morse messages were sent into the navy receiving hut (Hut 8) at BP. The navy intercept stations also fed directly into Naval Intelligence, in the Citadel, a bleak bomb–proof operations centre which stood (and stands) on Horse Guards Parade, in London, just round the corner from Downing Street and Churchill's own command bunker. The Citadel, coupled with Bletchley Park and Western Approaches HQ at Liverpool, was where the Royal Navy planned its war.

There were also various naval HF/DF stations in Britain and abroad. HF/DF – generally called Huff-duff – stands for high frequency direction finding. That is to say, the plotting of the direction that a transmission is coming from. Huff–duff enabled an operator to determine the direction of a radio signal, *regardless of whether the content could be read.* The distinction is important. This was done by using a rotating aerial, or a number of fixed aerials. Ideally, several different tracking stations would get a fix on the same enemy radio transmission so that its origin could be plotted as exactly as possible.

In Britain, Huff–duff had been developed at the same place as radar – Ditton Park in Datchet, near Slough – where Robert Watson Watt was in charge. In fact, it was what the other half of what Ditton Park did – those who weren't developing radar worked on Huff–duff. A quarter (24%) of all the German U–boats which were sunk during the war would be detected by Huff–duff. It was just as effective against Germany's surface navy, as we shall see.

The army

The chief listening post for army Y service intercepts was at Beaumanor in Leicestershire. Here, too, intercepts were received and passed on from a number of other sites, before going on to BP by teleprinter. Originally sited at Chatham, in Kent, the listening post had been relocated into the Intelligence Zone because of bombing. By the end of the war there were about 1,000 ATS (women, army) operators and 300 civilian men working there. They worked round the clock (wo)manning five receiving rooms and many radio receivers. Beaumanor also managed the Huff–duff stations which the army had in many parts of the country.

The primary mission of Beaumanor was to pick up German military communications, which included those of the German Police. It is said that Beaumanor picked up the first report of the Katyn massacre – when Russians troops murdered virtually the whole of the Polish officer corps – 22,000 officers – in the forest of the same name.

Additionally, the army had DF stations in many parts of the country, often in tiny huts in isolated locations.

The air force

The chief RAF Y service intercept site was at Chicksands Priory in Bedfordshire. An anonymous description of Chicksands at the time says :

'As all of the work had to be carried on in the upper rooms of the Priory, masts were erected all around the building and ...dozens of straight wire aerials of 70 to 100 feet in length trailed to the upper windows until the whole looked like a spider's web.'

This web trapped not insects, but the thoughts and commands of the enemy.

Linked into Chicksands were other RAF tracking sites; notably RAF Cheadle, which also had a satellite station at Marston Montgomery in Derbyshire, which was dedicated to identifying the peculiarity of call signs – the 'fist' of the operator. So, if a signal was received from an operator who had been previously identified as working on the battleship *Bismarck*, then that signal had almost certainly come from the

Bismarck. Another section concentrated on the 'fingerprints' of the transmitter itself – minute differences in components giving different results. In practice, German radio transmitters were remarkably uniform, but Italian ones were often quite individual.

Huff–duff and the fine tuning of 'fists' and 'fingerprinting' were all linked to Gordon Welchman's traffic analysis work at Bletchley. Welchman had a lot of contact with the Huff–duff sites.

***

Each of the armed forces were intercepting messages not only in Britain but wherever they were fighting. In Europe, Africa and Asia, static and mobile units were stationed to pick up Axis broadcasts and pass them back to BP. There were naval monitoring units in America and Australia too.

The description I have given of which site dealt with which armed force is in fact a simplification of what was in truth a highly complex network. This 'gloss' will perhaps cause pain to some of my most knowledgeable readers. I can only admit my guilt and plead the exoneration that if I were to explain the network in greater detail, it would not fit into the space I have here and would be tedious to all but the initiated. If you, dear reader, wish to become initiated, I recommend the books (they are often superb) which I list as sources for this and the next chapter – and a goodly stock of candles and coffee.

The RSS

In addition to the three military Y services, there was a civilian one – the Radio Security Service (RSS). This was run by the secret services and its history is in the finest tradition of skullduggery. At the outbreak of World War Two the secret services were worried about German spies. It was an old fear; as far back as 1903 a novel dealing with it – *The Riddle of the Sands* – had been a best–seller. To counter this very real threat, MI5 tasked an officer from the Royal Signals, Major Worlledge, to set up and run the Radio Security Service. His brief was to 'intercept, locate and close down illicit wireless stations operated either by enemy agents in Great Britain or by other persons not being licensed to do so under Defence Regulations,

1939'. As a security precaution, RSS was given the cover designation of MI8(c).

The RSS was originally based in London, in His Majesty's Prison Wormwood Scrubs (the prisoners were annoyed at being turfed out) to record and track down spies broadcasting from and to Germany. The organisation used resources and knowledge from the GPO and the army. The links between the army and the GPO had always been very close. The GPO provided training for army signallers – many of whom ended up working for the Post Office after they had finished their army service.

The RSS used GPO intercept vehicles (whose civilian purpose was to see whether anyone was broadcasting illegally – that is, not paying a fee to do so) and also GPO fixed stations.

The RSS's fears were well founded. The Germans were indeed dropping spies into England. Of the twenty–three German agents working in or dropped into Britain during the war, RSS monitoring led to the capture of five, and the identification of two more. These men were either executed or 'turned' to operate as double agents under the 'XX' (double cross) Committee. One of the captured agents broadcast for a while from Aylesbury police station. Later in the war this side of the RSS's work would aid greatly in deceiving the Axis powers about where the Allies were going to strike next.

By May 1940 it was clear that the RSS's initial mission – to locate enemy agents in the UK – was complete. However, BP was very interested in the large number of German messages that were delivered to them via Wormwood Scrubs. These were being recorded from hundreds of points in mainland Europe. The RSS had found their way into various radio networks, among them the Abwehr (German military intelligence), Hitler's private army (the SS), and the Nazi terror police – the Gestapo.

Among the staff at Wormwood Scrubs was Hugh Trevor–Roper, an Oxford historian and fluent German speaker who had been called up for the duration. Major Roper put the cat among the pigeons by decoding some of the messages, thus trespassing on Bletchley Park's territory. This led to a rebuke from BP and the immediate annexation of the RSS by SIS (MI6).

As with all of the Y services, the RSS grew rapidly. The organisation was developed by Ralph Sheldon Mansfield, the 4th Baron Sandhurst – a name which will re–occur. Lord Sandhurst had been a signaller in the first war and was an enthusiastic radio amateur. In his insatiable search for more listeners, Sandhurst approached the President of the Radio Society of Great Britain (RSGB), Arthur Watts, who recommended that he recruit the entire RSGB council, which he did. He then put the council to work recruiting their members from around the country to serve as Voluntary Interceptors (VIs). There was very little private internal radio traffic in the UK as all private transmitters (but not receivers) had been confiscated by the authorities at the outbreak of war.

With the giddying growth in radio intercepts and transmissions, all of the radio intercept services were on the lookout for good operators. Some were radio amateurs – 'Hams', some were found by aptitude testing in the services, some were recalled or existing service men and women, some were from the Post Office, some were refugees from Europe. The German language was, of course, a prized attribute.

As it grew, the RSS took over the GPO intercept station at Arkley View near Barnet (in 1940) and Hanslope Park in Buckinghamshire (in 1941). Apart from army and GPO signallers, they also had many hundreds of part–time civilian listeners, the Voluntary Interceptors (VIs) whom I mentioned earlier. The VIs usually operated from home (in secrecy, often from their bedrooms or garden sheds) for as many hours as they could spare. They were asked to provide intercept logs (of the Morse transmissions) at least three times a week.

The RSS controlled the VIs from 8 regional offices (for example, Cambridge), each of which controlled up to 200 listeners. Some VIs were co–opted into full time, paid, service, often at Hanslope. To qualify for this, they had to pass rigorous tests. In order to be classified grade 'A', RSS operators had to have a speed of 23 words a minute when transcribing signals, as well, of course, as to be able to separate out those signals from the surrounding airwave mush. These RSS recruits were paid £7 a week, free of income tax, plus meals and accommodation. That was 3 or 4 times what an army recruit was making – so

191

those who were recruited in this way were advised to keep quiet about their pay rates (sometimes they were working beside service men and women doing the same job on service pay).

At the main RSS interception station, Hanslope, and indeed at all of the listening posts – such as Forfar, Thurso, St Erth and Gilnakirk – it was found that the American HRO receivers were by far the best for precision tuning and the ability to 'lock onto' the wave bands. In fact, the RSS employed four American engineers (based at Whaddon Hall) to look after these and other American equipment.

Hanslope was to have lots of 'top brass' visits during the war, including Montgomery and Eisenhower.

The RSS was managed by SIS's communications section – and specifically by the larger–than–life figure of Richard Gambier-Parry – 'Quex' Sinclair's head of communications – who also presided over the communications 'factory' at Whaddon Hall, a couple of miles from Bletchley Park, which I will talk about in my next chapter.

The Y services were large enterprises and were allocated a high priority in staff and resources. In January 1942 the Chiefs of Staff authorised the recruitment of 7,150 additional personnel. In 1943 came a second increase. In all, around 50,000 men and women worked on 'Y' and huff–duff during the war.

The wider war picture

The immense effort that Britain had gone to in setting up and integrating its Y and huff–duff services with Bletchley Park's code-cracking would pay greater and greater dividends during the war.

One of the earliest proofs of the value of the intelligence revolution was in May 1941, at a time when things were not looking too good for the British war effort. Britain (in which I include, as ever, Canadians, Australians and other members of the Commonwealth and Empire) was still fighting alone. While it was true that she had achieved significant victories against Italy in North Africa and the Mediterranean, this had provoked Hitler to commit German troops to those areas. German armies had thrown the British out of Greece. A second Dunkirk had been needed, with Admiral Cunningham arranging the evacuation of 50,000 troops – at a great cost to his ships.

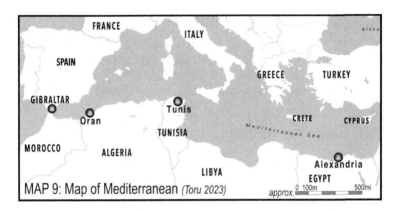

MAP 9: Map of Mediterranean *(Toru 2023)*

The Germans had also launched a parachute assault on Crete. BP, knowing that the attack was coming, had told the army where and when the parachutists were going to drop – so it was hard to imagine how that attack could possibly succeed: but in May 1941 the battle still hung in the balance.

In North Africa, the arrival of the German general Rommel had reversed the series of victories and advances the British had won over the Italians, causing Churchill to reshuffle his generals.

The Spanish fascist dictator, General Franco, who had been aided by the Nazis in his seizure of power, seemed on the point of committing troops to the German and Italian cause. Should Spain join the Axis, there would be little to stop her taking the tiny (two square miles) Rock of Gibraltar, the key British outpost which overlooks the western entrance to the Mediterranean. The Rock, a British colony since 1830, is part of the Spanish mainland. Without 'Gib' with its fortress and harbour, the Mediterranean would be denied to the Royal Navy, leading to the near certainty of British defeat in North Africa.

Generalissimo Franco had already made a formal offer to join the Axis – but he and Hitler had yet to agree on the terms. Hitler wanted Gibraltar, of course, and also the use of Spanish naval bases in the Azores, from which he could attack America.

193

Franco wanted oil, arms, food, and large parts of the French colonial empire in Africa. The Generalissimo had set his price high: but then he was taking a big risk – fighting England in the past had not been profitable for Spain. Franco had told Hitler that he wanted to wait until Britain "was on the point of collapse" before attacking her. Perhaps now, with the German invasions of Greece and Crete (although this was still in the balance), that moment had arrived? It depended, perhaps, on how the German navy fared in the next round in the North Atlantic...

Crisis with the convoys

The primary objective of the German surface navy in World War Two was the disruption of the Atlantic convoys which brought food and fuel from the Americas to Britain. For Britain, Germany and indeed America this was a rerun of what had happened twenty years earlier. In the first war, Germany had come near to starving Britain into submission: but in doing so had helped to provoke the United States into joining the war on the side of Britain and France. In the end, it had been Germany that starved.

In the first eighteen months of the second war, German surface ships made three significant raids on British convoys in the Atlantic, in which they sank two British light cruisers and sank or captured 36 merchantmen. In return, they lost a heavy cruiser (the *Graf Spee*). Now, two new German heavy warships, the *Bismarck* and the *Tirpitz*, were ending their sea trials and would soon be ready for use. If the two monsters got into the Atlantic (which has an area of 30 million square miles), the fear was that the Royal Navy would not be able to hold them. The carnage that they were capable of inflicting could lose Britain the war.

To protect her convoys, Britain's had several battleships, of which the most powerful was HMS *Hood*.

The *Hood*

HMS *Hood* was the pride of the Royal Navy. She was 860' long – the length of three football pitches – and 95' wide at her deck.. One of the statistics which was regularly trotted out to her visitors was that if she sank in the middle of the English

HMS Hood

Channel, 80' of her would still be above water. Her main armament was eight 640" long (53') guns with barrels of 15" diameter. These threw shells which weighed nearly a ton and travelled for up to 19 miles.

However, this giant had shortcomings. She was, by now, nearly twenty five years old – and even while she was still being built, back in 1918, tests had shown that her upper armament was too thin: she would be especially vulnerable to plunging heavy shells fired from a long distance. Thicker armour should have been thought about at the design stage – but on the basis of 'better late than never', it was added shortly before she was launched. This addition – which was still insufficient – added greatly to her top weight. Because of this she was 'a wet ship' – i.e. one that was affected by storms at sea, prone to waves on her main deck and to rolling. This affected her stability as a gun platform, especially in high seas.

Her fully laden weight was around 48,000 tons. She had a crew of 1400 men.

From her launch, and until the *Bismarck* came off the blocks, HMS *Hood* was the most powerful ship in the world.

The *Bismarck*

The *Bismarck* came down the slips in August 1940. Although the British did not realise it at the time, it was now the biggest, heaviest and most powerful ship on earth. When an officer in her crew, Baron von Rechberg, met her captain, the latter asked him: "'Do you know how big the *Bismarck* really is?"

The answer is recounted in Rechberg's superb book – *Battleship Bismarck*:

"'Well, I answered, 35,000 tons plus fuel and water, I think." Not without pride, the captain said, "53,000 tons, fully equipped …but that is strictly secret information."'

The *Bismarck*'s captain was Ernst Lindemann. Captain Lindemann advised secrecy because, according to a written treaty between the world's naval powers, his ship was supposed to be no heavier than 35,000 tons. However, as was often the case with the treaties they signed, the Nazis' pledge had been a lie. Lindemann was quite happy to share the deception with Baron von Rechberg – for the latter was, as well as being a gunnery officer, the captain's personal adjutant and therefore privy to all of the ship's secrets.

Captain Lindemann, was a gaunt, rather delicate–looking man, who had made his life in the navy. Unlike many German naval officers, he was not a martinet and, in a tough service, he was generally liked by his crew. His specialist field was gunnery and he reckoned his ship to be the best gunnery platform in the world. The surname Lindemann is, of course, German – but it's not that common. Ernst Lindemann was, perhaps, related in some way to Churchill's scientific advisor, Frederick Lindemann.

Bismarck

Bismarck was a little shorter and a little wider than the *Hood* and carried a similar main armament. It was constructed of a honeycomb of watertight compartments, heavily armoured and was structurally much stronger than the *Hood*. It carried four seaplanes and had a larger crew (2,064) than the *Hood*. The top speed of the *Bismarck* was 30 knots, the *Hood* 28 knots. Only in radar was the German ship less advanced than its British adversary.

Bismarck was named in honour of Otto von Bismarck – the 'iron chancellor' who had forged a unified Germany from its disparate states in 1870. Lindemann insisted that his ship be referred to as 'he' (ships are generally referred to as 'she'). This was no weak, effeminate object, this was masculine force personified – Hitler's steel fist. 'He' was the most powerful weapon in Hitler's armoury – except, perhaps, for the *Tirpitz*, which was a couple of months newer and slightly behind *Bismarck* in terms of readiness.

B-Dienst

The forthcoming confrontation between the two behemoths was not just to be ship against ship – but also between the German and British intelligence services. Knowing what the world knows now, it is tempting to suppose that Bletchley Park was always going to come off best in this tussle. In fact, at the start of the war, Germany had the lead in code breaking. Germany's B-Dienst ('observation service') – Bletchley Park's equivalent – had both the hardware and intelligence service to spot British shipping. The hardware were tracking towers on the German coast – while B-Dienst was able to read codes used by the Royal Navy. The code cracking was down to the head of B-Dienst, Wilhelm Tranow. Among Tranow's accomplishments was reconstructing the Royal Navy Administrative Code prior to the war, the breaking within six months of the new Navy Cipher, and, by May 1940, cracking the British Merchant Navy Code, which allowed the U-boat command and surface fleets to track and anticipate the routing of allied convoys.

In Britain's corner was what I have called Britannia's sixth sense – the most complex network for capturing information that the world had ever seen – spun from the Y services, radar and Huff–duff. And, of course, the place where much of that input was interpreted and put together – Bletchley Park.

The enemies met head to head in May 1941.

The *Bismarck* sets off

When Adolf Hitler inspected the *Bismarck* on May the 5th, 1941, he was welcomed aboard by the Captain, and Lindemann's superior officer, Admiral Günther Lütjens. Both officers were to sail in the ship on *Exercise Rhine*, their forthcoming sortie into the Atlantic. Lütjens explained that with ships of the strength of the *Bismarck* and the *Tirpitz* (which Hitler also inspected that day), the German fleet would no longer be forced to avoid well protected convoys. When Hitler asked how Lütjens was going to address the fact that there were many more British than German warships, the latter stressed again the strength and speed of the new German fleet. The British could not physically protect each convoy with enough of her fleet to deter his ships.

His main problem was not, he said, out in the open Atlantic, but how to get there without having to take on the Royal Navy's main battle fleet, which was based at Scapa Flow, off the north

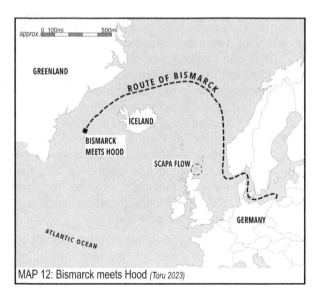

MAP 12: Bismarck meets Hood *(Toru 2023)*

of Scotland. He added that he was also worried about the dangers of torpedo planes from British aircraft carriers (the Germans had no aircraft carriers of their own).

Hitler didn't know enough about ships to probe Lütjens further: but that didn't mean that he was blind to the dangers his fleet faced, as his comments about British numerical superiority had already made clear. Just as tellingly, perhaps, he had recently ordered that the heavy cruiser *Deutschland* should be renamed (to *Lutzow*). The propaganda risk of a ship called 'Germany' being sunk by the Royal Navy was too great. (In the event, the Royal Navy didn't sink the *Lutzow*. The Royal Air Force did.)

The *Bismarck*, escorted by the heavy cruiser, the *Prinz Eugen* and several destroyers, began *Exercise Rhine* on the 19th of May 1941. On that day eleven convoys were at sea between Britain and America. Admiral Lütjens' original intention had been that the battleships would meet up with two other German heavy ships – the *Gneisenau* and *Scharnhorst* – sailing from the French port of Brest. This group of four of the fastest, newest and most heavily armoured ships in the world would have been a serious challenge to anything that the Royal navy could put against it, especially as the route of the British convoys were known to the Germans, courtesy of B-Dienst and their cracking of Royal Navy codes. However the *Gneisenau* had been damaged by RAF Bomber Command and the *Scharnhorst* had machinery problems, so the German heavy assault was halved before it had begun. Supporting the German thrust were eight tankers and supply ships – as well as several U-boats which they were scheduled to meet at sea.

Lütjens' force was twice sighted and reported to London before they cleared the Scandinavian coast; firstly by a member of the Norwegian resistance (who photographed them), secondly by a Swedish naval officer. Aboard the *Bismarck* – and as a result of their sighting – a report from B-Dienst informed Admiral Lütjens and Captain Lindemann that the RAF knew that they were on the move and to expect British reconnaissance planes. An RAF plane duly appeared, photographing the ships in a Norwegian fjord.

Death of a battleship

The *Bismarck* and the *Prinz Eugen* headed due north, intending to enter the Atlantic north of Iceland. Then, in accordance with Lütjens' plan, their escorting destroyers turned for home. This was not Lütjens' first trip into the Atlantic against the convoys – he had been out on the successful raids of the *Scharnhorst* and *Gneisenau* – the ships currently laid up in France.

The Royal Navy had patrols to the north and south of Iceland. To the north – Lütjens' route – lay the British cruisers *Norfolk* and *Suffolk*. The *Suffolk's* radar picked up the German ships as they passed between Greenland and Iceland – through what is confusingly named the Denmark Strait. In the freezing and often foggy seas, among heavy squalls that cut visibility, and further constrained by the closeness of the permanent icepack and British minefields, the Germans could neither throw off nor engage the British ships. In the words of Baron von Rechberg on the *Bismarck*:

'Lütjens concluded that the British had an efficient long–range radar system, a conclusion that threw his whole concept of surface warfare in the Atlantic into a disturbing new dimension. In fact, only shortly before, the *Suffolk* had had a modern traversable radar installed, by means of which she could reconnoitre up to 22,000 yards (over 12 miles). We were haunted by concern as to what other ships they might have called up to join them.'

Lütjens was right to be concerned by radar. The Royal Navy's heavy response to the *Bismarck* and the *Prinz Eugen* – the battleship HMS *Hood* and the cruiser the *Prince of Wales* – were already steaming from Scapa Flow.

Ted Briggs was a sailor aboard HMS *Hood*. He had been entranced by the big ship ever since he had first seen her steaming off Redcar, in Yorkshire, in 1935 – and had wanted to join up and sail with her there and then, but had had to wait until his fifteenth birthday before joining the navy. When he was posted to the *Hood* in 1939, at the age of 16, he had fulfilled the ambition of his young life:

'I was staring at my destiny... this grey, gargantuan creature of beauty, grace and immaculate power... she epitomised pride – pride of the Royal Navy, of king and country and empire... the mess decks were colossal; a series of scrubbed wooden mess–tables reached out to me like massive conjurer's fingers... one of the first tasks of a newcomer on the *Hood* was to find his way round the thousand–plus compartments, although to my knowledge no one had ever seen them all.'

Like the *Bismarck*, the *Hood* carried a captain, Ralph Kerr – a decent man who "did not want everyone to get out of his way just because he was captain of the *Hood*." – and an admiral, Lancelot Holland; a slim, taciturn man who had never recovered from the death of his only son from polio. Both were new arrivals to the *Hood*.

As she steamed towards Iceland from Scapa Flow, the crew of the *Hood* were confident. In Briggs' words:

'The *Hood* was capable of handling any jumped up German battleship... what we did not know was that the *Bismarck* was in every way superior to the *Hood* and also to the *Prince of Wales*.'

Guided by the *Suffolk* and *Norfolk* (which had been fired on by the German ships but not hit), the *Hood* and *Prince of Wales* moved closer to their enemy. The Germans were unaware that the heavy enemy ships were approaching.

The enemies first sighted each other at 0535 on the 24th of May 1941. As soon as he saw the German ships, Admiral Holland ordered a direct attack at full speed. His tactic would seem to have been to force the German ships to fire at as close a distance as he could: thus making the trajectory of the enemy's fire flatter and so reducing the chance of Hood's thin top armour being hit by plummeting shells. In order to offer as small a profile as he could to the enemy ships, he approached them bow first. This meant *Hood's* after gun batteries could not train on the *Prinz Eugen* and *Bismarck*.

Aboard the *Bismarck*, Baron von Rechberg thought:

'To approach nearly bow–on, as they were doing, appeared to me absolutely foolhardy; it reminded me of an enraged bull charging without knowing what he's up against... on the telephone I heard Albrecht (the second gunnery officer) shout: "The *Hood* – it's the *Hood!*." There she was, the famous warship that had been the terror of our war games.'

Lindemann gave permission to fire. The rumble of gunfire from the four ships was heard in Reykjavik, the capital of Iceland.

Aboard the *Hood*, the eighteen year old Ted Briggs asked a shipmate how long the battle would last. "I think it will be over in a couple of hours, Ted," Yeoman Wright replied. In fact the *Hood* started burning just five minutes into the battle. Briggs, on the compass platform, saw hits on the base of the mainmast.

'Fear gripped me as agonised screams of the wounded and dying emitted from the voice pipes... who the hell do they think they are, hitting our super ship, I thought, ridiculously... a blinding flash hit the outside of the compass platform. "Steering's gone sir." The *Hood* heeled over. The reply of "very good" showed no sign of animation. Immediately, Captain Kerr ordered "change over to emergency steering." Slowly the *Hood* righted herself, only to cant to port. On and on she rolled, until she reached an angle of forty–five degrees. There was no order to abandon ship, nor was a word uttered. It was not required. Some tried to kick their way through the reinforced glass to escape. *Hood* was finished and no one needed to be told that.'

Briggs went down with the ship: 'The pressure on my ears was increasing each second... I was going to die... I struggled madly to try to reach the surface... I got nowhere... I opened my mouth and gulped in a mouthful of water... I was going to die. I was going to die... What was the use of struggling? The water was a peaceful cradle. I was being rocked off to sleep. There was nothing I could do about it – goodnight mum.'

Then he was shot to the surface.

Three men: Ted Briggs, William Dundas and Bob Tilburn, were picked up by HMS *Electra*. They were the only survivors from the *Hood*.

Aboard the Bismarck von Rechberg watched the end of his enemy with incredulity:

'At first the *Hood* was nowhere to be seen; in her place was a colossal pillar of black smoke reaching into the sky. Gradually, at the foot of the pillar, I made out the bow of the battle cruiser projecting at an angle, a sure sign that she had broken in two. Then I saw something I could hardly believe: a flash of orange from her forward guns! Although her fighting days had ended, the *Hood* was firing a last salvo. I felt great respect for those men over there.'

The battle had lasted six minutes.

The *Prince of Wales* had also been hit – seven times – by German shellfire. Her captain, John Leach, ordered her withdrawal.

In later life, when Briggs wrote *Flagship Hood,* he mentioned two Lindemann's in the loss of his beloved ship. One was, of course, the captain of the *Bismarck.* The other was Churchill's scientific advisor. 'The Prof', an advocate of rockets as an anti–aircraft device, had championed the development of the UP (Unrotated Projectile) weapon. This was a gun which fired rockets which exploded in mid–air to release wire cables, parachutes and mines. Its intention was to create an aerial minefield in front of attacking aircraft.

The Ups sitting on a gun turret on HMS Nelson (they look like sphinxes here)

The UPs were fitted on top of the turrets of the main guns on the *Hood*. Briggs says that stocks of these 'rockets–on–a–string' were lying about on the *Hood*, waiting to be used. He says that Captain Leach, of the *Prince of Wales*, at his debriefing at Scapa Flow, is alleged to have stated:

'The rocket weapons

and the unsafely stowed ammunition were the direct cause of the loss of the ship, probably through the explosion of the ready–use cordite penetrating the flash proofing of X turret.'

References to these rockets are few: and the ones that I have seen are universally negative. Wind caught the parachutes, so that the trailing wires and explosives tended to end up at or near the point from which the rockets had been fired. However, they were Prof. Lindemann's 'baby' and therefore backed by Churchill. The UPs had never bought down an aircraft: did they sink HMS *Hood*? Captain Leach was not asked for his thoughts on the matter at the official enquiry. After the *Hood* went down, they were removed from all ships.

Briggs also says: 'Our heavyweight champion had a knockout punch but a glass chin and a paunch which was too heavy for her.'

She was certainly no match for the *Bismarck*. Brigg's mum in Derby heard that her son was safe just 60 minutes after the loss of the *Hood* was announced. Fourteen hundred and fifteen other mothers were not so lucky.

The German navy emasculated

On board the *Bismarck* the sailors:

'Stared at each other in disbelief. Then the shock passed and the jubilation knew no bounds. Overwhelmed with joy and pride in the victory, they slapped one another on the back and shook hands.'

The battleship had not escaped scot–free, however. Although no one had been killed or seriously injured, the ship had taken three hits, two of them significant. The hull was breached above the water line and several fuel tanks were flooded, meaning that 1000 tons of fuel was inaccessible. Two thousand tons of water flooded the forecastle. The battleship was down 3 degrees at the bow and listing 9 degrees to port, the tips of one propeller's blades turning above water. The giant was trailing oil and its maximum speed was cut to 28 knots. These were not mortal blows, but Lindemann needed to get his ship back to port. On top of that, he was still being trailed by the British cruisers *Norfolk* and *Suffolk*. The *Prince of Wales*, too, was still within striking distance. The Royal Navy was unlikely to take the loss of the pride of her fleet lying down. B-Dienst confirmed that the British ships could still 'see' the *Bismarck* by radar.

It seems odd, at first, that Admiral Lütjens decided to head for Brest, a French port 2000 miles away when the nearest alternative, Bergen in Norway, was only half that distance. It makes sense, though, when one realises that the shorter route would have taken him close to Scapa Flow and the undoubtedly powerful response that the Royal Navy was planning for him. Given that *Bismarck* was trailing oil and readily tracked by air, Lütjens decided to separate his two ships. The *Prinz Eugen* departed. The *Bismarck* slowed down to conserve fuel and headed out into the Atlantic, where there were several U-boats which could help to protect the ship.

Later that same day – in the late evening but still light – the first British reaction came; from the Aircraft Carrier HMS *Victorious*. Aircraft carriers were a fairly recent development in 1941 – the first purpose-built one having been launched (by the Royal Navy) just 17 years earlier. Nine Swordfish biplanes came from the carrier. These, slow, antique looking open biplanes hardly seemed to have a place in the latest war – but they had already played a key role in the Battle of Taranto which had badly damaged the Italian fleet. They were guided by airborne radar (pioneered, as I mentioned earlier, by Taffy Bowen at Bawdsey).

The Swordfish - known to its pilots affectionately as 'the Stringbag'

The Swordfish was a plane that was regarded with great affection by its aircrew, who called it 'the Stringbag', as, like a housewife's string shopping bag of the time, it could carry just about anything; but it couldn't carry everything at once – certainly not a torpedo at the same time as a bulky airborne radar set. Consequently one Swordfish carried the radar and guided the others.

Only one Swordfish's torpedo hit the *Bismarck*, killing a crewman – the first to die on the battleship. Other than that, the attack did little material damage, except for opening up the patches which had been put over the holes in the hull. The ship slowed down while they were repaired.

The *Prince of Wales* fired on the *Bismarck* and the *Bismarck* replied. All the shells missed.

That night, *Bismarck*, by steaming in a circle, succeeded in giving the trailing British vessels the slip. Admiral Lütjens, however, did not realise this and the next morning (which was his birthday), believing his ship still to be under observation by British radar, he made the error of sending out two long signals. These radio messages gave plenty of time for the Huff–duff sites to lock onto the transmissions. The messages were picked up by HF/DF stations in Scarborough, Iceland, Newfoundland, Ascension island and West Africa: allowing the listeners to map *Bismarck*'s position exactly. The actual Morse content of the transmissions was recorded at RAF Chicksands and passed to Bletchley Park, who confirmed that the messages were from *Bismarck*. They knew this not from the messages themselves – which would not be read until several days later – but by traffic analysis in conjunction with the RAF 'Y' service.

Britain's signals net had found its biggest fish. The *Bismarck*'s position was sent to naval intelligence in the Citadel, in London, which passed it on to the searching warships. There were lots of these by now, the *Suffolk*, *Norfolk* and *Prince of Wales* of course: and another group sailing from Scapa, a third from Gibraltar, and yet others pulled from convoy protection duty.

Lütjens had told his enemies exactly where he was; now the British made an equally massive error – the *Bismarck*'s position was wrongly transposed on the ships' charts of the pursuing main fleet. The British ships should have headed south–east to cut off the German battleship. Instead they turned north–east, away from the German ship.

There were mixed feelings aboard the *Bismarck*. Everyone knew that they had stirred up a hornet's nest – and that they were holed and trailing oil. Baron von Rechberg tells us, however, that there was cautious optimism on the bridge. B-Dienst was keeping the commanders abreast of the Royal Navy's movements – and they believed that they had a better than fifty–fifty chance of reaching France:

> 'Only one thing should not be allowed to happen under any circumstances: the *Bismarck* must not lose speed or manoeuvrability. If that were to happen, the slow but heavily armed British ships astern would be able to close and concentrate more fire power on us than we would be able to withstand.'

Bismarck had had, all in all, a pretty lucky day. That luck was about to change, however – and for an odd reason. The other great war event which was taking place at the same time as *Exercise Rhine* was, of course, the German invasions of Greece and Crete. One of the senior Luftwaffe officers who was taking part in these was based in Athens, and was concerned about the safety of his son, who was on the *Bismarck*. He sent a signal to the German high command in Berlin to ask after the boy. The reply – which was in the Luftwaffe's Enigma code – was deciphered at Bletchley Park. This made it clear that the ship was heading for France.

Bletchley, of course, already knew the battleship's previous position. Now that her destination was also known, the code breakers were able to deduce her likely course and location. They arranged for an aircraft to be sent out from Northern Ireland to search for the ship. The plane was an American flying boat, a Catalina, an early fruit of the American lend– lease program. The Americans had sent 80 aircrew with these planes, to train the RAF in their use. The Catalina was piloted by an American, Ensign Leonard Smith and co–piloted by an RAF flight lieutenant, Dennis Briggs. They spotted the *Bismarck* at 1015am. Bletchley Park informed the admiralty who, having already recognised that they had earlier made a mistake, rerouted their ships towards the *Bismarck*.

Were they too late? Aboard the *Bismarck*, messages were repeatedly broadcast to the crew that they were getting nearer to supporting U-boats, land based aircraft and German naval units – and their pursuers were a long way behind.

The only chance – the last chance – the British had of stopping the *Bismarck* from reaching France was to attack it again with carrier–based aircraft. If the ship were crippled, then the battleships could finish it off. Accordingly, the aircraft carrier, HMS *Ark Royal* flew aircraft off towards *Bismarck*'s position. What the *Ark Royal* didn't know was that a British cruiser, the *Sheffield*, was now between them and their prey.

As before, the planes were Swordfish – biplanes with three crew in an open cockpit. As before, one Stringbag carried the airborne radar, the others, torpedoes. No other nation had airborne radar at this time – and the first sets were big and relatively unsophisticated; they couldn't tell friend from foe. When the aircraft found *Sheffield* where they expected to find *Bismarck*, while some recognised her and held their fire, others attacked. One torpedo hit the British ship but failed to explode.

The planes returned to the Ark Royal, were rearmed and set off again. The pilot of the radar–carrying Stringbag finally guided his flock onto the *Bismarck* at about 9 o'clock at night (GMT), as daylight began to fail.

The aircraft attacked from several directions at once. Von Rechberg, aboard the *Bismarck* watched them come in:

'The antique–looking Swordfish, fifteen of them, seemed to hang in the air, near enough to touch… they flew low. The spray of the heaving seas masking their landing gear. Nearer and still nearer they came, into the midst of our fire. It was as though their order was: "get hits or don't come back."'

The Swordfish had a maximum powered speed of 143 miles per hour when carrying a torpedo, slower than many modern cars. Of course they might be a good deal faster – or slower – depending on the wind. Their leisurely (or suicidal, depending on whether the view was from inside or outside the open cockpit) approach was so slow that the predictors on the battleship's guns could not register on them. The *Bismarck* was twisting and writhing so much that it was far from the steady gun platform it had been when it had sunk the *Hood*. Until the final run–in (which had to be straight), the pilots did their best to go over or between the incoming shells. The Stringbag could turn almost in its own length and carry out manoeuvres that made other aircraft stall.

The release altitude for the torpedo was 18 feet above the water. By then, the Stringbags were too low for the German guns to train on them. The biplanes would not have lasted five minutes against fighter aircraft: but they had found the *Bismarck*'s Achilles heel.

Von Rechberg again:

"All ahead full! All stop! All Astern full! All stop!" – were the ever changing orders by which Captain Lindemann sought to escape the malevolent eels…. The attack must have been almost over when it came – an explosion aft. My heart sank. I glanced at the rudder indicator. It showed 'left 12 degrees.' It did not change. Our increasing list to starboard soon told us we were in a continuous turn.'

A torpedo had hit the *Bismarck*'s stern, blowing a hole in the hull so big that all the steering compartments were flooded. The pumps were unusable and all attempts to enter the steering rooms were in vain. The *Bismarck* was slowly turning in a circle, back towards her pursuers. High seas meant that it was impossible to plug the hole in the hull from the outside either; the seas and the suction under the stern was too strong for divers. The *Bismarck* continued to turn. Could the hangar door be removed and somehow welded to the stern to act as a counteracting rudder? The sea was too rough.

The wind rose strongly during the night, pushing the crippled German ship back towards the pursuing battleships, destroyers and cruisers. Divers continued to try and get into the steering rooms as water washed in and out from the ocean; but, despite trying until the point of collapse, the men could not shift the rudder. By now a wind of about 50mph – gale force 9 – was blowing. The captain ordered only enough speed to keep the ship from being blown about.

The first of *Bismarck*'s pursuers – destroyers – arrived less than two hours after the torpedo strike. The gunners on the greatest gun platform in the world now found that in the heavy seas, at reduced speed, listing, and swinging back and forth, they could not hit them. Again and again the British ships launched torpedoes against the German battleship. The seas were too heavy and the night too dark – they all missed. The destroyers fired star shells, to guide in the heavyweights for the kill.

Von Rechberg:

'Most of the time between destroyer attacks we proceeded at very low speed, but occasionally we stopped. At such times the *Bismarck* lay athwart to the seas and rolled quite heavily. Of course... it did not matter whether we made headway or not, because when daylight came on 27th May, Tovey's battleships would find us one way or another... some distance below me on the upper deck a heavy door was making a metallic clang as it swung to and fro with the movement of the ship, It was enough to get on one's nerves. A symptom of slackening discipline? Of course not. A death knell for us? That was more like it. Thank goodness, someone finally closed it tight.'

And so the night wore on. At around midnight, all attempts to free the rudders were pronounced to be useless:

'When it was announced that work on the rudders had ceased, hope evaporated. The older men took the news as sentence of death for ship and crew. Later in the night permission was given for everyone to help himself to anything he wanted. This was a clear sign that the ship's command knew that the end had come.'

An attempt was made to send the fleet diary off to France but the light aircraft that the *Bismarck* carried could not get aloft in the gale force wind. At 0710 Lütjens radioed Group West asking for a U-boat to pick it up. It was his last signal home.

Shortly after this, Baron Rechberg saw his captain on the bridge, wearing a lifejacket. The baron saluted him but Captain Lindemann did not acknowledge him:

'I was greatly disturbed and puzzled. After all, I had been his personal adjutant and the situation we were in seemed to me unusual enough to merit some remark.'

Rechberg threw a last glance at Lindemann and Arthur Meier, the captain's personal servant – a good natured ex–publican from Hanover who kept Lindemann stocked with his favourite cigarettes, Three Castles:

'Arthur Meier was always ready for a little chat. He could imagine much nicer things than the war and being in the navy, but, as he said resignedly, one had to be somewhere, and being in the *Bismarck* was quite all right with him. Such a big ship and such heavy armour. It would be hard for anything to happen there. How often he said that. And now his last dawn had broken.'

Then Rechberg moved to his action quarters in the gunnery station. On his way, he passed Admiral Lutyens. He was silent too:

'Then the alarm bells began to ring shrilly. It seemed as though they would never stop.'

Two British battleships – HMS *King George V* and HMS *Rodney* – spotted the *Bismarck* at 8.43 am. The *Bismarck* was now hemmed in by the battleships, two heavy cruisers and numerous destroyers. A broadside fired from all these ships together would have weighed about twenty tons.

Then it started. Shells came in from all directions. The *Bismarck*, the greatest gun platform in the world could not, due to her list to port and unpredictable movements, effectively reply. Nor could she steer to avoid fire. The British moved nearer. Shell after shell hit the German ship and two of her main guns were quickly put out of action. Rechberg, directing fire from the other two main guns, was frustrated as a heavy shell took away the range finder for his giant weapons:

'Nothing could have been more devastating to me than being put out of action just when I had every hope of hitting the *King George V*… unable to leave our station because an inferno was raging outside, we knew little of what was going on elsewhere.' Sailors clambered up the iron rungs into the baron's armoured fire-control compartment to escape the carnage: 'Many so badly wounded that one could only marvel that they did it.'

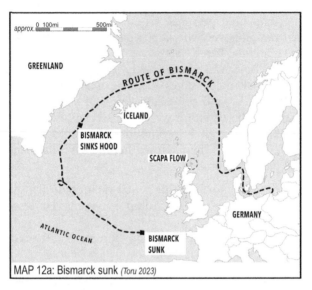

MAP 12a: Bismarck sunk *(Toru 2023)*

For half an hour, the *Rodney* steamed back and forth firing salvo after salvo of heavy shells into the dying *Bismarck*. Other ships shelled and torpedoed the ship too. Aboard the *Rodney*, her air defence officer, Lieutenant Donald Campbell (who had captained a small boat in the Dunkirk evacuation, where three of his five Royal Navy companions had died), watched as the crippled ship took more and more hits without reply. As shells crashed through the enemy's armour, he screamed involuntarily:

"My God, why don't we stop?" As if in answer, the cease–fire gongs rang.

The order came to abandon the *Bismarck*. The men in Rechberg's turret exited onto the main deck. The firing had ceased:

'…It was chaos and desolation. The anti–aircraft guns and searchlights had disappeared without trace. There were holes in the stack and whitish smoke indicating where fires must be burning below …I had to clamber over all manner of debris and over holes in the deck. Across the water, only around 2,500 metres away, was the *Rodney*, her guns still pointing mistrustfully towards us.'

Above Rechberg, on platforms where access ladders had been blown away by the shelling, men tried to escape the fires and exploding ammunition, while the ship listed ominously. The munitions stores on the *Bismarck* were on fire, their external temperature gauges registering 80 degrees centigrade. Flooding was ordered – even though men were trapped inside. The alternative was to go sky-high.

A few minutes earlier, a machinist in the lower part of the ship, Josef Statz, had climbed several decks up a cable shaft with two companions to escape:

'The *Bismarck* had a steadily increasing list to port, so that the men, hanging onto the rungs on the opposite side and repeatedly snagged by cable housings, had to expend three times the usual amount of energy to clamber up.'

They reached fresh air earlier than expected, shells having blown away several decks. Shells were still coming in. Men lay dead, 'massed at their action stations.' A friend, Heinz Moritz, who had climbed with Statz was wounded then: his whole chest torn open. Statz had no idea how he could help his comrade. He simply stroked his face, 'as one would a baby.'

'Moritz smiled at me gratefully, gasped: "Say hello to Cologne for me." And died.'

Then the firing stopped Josef Statz and his other remaining companion, Friedrich Cardinal, leaped into the boiling sea. They were swept apart and then closer. Statz saw that Cardinal's head was hanging slackly; he was already dead. Statz, who worked in damage control, was wearing leather clothing. The air pockets in his leathers, especially at the arms and knees, supported him, taking over the job of his life jacket, which had been completely shredded by shell splinters.

Rechberg, too, jumped into the sea. The *Bismarck* was turning over. Captain Ernst Lindemann was seen climbing onto the ship's side, saluting and going down with his ship. When he was a boy, Ernst had often told his companions that his greatest

213

wish was to command a ship and to go down with colours flying. Now he had fulfilled his wish. An observer remarked:

'I always thought such things happened only in books, but I saw it with my own eyes.'

Bismarck had taken 2876 shells and 58 torpedoes in 90 minutes. Scuttling charges went off in the ship, even as torpedoes from HMS *Dorsetshire* hit 'him'. He had finished his first and last operation. It had lasted nine days.

Rechberg and Statz were pulled from the sea by the *Dorsetshire*, Moments after they were rescued, the ship pulled away leaving hundreds more in the water. A U-boat had been spotted. Luckily for the British the U-boat (of which there were several in the area) had already used all its torpedoes against the convoys.

Of the 2,200 men, aboard the *Bismarck*, 115 were saved.

Incidentally, every single Stringbag that had attacked the *Bismarck* survived to return to its carrier. They would also survive many attempts to replace them with 'better' aircraft. By the end of the war, they would sink a greater tonnage of Axis shipping than any other aircraft.

Franco's fateful decision

One of the last signals received by the *Bismarck*, just before the British battleships attacked, was to say that Germany had asked the Spanish government to send naval forces to their aid: 'As an assistance and a precaution.' So keen was Franco to curry favour with the Nazis that he obliged by sending Spain's flagship – the cruiser *Canarias* – and two destroyers. It is difficult to imagine a more stupid move. Franco was either an ill–advised naval simpleton or he did not rate his navy too highly. Surprisingly his ships managed to get through the waters between Spain and the battle unmolested. There wasn't a lot for them to see by the time that they arrived. The *Bismarck* had gone; but they did find the bodies of two German sailors – a bandsman and a signaller – floating in the water. They hauled the corpses aboard, and then re–consigned them to the deep with full military honours.

How did the fate of Hitler's great battleship fit in with Franco's decision on when – or whether – to come into the war on the side of the Nazis? There was quite a bit for the Generalissimo to weigh up. True, German troops were doing rather well in the Mediterranean area: they had taken Greece – and, after a struggle – it was now clear that they had taken Crete too. But on the other hand, look what had happened to the Italian navy of late... and now the *Bismarck*. The Spanish dictator's conclusion seems to have been that 'England' wasn't quite 'on the point of collapse.' At any rate, he did not send his troops to invade Gibraltar (although he did, later, send a division to fight alongside the Germans on the Russian Front).

Though I have never seen it discussed – hardly even mentioned – this, it seems to me, was one of the key decisions of the war. If Gibraltar had been taken – and it was indefensible against a serious landward attack – the Mediterranean would have been lost to Britain: which would have meant that they would also have lost North Africa. That would have meant that there could have been no attack on Italy and many, many more German troops on the Atlantic coast and the Russian Front. After that there can only be speculation. The war would, at best, have lasted a good deal longer.

In the event, history shows that from a personal point of view Franco probably made a good call. He died in his bed, of natural causes, forty–four years later.

The supply ships

The tracking down of the *Bismarck* had been made possible by a joint action between Britannia's sixth sense (her mastery of wireless radio technology – the 'Y' stations, huff–duff and radar) and Bletchley Park. Four different methods had been involved in finding the ship – direction finding, radar, traffic analysis and decryption. Scarborough, Chicksands, Bletchley Park, and the Citadel in London had all played their part – as well as the intercept sites around the Atlantic.

The sinking, of course, had been due to the bravery, competence and sacrifices of the Royal Navy: and most especially, perhaps, to the superb flying and shooting of the unknown pilot of the Stringbag who trundled up to the most powerful ship on earth and found its Achilles heel.

After the sinking, the code breakers took centre stage. It was Bletchley who guided the navy to the eight supply ships and tankers which had supported *Exercise Rhine*. Apart from supplying the great battleships and cruisers these craft also resupplied smaller commerce raiders and U-boats. The hunting and sinking of every one of them in a matter of a couple of weeks was largely down to the foresight of one young man, Harry Hinsley. At the start of the war, Hinsley had been twenty years old and studying history at Cambridge. His studies were interrupted when he was summoned to work at Bletchley Park. He was instrumental there in getting the Royal Navy to capture a German weather ship and thus get hold of Enigma code books.

The capture of the code books from the German weather ship (the *München*) and the almost simultaneous capture of an Enigma machine from a U-boat (the U110) allowed Bletchley to decipher messages in the main German surface fleet code *on the same day that they were sent*. Bletchley called this code *Dolphin*. (BP had been breaking *Dolphin* for a couple of months already, but with a delay, meaning that *Bismarck's* messages weren't actually deciphered until after the ship had been sunk – hence the critical importance of traffic analysis, Huff–duff and radar in that sinking.)

This breakthrough came less than a week after *Bismarck* was sunk. It meant that when the German tankers told other German ships where they were – so that they could meet and refuel them – they inadvertently included Bletchley Park on the circulation list. Bletchley then passed the information on to the Citadel in London, who in turn told Western Approaches Command in Liverpool, who then sent out ships to track and sink their obliging informants.

The Royal Navy sank six of the supply ships in the week in which the code was broken and the other two a week later. They got another four later in the year. It didn't matter whether they were in the south, middle or north of the Atlantic, the Royal Navy found and sank them.

The cleanup was so successful as to be too obvious: the Germans were not so stupid to believe that the discoveries were all coincidental. They did not, however, conclude that their codes had been broken. Instead they blamed the tracking down of the supply ships on infiltration into the German navy by spies of the British secret service. The Germans tended to ascribe almost mystical powers to Britain's Secret Intelligence Service (British troops in North Africa regarded the German general, Erwin Rommel, in much the same way).

It is worth noting that the Germans' blind belief in the security of their codes was shared by the Royal Navy. Although the latter were told by both Bletchley Park and the American security services that their codes could be – and probably were being – broken, they did not change them until mid–1943.

After the *Bismarck* went down the Germans moved their warships from France to Norway, where they were hunted down by the RAF one by one. Only once more would the German surface fleet cause significant damage to Allied shipping (the hellish losses suffered by convoy PQ17, sailing from Britain to Russia).

Britain's lead in radio technology and code breaking had given Britannia a devastating edge. Her Royal Navy had now sent both the Italian and German surface navies either to Davy Jones' locker or back to port.

The use of intelligence in humanity's affairs

The marriage of communications and computing which began at and was centred on Bletchley Park was powered by wireless networks linked to sophisticated electro– mechanical devices and analogue and digital computers. The world had never seen anything like it. The first fruits of this intelligence revolution would be the defeat of fascism in Europe. It would also lay the foundations of the modern world. In terms of its effect on mankind, it can best be compared to the industrial revolution which had taken place at the other end of England, a couple of centuries earlier.

There are giants in the story – Tommy Flowers (I'll come back to him), Marconi, Welchman, Turing and Watson–Watt to name some of the obvious ones; although there are many, many, others.

A second revolution was taking place too: as important (arguably more so) as the first. This was a cultural, sexual, revolution. Here, in the Intelligence Zone, began the wholesale integration of women as equal contributors to the scientific progress of humanity.

When the men and women who operated Britain's communications web netted the Bismarck, it was not the end of a process but the start. Web? Net? I do not use the words lightly. It is no coincidence that the father of London–born Sir Tim Berners Lee – the inventor of the internet – was working on radar during the war and that his mother, Mary, was a mathematician, and that they met when they worked on the development of the world's earliest programmable computers.

The future started at Bletchley Park.

The success of Bletchley and its intelligence web was in a way a 'cold' victory. The men and women in Scarborough, Chicksands and Bletchley who did so much to place the *Bismarck* on the chopping board were remote from it: and often had the difficult task of explaining why they were not 'doing their bit for the war' while at the same time keeping absolute silence as to exactly what it was that they *were* doing in their safe havens, so far behind the lines.

Other dark horses from 'Quex' Sinclair's intelligence stable were running in an altogether more bloody race. So let's leave Bletchley for the moment and hack across country to SIS's communications factory at Whaddon Hall.

9: The many voices of the Whaddon Web

Quex Sinclair's conundrum

The towers and wires of the 'Y' services were only part of the extraordinary communications web that spread across the Intelligence Zone. There was another significant network working to defeat the Nazis. It was spun from Whaddon, a couple of miles from BP; and so I have called it the Whaddon Web. It, like many aspects of Britain's 'irregular warfare', owed its genesis to the head of Britain's Secret Intelligence Service (SIS/MI6), Admiral 'Quex' Sinclair.

The approach to war had posed a problem for Quex: while a few of Britain's overseas embassies had radio transmitters and receivers, his agents in the field – spies – had none. They had to rely on secret ink, codes and cover postal addresses. His biggest headache was getting messages in and out of Germany, where the Nazis intercepted and read all international mail going in and out. The only secure means to communicate with headquarters in London was by diplomatic pouch.

Fortunately Quex knew a man, Richard Gambier–Parry, who might be able to help him solve this conundrum. He was a chap that Quex could trust: they had both been to the same school – Eton; even better, they rode to hounds together. They hunted with the Whaddon Chase: one of Britain's most prestigious fox hunting packs. Quite a few blue blooded, or rich, men and women escaped London for the weekend and took a train north to Leighton Buzzard or Bletchley – where they stabled their horses. They would then ride to join 'the Whaddon'. It was the preferred hunt of the British secret services; Stewart Menzies, Quex's successor, rode with them, as did Gordon Welchman and Fred Winterbotham – to name but a few. Many of the key sites in the Intelligence Zone were identified and taken over because of their owners' membership of The Whaddon. The original owners of Bletchley Park, the Leons, hunted with the pack (the hunt would meet there on Boxing Day), as did Captain

219

Faulkner, the local builder who bought BP from them and sold it on to Quex. And so did a few others we shall meet along the way.

The master of Whaddon – 'Pop' Gambier-Parry

Richard Gambier–Parry, 46 in 1940, had, like most British men of his age, fought in the First World War. At the outbreak of that war, in 1914, he joined the Royal Welsh Fusiliers (Parry is a Welsh name) and was in action in France and Belgium.

Wounded three times and mentioned in dispatches twice, he later joined the Royal Flying Corps. After the war, he worked for the BBC as its sole press officer. Then he joined the American radio company, Philco (at the time the largest manufacturer of radios in the world), as its British sales manager. Both socially and technically, he looked to be the perfect man to sort out Quex's problem. When Quex summoned him to his offices in Broadway, London, in April 1938. Gambier–Parry reported that his briefing was ...brief:

'Pop' Richard Gambier-Parry

"I get a great deal of information. They drive it around Europe before it reaches me. Your business here will be to do something about it. Good morning."

Gambier–Parry resigned forthwith from Philco and joined SIS. Realising the size of his task, he took most of the Philco managers with him. The company was apparently very good about it.

Quex could not have chosen a better man for the job. Gambier–Parry began his work for SIS by setting up the Bletchley Park end of the military and civilian radio 'Y' listening posts. He was based for a while in the main house at BP – in a radio room in the tower (part of BP's museum now) –

but it was decided that it would be a good idea to move communications out of BP, partly because the aerial masts were a bit obvious. So on the 12th of September 1939 (less than two months before his death), Hugh Sinclair approved the leasing of Whaddon Hall and put Gambier–Parry in charge there. Whaddon was designated as section VIII: the communications section of SIS.

Gambier–Parry was a man of style. When he took over Whaddon Hall (which is about 4 miles from Bletchley Park), he took over as acting Master of the Whaddon Chase hunt too. In future years he would reputedly commandeer to his personal staff any huntsman who wished to avoid being called up. He also kept Whaddon Hall's butler. In the early days, evening dress was obligatory for the pre–dinner glass of sherry and the evening meal (black ties for the gentlemen, long dresses for the ladies).

Gambier–Parry was a colourful character. In the words of the witty and brilliant (but rather unpleasant) Hugh Trevor–Roper:

'In the world of neurotic policeman and timid placemen who rule the secret service, he moves like Falstaff, or some figure from Balzac, if not Rabelais.' (Trevor–Roper was a fellow huntsman and rode regularly with Gambier–Parry and the Whaddon hounds pre–war.) As a huntsman, Gambier–Parry was… 'a loud, Levantine figure in a risqué chocolate uniform, beltless and betabbed, his brass slightly awry, thrusting merrily forward on a heavyweight hunter and closely followed by two modish blondes, his secretaries… In the evenings afterwards he would bang the bottle on the table and boast of his success: "led the field all the way"… he lived like a colonial governor with a fleet of camouflaged Packards at his disposal.'

It is often said that troops 'worship' their generals. In truth, they more often fear, are ignorant of, or are rude about them. Gambier–Parry – 'Pop' as he frequently signed himself and as he was generally known – was, however, regarded with both respect and affection by his staff. The only fly in the ointment seems to have been a certain amount of tension among the wives in the section. Possibly this was because Pop had an eye for the ladies and – persistent local rumour suggests – the ladies liked him too.

Talking with an occupied continent

In the previous chapter, I wrote of the use of radio in its various facets to listen to and locate the enemy. In addition to listening to enemies, radio was also used to talk to friends. Talking (mostly in Morse code) was what Whaddon Hall and its wide–flung ring of communication masts was all about. Many of Whaddon's 'customers' were secret agents. From the agents came information about the enemy; in return, Whaddon would send them radios and radio operators, and arrange supply drops and the flying in and out of agents.

Britain supported two types of agents – 'passive' agents: spies who gathered information on submarine movements, troop deployment, aircraft and so on – and 'active' agents; saboteurs who blew up railway bridges and power lines and the like. The spies were controlled directly by SIS. Control of the saboteurs would pass from SIS to a new organisation, called the Special Operations Executive (SOE). Whaddon Hall set up communications for both the spies (SIS) and saboteurs (SOE) who operated in mainland Europe. The SOE communication stations were sited a few miles to the south–west of Whaddon, in the low hills towards Bicester.

Pop Gambier–Parry moved quickly to build an organisation that could handle an expanding amount of traffic; and, as the peoples of Europe took heart from Dowding's victory in the Battle of Britain, the traffic did grow. The conquered people of Europe saw that resistance could lead to the overthrow of their oppressors – and the bravest took action to make it happen.

The communications infrastructure that Pop built was to give succour, a voice – and hope – to an army behind the lines; an army without uniform whose every man and woman was an unpaid volunteer. An army of resistance to a power more brutal than any seen in Europe for a thousand years. An army whose troops, when they were captured, did not see a prisoner of war camp, but a butcher's hook, or a firing squad, or an oven, or a hangman's noose. Both spies and saboteurs were to suffer catastrophic losses.

Spies and saboteurs were not Pop's only customers. Whaddon Hall (Section VIII) also built stations for the Czech and Polish governments in exile. On top of this they supplied communications between BP and 'the top brass', such as Churchill, Montgomery and Patton. They also set up transmitters and studios for the broadcast of 'Black' propaganda.

Suitable sites were searched out for the numerous transmitting and receiving stations that were needed. Within a short period of time just about every major hill around the local market town of Winslow had its array of aerial masts.

To put up the masts, Whaddon had a 'small but merry' group of aerial riggers run by an Australian Army soldier, Sergeant Ernie 'Digger' Buick. He was described (by an engineer, Major Robin Adie) as:

'A remarkable man although his language, parliamentary and otherwise was fairly extensive …they would set off in the morning, winter or summer, rain or shine… how they put up with his language I don't know.'

Huts for radio operators were erected at the foot of the masts and fences put around them. Many of these compounds had armed guards. Lord knows what the old gaffers in local pubs such as the *Sow and Pigs* in Poundon or the *Shoulder of Mutton* in Calverton made of all this.

From huts at the SIS and SOE communication sites, radio operators listened and broadcast day and night, sending their (coded) messages in almost every European language. Predetermined airwaves were monitored, agents' reports received and instructions given. The operators (male and female) in those huts were the cream of the crop. They had to be quick and accurate; for this was the British end of those terrifying exchanges which lasted from the moment an agent went on the air to the moment he, or she, shut down. As soon as an agent in occupied Europe began to broadcast, Nazi detector stations would identify the approximate source of the transmission and instruct local detection vans to hunt them out.

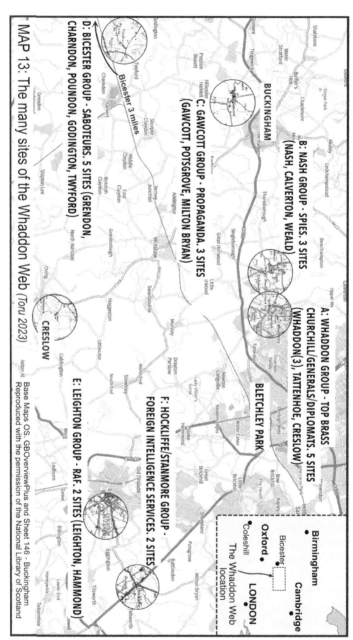

MAP 13: The many sites of the Whaddon Web (*Toru 2023*)

A: WHADDON GROUP - TOP BRASS
CHURCHILL/GENERALS/DIPLOMATS. 5 SITES
(WHADDON(3), TATTENHOE, CRESLOW)

B: NASH GROUP - SPIES. 3 SITES
(NASH, CALVERTON, WEALD)

C: GAWCOTT GROUP - PROPAGANDA. 3 SITES
(GAWCOTT, POTSGROVE, MILTON BRYAN)

D: BICESTER GROUP - SABOTEURS. 5 SITES (GRENDON,
CHARNDON, POUNDON, GODINGTON, TWYFORD)

E: LEIGHTON GROUP - RAF. 2 SITES (LEIGHTON, HAMMOND)

F: HOCKLIFFE/STANMORE GROUP -
FOREIGN INTELLIGENCE SERVICES. 2 SITES

BUCKINGHAM

Bicester 3 miles

CRESLOW

BLETCHLEY PARK

The Whaddon Web
location

Birmingham

Cambridge

Oxford
Coleshill
Bicester

LONDON

God help those agents if they stayed on the air too long, or garbled their messages and had to repeat, or if the operators at Nash, Weald, Poundon or Grendon weren't up to scratch. A 'repeat' could be a death warrant. Radio operators were the most expendable of secret service operatives in occupied Europe. Section VIII ran a school – at Hans Place in London – which trained over 600 of them during the war; and there were several such schools.

The communications network that Gambier–Parry set up had, in the words of the head of SIS, 'no rival in the world'. That the paperwork did not always keep up is not surprising: and the bean–counters at head office could have shown more forbearance than they did. Gambier–Parry certainly thought so, as his volcanic reply to the paymaster of SIS (Commander Sykes) in July 1941 shows (he had been accused of poor record keeping):

'No consideration at all is given to the fact that during the period our annual estimates... tripled... and we were working at the highest pressure, forming a military unit, equipping some 60 technical vehicles, putting up two broadcasting stations and a recording centre, at a speed which many experts would believe impossible, carrying ever–increasing telegraphic traffic, developing the new science of agent communications, coping with SOE communications, carrying an expanding circulation of Polish signals at home and abroad, and endeavouring to contribute to the process of winning the war. But then the auditors wouldn't want to know what we do in any of these fields. It seems to be of greater importance to them that one order has become entangled with another.'

'Pop' does not mention here the work he and his section had also carried out in providing radio communications for the 'stay at home' resistance organisation based in Coleshill, Wiltshire. Peter Fleming (brother of Ian) was in charge at Coleshill. His section set up a nationwide network of camouflaged underground lairs and trained and supplied men to go to ground in them. If the Germans had landed, Fleming's saboteurs would have emerged at night to fight them behind the lines. Their survival rate would not have been good – but at least they had radios. Desperate stuff.

Gambier–Parry lived for much of the war at Wavendon Towers, a large country house a couple of miles east of Bletchley (which in a way is where I come in, as Wavendon was the first home of the Milton Keynes Development Corporation, the builders of the new city, for which I was the I.T. manager).

In essence, then, apart from the stay-at-homes at Coleshill, the 'Whaddon ring' of communication towers served five clients. I will devote entire chapters to what the foreign governments and SOE were up to in the sequel to this book *A New World After Pearl*. In this chapter, though, I want to talk a little more about the other three of Gambier Parry's 'customers'; 'Black' propaganda, the generals and the spies.

Black propaganda – PWE

'Black' propaganda was the broadcasting of programmes to try to sow alarm and despondency in the Nazi ranks. It could – and did – use lies to achieve its ends. Originally one of SIS's many responsibilities, black propaganda was taken over by an organisation called the Political Warfare Executive (PWE). The broadcasts were managed – and often made – by Sefton Delmer – who, it may be remembered, had been rather rude to Adolf over the BBC airwaves on Hitler's offer of peace shortly after the collapse of France. The programmes were mostly in German and mostly aimed at German troops. Most PWE broadcasters were native Germans, some Jewish, others disaffected Nazis.

Of all the British intelligence initiatives, black propaganda was arguably the least successful. Delmer knew that it was pointless trying to discredit Hitler. The Fuhrer was beyond criticism inside the Third Reich; regarded as a god amongst many of his followers. I do not use the word 'god' lightly. Many Nazi households had flower–decked shrines set up to Hitler, with his portrait as the altarpiece. His picture was hung everywhere in public places and offices.

Delmer set up stations which would attract enemy troops – particularly submariners. They were enormously popular with the sailors – probably the most listened to of any radio stations, including the German ones. The problem was, they didn't really achieve much. They sowed some alarm and despondency it is true. The U–boat crews couldn't believe how much information was known about them (including, sometimes, the date of their sailing and who had won the inter–submarine football match the night before) but mostly the radio stations provided first class light entertainment; for instance the music of Glenn Miller and a forces' sweetheart.

Perhaps PWE's greatest moment was towards the end of the war, when it used the enormous power of its giant 'Aspidistra' transmitter to swamp the air waves over Germany with fake instructions. German night–fighter controllers could only listen helplessly as their pilots were routed away from the Allied bomber swarms.

The fact that Sefton Delmer could not directly indoctrinate the Germans to rise against the Nazis is no reflection on the man himself. It is sobering to realise that a great part of the population can be led to believe just about anything by constant repetition. This is probably true of any society, anywhere; but the Nazis also had preachers of genius. Both Hitler and his propaganda minister, Joseph Goebbels, could fool most of the people most of the time. Goebbels reckoned that after an hour of speaking to an audience; "I can make them climb trees if I feel like it".

To try and make a deluded society – or religion – question its beliefs is not only virtually impossible but dangerous and mostly pointless: which is why most visitors to Germany raised their arm in the Hitler salute. Ellic Howe, who worked in PWE during the war and who wrote the definitive book on the subject – *The Black Game* – says that while we did 'confuse and disturb them and soften them… black propaganda is not a war winner and only becomes effective when the enemy is losing confidence.'

Very few Nazis (and not enough Germans) lost confidence in Hitler until Germany lay in ruins and their master had shot himself.

Churchill and the generals

At Whaddon itself, SIS passed information from Bletchley Park to Churchill and high–command posts in London, Moscow and New York. This information was classified as 'Ultra'. Whaddon also communicated with generals and admirals at the battle fronts. Secrecy was the key here. Very few people knew about Bletchley Park. Most of Churchill's cabinet, for example, knew nothing of it – and only the highest of Allied commanders were in the loop. Any information which was sent overseas was handled on receipt by radio operators trained and provided by Section VIII at Whaddon. This system had been suggested very early in the war by Fred Winterbotham, who was at that time in charge of SIS's security; including Bletchley Park.

The military commanders included Admiral Cunningham and, later in the war, generals Montgomery and Patton. These two generals loathed each other. Bernard Montgomery (British) was not well regarded by SIS operators, being neither friendly nor very receptive to the information he was given. George Patton (American) was much more welcoming and much more likely to act on what he had been told. He hoovered up any information that was passed to him from Whaddon.

Whaddon had its own engineering workshops nearby (at Little Horwood, on an estate which belonged to yet another member of the Whaddon Chase hunt, George Gee). Here engineers (mostly poached by 'Pop' Gambier-Parry from his old company), made and fitted radios into the cars of high ranking generals so that they could be contacted securely with Ultra information.

American radio receivers and some of their machine tools were, at the start of the war, the best in the world and Gambier–

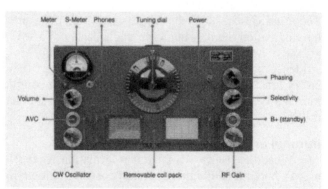

The American HRO5 - a thing of beauty and utility

Parry managed to charter a ship's hold full of 'goodies' across the Atlantic just before fighting started. There was a section of five American engineers at Whaddon, who serviced the American HRO radio receivers across the Intelligence Zone.

The radio car of choice was another American wonder, the Packard – a luxurious beast of which Gambier–Parry bought the entire British stock. Whaddon, which until then had been more used to horses than cars, would quickly become accustomed to these sleek beauties – and the sleek beauties who Gambier–Parry employed to drive them.

Gambier–Parry spread his feelers far and wide to find the best radio operators. His most fruitful source was the army (his brother, Michael, was a general). The radio operators and intelligence officers (Special Communication Units) that were sent from Whaddon to embassies and allied generals in the field were a key link in running the war. To give you a taste of what they did, I will tell you a little about the activities of two of them, Bill Miller and Edgar Harrison.

Bill Miller in Spain

Bill Miller loved radio – in fact he practically lived for it. As a boy, he made his own cat's whisker sets, learned Morse and had the ambition to eventually open his own amateur wireless station. He was called up as a wireless operator in the London division of the Royal Corps of Signals at the start of the war. He was 19 years old. As a lowly trooper, he was paid two bob (10p) a day – £37 a year.

He was an exceptional radio operator and was soon told to report to Bletchley railway station, from where he was eventually escorted to a man referred to as 'Pop' at a property nearby (Whaddon). After an initial talk, Pop (Gambier–Parry of course) showed him a map of the Spanish/French border area, shook his hand and welcomed him to 'The Firm' (as SIS was known amongst its members). Bill was staggered to learn that his pay would be £300 a year in Britain and £400 a year when abroad. That was more than most officers received.

Before being sent into the field, Bill was trained in codes – his own code was based on a paperback book, *Poet's Pub*, by Eric Linklater. If he wanted to use a word, he would code the page, line and word number where it occurred. Recurring information, such as an aircraft type or general's name, was covered by a separate list.

Bill's first posting was to the British consulate at Bilbao, near Spain's border with France. His task – to act as the tripwire which would give the Royal Navy as much time as possible to get out of Gibraltar – carried enormous responsibility. His orders were to alert Whaddon the moment that German troops marched into Spain. At the time this was regarded as being a near certainty. He was in Bilbao when the *Bismarck* sank the *Hood*. As Spain was very pro–Nazi at the time, the local paper splashed the story all over the front page. The offering at the local cinema was a German propaganda film, *Victory in the West* (about Dunkirk) with footage from the planes strafing the beaches. When the *Bismarck* was sunk, it merited just a few lines on an inside page of the paper.

Bill watched as ships from South America which had bypassed the Royal Navy landed at Bilbao's docks. At the bottom of the gangplank any German passengers were greeted by uniformed Hitler Youths and put straight onto buses to France.

Bill was a quiet, bespectacled, lad. Not the stuff of heroes, nor one to put himself into dangerous situations – hardly the stuff of Hollywood. Nevertheless, he had an eventful war where he spied and was involved with sabotage and saw a world far, far beyond his native land. He learned Spanish and some Arabic, made a bob or two and married a Spanish girl, Ramona. Bill Miller's love of 'the wireless' had pitched him from the daily grind into the world of espionage and the pages of history.

Edgar Harrison – Greece and Crete

Edgar Harrison was another signaller whose life was spun in a new direction by Whaddon and the war. His experiences were so extraordinary that a book has been written about him. Of all the people of Whaddon, Pop Gambier–Parry included, I think he is the only one who has been the subject of a personal biography.

Harrison was a Caerphilly lad, the eighth of ten children. He joined the army at the age of 14, in 1929. He was a corporal when he was poached by Gambier–Parry's section VIII at Whaddon Hall. The Royal Corps of Signals was to provide a good number of Pop's radio operators.

Edgar began his time at Whaddon fitting radios into the Packards which were to have been used as command posts behind the lines in the then–likely event of German invasion. The Packard was roomy. The rear was stripped out (at Little Horwood) and turned into a three man radio room – with a transmitter and a receiver. After Whaddon, Edgar Harrison was sent abroad, to pass Ultra to generals in the field. He was to take part in six retreats and become Winston Churchill's Ultra wireless operator.

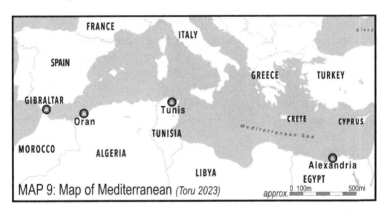

MAP 9: Map of Mediterranean *(Toru 2023)* approx. 0 100m 500mi

His first posting – and retreat – was from Norway. Then he was sent to Brussels – and retreated via Dunkirk. Then he was posted to the British army headquarters in Greece (commanded by Gambier–Parry's brother). British troops were in Greece at the request of the Greek government, who had asked for help when Italy had tried to invade their country. The Greeks, with British aid, repulsed the attempted Italian invasion. That caused Hitler to send German troops to do the job properly – which they did – pushing the British into the sea. The Royal Navy evacuated the army, suffering major losses whilst doing so. It must have seemed a bit old hat for Edgar Harrison, this being his third retreat.

From Greece, Edgar Harrison was sent to the island of Crete as part of Whaddon's liaison team there. Their job was to receive Ultra information and pass it on to the commander of the Allied forces in Crete (Major–General Bernard Freyberg). The team duly informed the commander that there was about to be a co–ordinated German and Italian sea and air attack on the island. The air attack was to be a mass landing of German parachute troops on Crete's two airfields. The defenders outnumbered the attackers. The Germans took the island anyway.

Stuart Milner–Barry, one of the senior staff in (and later head of) Bletchley Park's Hut 6 said of this debacle:

'The Cretan episode was, from the Hut 6 point of view, the greatest disappointment of the war. It seemed a near certainty that with General Freyberg warned that the crucial point of the invasion was to be the airborne attack on the Maleme airport, and the time and every detail of the operation spelt out for us in advance, and given the appalling difficulty and danger of any airborne invasion in the best of circumstances, the attack would be ignominiously thrown back: and we awaited the operation with anxiety but also with a considerable degree of confidence.'

Crete was one of the great failures of British arms and planning in the Second World War. The defeat was costly. Eleven thousand defending troops were taken prisoner and the Germans took bloody revenge on any civilian who had opposed their landings. There were many of these, for the civil population of Crete were brave fighters who fought alongside the soldiers to defend their homeland, attacking the paratroops with billhooks, sticks and spades – whatever weapons came to hand. The German invaders replied both individually and systematically. According to their own records they shot 3,474 civilians in front of firing squads. One Cretan source lists 8,575 killings: of which around 2,000 were women and children.

The Royal Navy, too, took terrible punishment in the defence of and evacuation from Crete. Admiral Cunningham's forces lost 6 destroyers and 3 cruisers to German and Italian bombers while evacuating 14,500 British troops. These shipping losses were considerably higher than at Dunkirk. One of those who got away was Edgar Harrison. It was his fourth retreat from the Germans in twelve months.

Crete (in May 1941) showed conclusively – if further proof was needed – that superb signals intelligence could only go so far in defeating the German war machine. Sufficient weapons and troops, both of the right quality, were needed too. So was proper leadership of the troops; and that was missing in Crete.

On the plus side, in diverting his armies to take Greece and Crete, Hitler was forced to delay his attack on Russia by several weeks. The German Field Marshal Wilhelm Keitel (who was eventually hanged at Nuremberg for his war crimes) said that the delay cost Germany the war. Keitel's words carry a lot of weight as he was Hitler's Chief of Staff at the time of the invasion of Russia.

Edgar Harrison, ever at the front, would get involved in Russia too. He would shortly be seconded to the Russian Front, partly to put radios into British tanks for Stalin's beleaguered armies.

The British army was not doing terribly well in its head–to–head confrontations with the German army. That concentrated Churchill's resolve to win by other means – which brings me back to Whaddon and its key role as the hub of the European resistance movements.

A shortage of spies

Whaddon was eminently capable of supplying all of the communications, radios and radio operators that Europe's resistance movements needed. Initially, though, they were somewhat short of agents to talk to. SIS had been running several spy networks in Europe pre–war; but all of them had suffered in one way or another – some of them very badly. Their German operations were very seriously damaged by the rise of Hitler and the Nazis. Then, in 1940, the heads of their Dutch operations were captured in a Nazi 'sting' operation at Venlo in Holland. Scandinavia fared somewhat better – the spies there fed back a great deal of useful information: for example, the spotting of the *Bismarck* by a Norwegian agent which I mentioned earlier.

Crucially, military information was needed from France. That country was the easiest route for a ground attack on Germany – and the German surface and submarine fleets were largely based there. France, it is worth repeating, had been split into two by the invaders. The north and coastal areas were ruled directly by the Nazis while the south, the 'Zone Libre' was governed from the city of Vichy, by the French themselves, (as long as they did what they were told) under Marshal Pétain. Pétain and his government thought that Britain could not hold out against Germany and aimed to take advantage of the new realities of a Nazi–ruled Europe by collaboration with their invaders.

A couple of areas of France had been annexed by the Germans and Italians.

MAP 7: Vichy France showing German Submarine bases *(Toru 2023)*

Britain was not without information from France. An astonishing example of courage in the intelligence war was the work carried out in the South of France under the leadership of

Captain Gustave Bertrand. Bertrand, who we met briefly in the chapter about Bletchley Park, was the head of France's radio intelligence service: Gambier–Parry's French opposite number. He led a team of 30 'stay behind' agents, comprising French, Poles (including Marian Rejewski, whom we also met in the chapter about Bletchley) and Spaniards. The group gathered information by putting line taps on the main telephone routes to Berlin. Nearly 3,000 messages were transmitted by these brave men to the RSS's listening post at Hanslope (which was also administered from Whaddon) between October 1940 and November 1942.

The *Alliance* network: the flower of France

Then there was *Alliance*, a complex, powerful and knowledgeable French resistance network which seemed to have sprung from nowhere. *Alliance* would quickly become the Allies' best source of resistance intelligence. I will tell a little of their remarkable – and too little known – story through the experiences of their founder, 'Navarre' and his deputy, Marie–Madeleine Fourcade who would take over as leader after his arrest.

Marie-Madeleine Fourcade's false identity card

'Navarre'
Georges Loustaunau-Lacau

'Navarre' was the code name of Major Georges Loustaunau–Lacau, a French army officer whose patriotic work had started before the war. He owned and published magazines which were devoted to raising awareness of – and fostering resistance to – Communist and Nazi infiltration into his country; especially in the armed forces. Marie–Madeleine Fourcade (nee Bridou) worked for him as his manager and second–in command. Navarre relied on her explicitly. Both of them could see what was coming:

> 'It was pretty obvious,' wrote Marie–Madeleine of Nazi Germany, 'that anyone who preferred guns to butter would end up spitting fire.'

Navarre, who spoke five languages, had worked alongside the French secret service (the Deuxième Bureau) in the past and by the time he began his magazines, effectively ran his own secret service. He commissioned articles to be written by Berthold Jacob – a German Jew who had fought for Germany in the first war and would later be murdered by the gestapo. These articles listed the battle order of all three German armed forces.

When the German armies broke into France, Navarre relocated his staff to Vichy, where, as I have mentioned, the collaborationist government of Pétain had its headquarters. From that first day of defeat his intention was to work to foster resistance and armed uprising against the Nazi invader, with the help of the Vichy government if he could get it.

Marie–Madeleine took part in the flight from Paris of 1940, when the roads were clogged with refugees. There were a few men, but most had been called up – the refugees were mainly children and the old. The pace was slow – a seemingly endless file of cars, carts, loaded prams and pedestrians. The Luftwaffe routinely machine–gunned these columns from the air. Marie–Madeleine's column was bombed by Hitler's Italian allies, who were only too happy to ingratiate themselves with the Fuhrer by attacking such an easy target.

Navarre and Marie–Madeleine began the *Alliance* resistance network in October 1940. At the beginning, it was difficult to find anyone to join them. The great majority of the European population believed that the invasion of Britain was imminent, which made it pointless to resist the Nazis. All of the evidence supported this view: but Navarre and Marie–Madeleine Fourcade were prepared, from the first moment, to put their lives on the line to throw the enemy out of their country.

To build his resistance group, Navarre targeted those whom he thought might be sympathetic. To get to talk to his target audience, he first played a dangerous trick on the man at the top – the leader of the Vichy regime, Marshal Pétain – the very man who had negotiated the French surrender.

Marshal Philippe Pétain was a French national icon, revered for stopping the German army at Verdun in the first war. He was first and foremost a soldier; but an old and weary one (84 years old when he came to power) who no longer believed that France could beat the Germans. Navarre was well placed to approach him, having previously served as his adjutant in the army (as had de Gaulle).

Navarre intended to use his closeness to Pétain to bring about the defeat of Nazi Germany and the liberation of his country. He began by asking Pétain to allow him to set up a club, at Vichy, for veteran warriors. Pétain agreed to the request, not realising that he had been duped; for far from being a talking shop where old soldiers refought old battles with their tongues, Navarre used his organisation to pinpoint men who were prepared to fight the Nazis. The group – the core of the *Alliance* resistance network – grew from six to fifty in three months.

Navarre gave Marie–Madeleine Fourcade the job of carrying out the next phase of his plan – setting up and staffing further branches in both the free and occupied zones. To do this she had to pass through the zone of demarcation – the area policed by the Germans between occupied France and Vichy. Through his contacts in Vichy, Navarre had got hold of an *Ausweis*, the German document which allowed free passage between the two zones.

What Navarre and Marie–Madeleine didn't know was that the official who had supplied the document didn't trust Navarre and had issued an *Ausweis* with the suffix 'xxxx' – which meant that the carrier was highly suspect. Consequently, every time that she crossed this internal border, Marie–Madeleine was strip searched by the female German security police – 'the grey mice'. *Les souris grises* searched her clothes as well as herself, so she could not carry documents; to do so she would revert to stratagems like befriending women with babies and putting papers in the pram. Every time she crossed the line she was subjected to this disgusting and terrifying experience until she finally tore up her pass.

From the start Navarre, although he did not yet have anyone to give the information to, circulated a checklist of things he wanted his agents to find out. He wanted to know which enemy military units were stationed where and, if they moved, when and to where. He also asked for information about airfields (including dummy airfields) and aircraft, guns and artillery, tanks and U–boat installations.

Navarre was a truly remarkable man. Apart from passive intelligence gathering, he was also looking to stir up a military revolt in the French colonies of North Africa. He aimed to persuade the senior officers there to abandon collaboration with the Nazis and fight shoulder to shoulder with the British against Germany and Italy. He urged them to turn their troops – over 100,000 of them – out of their barracks and march them to war. Enough of acceptance, cowering and turning the other cheek – it was time France fought for her freedom.

With a network and ambitions on this scale, Navarre needed a good deal of help. The place to get it was London.

Marie–Madeleine suggested to Navarre that the ideal person to send to link up with the British was her brother, Jacques, an army officer who was married to an English woman (Sylvia Jeavons) and who himself spoke English well. Navarre agreed and, after some adventures, Jacques reached England (by way of Morocco and Gibraltar). No one was expecting him in London and he was not received with much enthusiasm. He ended up at the Royal Patriotic School, on the edge of Wandsworth Common, in London. This was the interrogation centre for arrivals from overseas: its purpose to sift out German spies. In Marie–Madeleine's words:

'England, more than ever, was an island that only operated by radar, their defence secret. Another radar, Scotland Yard, His Majesty's efficient police, was charged with plucking and confounding anyone who had the cheek to arrive unannounced.'

Jacques, with information which would condemn many to death if it got into the wrong hands, refused to talk to anyone except the head of the French resistance in London, Charles de Gaulle; or, failing that, to a friend of Navarre's, Admiral Pass. As neither was forthcoming, Jacques's interrogation didn't get very far. In the end, his wife's father was sent for. The trouble was that Jacques had never met his father–in–law, who was not introduced. To Jacques, he was just another stranger who sat in during yet another interrogation. Then the older man shot several questions at him – ending with:

"And this Sylvia – has she still got a beauty spot on her left buttock."

This was too much for Jacques: "How do you know that, you old pig?" he shouted and was on the point of leaping over the table and attacking the insulting Englishman. Luckily, Mr Jeavons beat him to it. "My son!" he cried, pulling Jacques into his arms. Meanwhile, Marie–Madeleine tells us:

'A choir of guardian angels proclaimed – "jealousy cannot be pretended – he's definitely the husband."'

A fine, Gallic, denouement.

When Jacques did get to meet General Charles de Gaulle, the meeting was to neither man's taste. I've mentioned friction in French affairs before. *Alliance's* place in the fight against the Nazis caused more. Jacques passed on Navarre's message: which was that he was happy to keep de Gaulle in the loop – but wanted to be free to run his dangerous show with the minimum of interference. He did not want an extra layer between himself and British command. Marie–Madeleine tells us:

'He wanted to send information direct to the *Anglais* (sic), who alone were running the war, so as not to lose time.'

Navarre did not want – nor would he accept – de Gaulle's leadership. He didn't need a boss. There may have been more than operational issues in his declaration of his independence. His organisation was streets ahead of anything the general had. While De Gaulle was safely in Hertfordshire with his wife and daughter, Navarre was the one in the front line risking his life; so why should he play second fiddle to the general? Nor did he think de Gaulle his superior. The two had been in the same officer intake at the French military academy – the *École de guerre* – the French army's staff college. Navarre had been the star of that intake of 129 pupils – *Major de Promotion* – the best in his year, *la crème de la crème*; Field Marshal material. De Gaulle had been rated assez bien (good enough) at number 52 (he had lost marks for 'his harsh dismissal of the views of others').

Whatever Navarre's motives, his independence was not at all to de Gaulle's taste. The general was in the process of setting up his own spy network – he did not want an equal: much less a potential rival.

Jacques had brought with him a leaflet entitled 'the crusade' – an epistle written by Marie–Madeleine, which Navarre wanted the RAF to drop over French cities. It announced that a French resistance network was already operating right across France and had been ever since October 1940. De Gaulle didn't like the idea – or the text – in the least. He, Charles de Gaulle, was the leader of *France Libre*. He would do things his way. His final remark to Captain Jacques Fourcade was dismissive:

"All those who are not with me are against me."

SIS, however, were more welcoming. At Jacques' interrogation, their spymaster, Commander Kenneth Cohen, had been very interested to hear of this large, coordinated, working resistance group which seemed to have risen, fully formed – as wonderful as a phoenix – from the very ashes of France's defeat. The offer of help from the charismatic Navarre who could not only furnish intelligence about German troops, but had the ear of Pétain and the ambition of bringing the French armies in North Africa across to the side of Britain was very, very, welcome indeed.

Jacques was given a course in parachuting (3 jumps), some money, information on radio usage and contacts, and parachuted back into France. He took with him an invitation from Commander Cohen of SIS. Cohen wasn't interested in inter-French rivalry – but information. Navarre's spy group was far in advance of anything that de Gaulle had. If Navarre and de Gaulle would not work together, then Britain might well be interested in working with them separately. Cohen wanted to meet Navarre in neutral Portugal in a couple of weeks.

When Jacques had finished telling his boss the ins and outs of all of his adventures, Navarre told him that he wished that he could pin a medal on him. Jacques said he'd prefer a decent glass of wine.

The meeting between Cohen and Navarre in Portugal in mid–April 1941 was friendly, open and to the point. Cohen told Navarre that Britain had lost the land war, that the air war was in the balance but that the Royal Navy was doing well at sea. He also said that the British would fight, if necessary, to the last man. However, they were very short of information from France. Much of SIS's French network had been taken down by the Nazis when the records of the Deuxième Bureau (the French equivalent of SIS) fell into German hands after the French defeat. SIS would be more than happy to help Navarre. In return, they desperately needed information on what the Nazis would do next: would they launch their troops into Spain – possibly with Vichy help?

Navarre made the same points to Cohen as Jacques had to de Gaulle. *Alliance* didn't need direction – just help. In return for that help, he would gather and pass information to SIS; but he would also give the same information to de Gaulle. That was fine by Cohen, who promised that Britain would give *Alliance* all the money, radio equipment, radio operators and supplies that they needed (they would subsidise de Gaulle and Navarre on equal terms). Everything was ready. Gambier–Parry had made sure of that. Navarre would have absolute freedom of action. The gentlemen's agreement was made.

Both sides would honour their word. *Alliance* would supply the most important information to come out of France. SIS would give them material help, but they would not try to run *Alliance*. 'Never' says Marie–Madeleine, 'did SIS issue orders. Just suggestions.'

Navarre came back from Lisbon with a present for Marie–Madeleine. It was the book she would use as the basis for composing her messages – *La dame aux camellias*. The method of coding was the same one Bill Miller was using in Bilbao.

SIS and Navarre were now in perfect harmony. De Gaulle, however, would take their accord as an affront. The general was often affronted. It was in his character to be so. As the French Staff College had noted, he did not understand nuance or compromise. He saw things in simple terms of right and wrong; he was right, others were wrong. As he had said to Jacques: "All that are not with me are against me." And he had an obvious chip on his shoulder with regard to 'England'. Clementine Churchill, like her husband a great lover of France, said to him once: "General, you must not hate your friends more than you hate your enemies." Sadly her advice was wasted.

The general justified his lack of empathy on the grounds of the needs of his country: and his own divine mission. On occasion he is reported to have said that he was not only French, but France itself "*Je suis la France*."

So de Gaulle would build up his own, separate, spy network: which would not share information with any other. *Alliance* would tell him what they were doing – but the passage of information was one way. Marie–Madeleine described the in–fighting as being 'criminally puerile'. Later in the war, De Gaulle's own spy group knew of, but did not pass on, the identity of a Nazi informer who had infiltrated *Alliance*. Several of the network would pay for this with their lives. That would lead to an explosion in the corridor of de Gaulle's London headquarters when Marie–Madeleine Fourcade would confront the general's head of security ('Passy'). An onlooker would describe them as being 'like two angry pythons'. But that was in the future.

The growth of *Alliance*

In the early days, *Alliance's* recruiters took in anyone who volunteered their services. Because of this, they would recruit a few who would betray them; some for money, a couple for ideological reasons – but betrayal was not always from bad will; the betrayers often turned out to be those who simply couldn't keep their mouths shut. Many were naïve, untutored, and trusting, taking others to be mirrors of themselves: saints seeing saints. Marie–Madeleine herself was trustful in the beginning: 'I wanted to open my arms to everyone. I felt ashamed to doubt.'

Marie–Madeleine Fourcade and her deputies would learn to be very, very suspicious – but only after the betrayals had cost *Alliance* many lives. Even so, caution could only go so far – they had to trust *some* of the people who pledged their aid, or the fallen could not be replaced. Alliance would need a lot of replacements in the years to come.

Marie–Madeleine had to cross a class barrier. She was from the elite, the moneyed, the educated, the officer class. Her troops were not. In her own words 'it was not the grand or the fortuned but the modest who became our family.'

And there were other, unique, problems, for a woman. Marie–Madeleine describes an evening when she was driving one of her men from Pau to Bergerac. She liked the fellow, Coustenoble – an NCO in the air force – a no–nonsense Parisian who had a clairvoyant's knack of reading people. He would become a key player in *Alliance*. Darkness fell early that night, great black clouds covering the countryside, while rain fell more and more heavily. The road was potholed and badly maintained. Marie–Madeleine slowed down – but to no avail. A rear tyre blew–out, slewing the car to the edge of a ditch as the storm grew wilder:

'My companion put on his leather jacket. I reached for my loden coat. "Are you cold?" he asked. "No," I answered, "we'll change the tyre together. It'll take half the time."

Ignoring his protests, I helped him with the job and, after an hour – of course the repair tools worked badly – we were on our way, soaked, filthy and chilled to the bone. Coustenoble was coughing in a way I didn't like to hear, but seemed happy:

"We thought you were an officer's floozy – a good time girl if you like."

His remark made me laugh: "Good times and bad." I said.

I blessed that tyre. When it blew, so did the social barrier between us.'

Marie–Madeleine Fourcade was an astonishing woman. She was married and divorced – rare in those days – and already had two children, a boy of 11 and a girl of eight. She gave up the guardianship of them to her mother so that she could do her work for *Alliance*. She describes her farewell words to her son, Christian, in the spring of 1941:

"'You understand, my love, that you are the son and grandson of officers. You must think of your family. If I don't write to you it's because I don't want to compromise you – so that they can't find me through you. I can't risk you like that"… even the flowering cherry trees could not soften the anguish. I would need to live with that hole in my heart; knowing that I could not turn from my path. Navarre's words haunted me – "**if I fall, you will go on without me, of course**.""'

She does not dwell on the parting from her eight year old daughter.

She wondered whether she was right to even try to fight. She, a leader, was endangering not only herself and her family but all those who followed her. What chance had they of survival? They were few and were being hunted not only by the Nazis but by their own government – Vichy. The population was largely resigned to its fate: it took a great deal of courage to swim against the tide of appeasement and collaboration. As she told one of her men:

'I believe we will win a series of victories. The first is not to choke under the weight of our enemy. To hold on at whatever the cost until we are freed from the outside.'

Marie–Madeleine considered that the real war started when *Alliance* received its first big, bulky radio set; made in Whaddon and delivered by parachute. Whaddon's range of agents' radios became smaller, lighter and more sophisticated as the war went on. Soon they would fit into suitcases – the movement of radios by train being a particularly dangerous undertaking in occupied Europe. Making agents' radios was only part of Whaddon's 'spy factory'. They also made sets to fit into the aircraft which flew into the landing grounds. Those secret flights were an epic in their own right – an epic which I will revisit when it better fits the wider story.

Alliance's brief – to spy but not to strike – was not always welcome to prospective recruits. Bravery and prudence do not always come in the same package. Navarre and Marie–Madeleine understood, and made sure their agents did too, that what Britain needed was not sabotage or open warfare but information on Axis troop movements, submarines and air force deployments.

Beyond Vichy, *Alliance* set up networks right across France. The big question of early 1941 was the one Cohen had put to Navarre in Lisbon: where would Hitler strike next: would he move his armies through Spain to attack Gibraltar? That, it will be recalled, was the eventuality that Whaddon had covered by moving Bill Miller into Spain. *Alliance* had the answer. They had contacts in the ranks of the 'White' Russians – mainly aristocrats who had fled to France after the Russian Communist revolution of 1917. They, in turn, had friends among the Nazis. One of *Alliance's* first intelligence coups was to tell Whaddon of the posting of the French–based German SS divisions to the east for the attack on Russia (in June 1941). This, along with BP decrypts, allowed Churchill to inform the Russian leader, Joseph Stalin of the coming attack (the warnings fell on deaf ears).

Another early *Alliance* coup was to report back on an order which one of their agents (who owned a company which manufactured camouflage), had received from the Germans for new works at Lorient, Brest and St Nazaire. These were for work on the submarine pens which the Germans were building on the Atlantic coast to shelter the 'wolf packs' which would soon threaten to starve Britain to death.

Marie–Madeleine spent much time on overcrowded trains and moving back and forth across France. Constantly tired, always having to fight fear. Once, in Paris, she went to Maxim's, the elite restaurant, to watch the German military aristocracy at play:

'The tank and Luftwaffe aces, their uniforms glittering with decorations, with an unquenchable thirst for blood and tears... that golden youth of Germany, the aristocracy who occupied us without shame with their only justification the words of Hitler in the name of the Grand Reich. Albert of

Maxim's tended them, served them wonderful dishes, and I thought of my poor devils who criss–crossed France in broken shoes and old raincoats with empty bellies.'

Intermingled with the Germans at Maxim's were French businessmen, happy to grow rich servicing the invaders. The French industrial base was put to the account of Germany. A few factory owners, such as Michel Hollard, would have nothing to do with the conquerors. Most collaborated. French factories were used, for example, to make tanks. The main German U boat aircraft-detection equipment, the Metox, was designed and made in Paris.

As Marie–Madeleine expanded *Alliance's* agent network, there were losses. A man caught in a submarine base here, a woman picked up while transmitting there.

Then Navarre himself was captured and imprisoned. He was arrested because of his attempts to stir up the French army in North Africa. Pétain didn't appreciate that. The (French) police got *Alliance's* boss through his weak link – his family. Normally he lived away from home, but missing his wife and children badly, he had arranged to meet them for Sunday mass in the cathedral at Pau. Armed police had followed his family. The police opened fire when Navarre ran for it; he surrendered to avoid casualties among the congregation. He had, of course, already briefed his deputy, Marie-Madeleine, on what to do should this circumstance arose: **"If I fall, you will go on without me, of course."**

Would she? Could she? Without Navarre they were lost. The odds were too great:

'What could we do against the strongest country in the world, against the accumulated wealth and manufacturing power of a dozen conquered countries. In the face of that, had I the right to throw my poor friends into a pointless bloodbath? We were fools, idiots.'

Her deputies advised her to stop – to draw back from almost certain ruin; but they did not question her right to decide. She was their leader.

Marie–Madeleine's story is one of the most inspiring of the Second World War. France is not noticeably a country of female
246

power. The French ruling monarch was always a king, never a queen – and France has never had a female president. Her greatest scientist – the genius Marie Curie, winner of two Nobel prizes – was refused admission to the French Academy of Sciences on the grounds of her sex. Indeed in France, in 1939, women were still not allowed to vote or own property in their own name. And yet Marie–Madeleine had risen, through her courage, intelligence and competence to become the undisputed leader of *Alliance* the earliest, biggest and longest running French spy network.

Now she faced this, the terrifying question: to fight or not to fight? She was not a warrior who had sought or fought for power. She can never have expected the question nor rehearsed her answer. For her personally resistance would more than likely end in death; if she was lucky, quickly, if unlucky slowly, perhaps after torture by the Gestapo in Fresnes or Montluc prisons; or consigned to the furnace in Mauthausen concentration camp. She knew the odds and was terrified – and yet she knew, too, that if all were terrified into submission the butchers, the torturers, the Nazis – Hitler – would have won.

She continued the fight.

Marie–Madeleine Fourcade was, when she decided to follow the narrow and dangerous road of resistance, the leader not only of Alliance but also, morally, of la France *entière*. When she heard of the loss of HMS *Hood* Marie–Madeleine sent London – via the radio room at Nash, near Whaddon – a message of condolence. In reply, the War Office, sent:

'THANK YOU FOR YOUR FRIENDSHIP – STOP – TOGETHER WE WILL AVENGE THEM – END'

'These exchanges across the battle lines allowed the expression of human sentiments. I vowed then and there to do whatever I could not to lose that contact.'

That was largely what Pop Gambier–Parry's ring of towers was there for. To allow a voice – and perhaps a future – to the brave men and women of Europe: the heroes (though most of them would have smiled at the word) who would rather die than live as slaves.

Marie–Madeleine sent London the information that she had been asked for, including a detailed construction map of the St Nazaire submarine pens drawn by the French engineer there, Henri Mouren. She also sent messages from her agent in Turin about an Italian squadron of aircraft flying to reinforce Rommel. They were shot down by the RAF. From her agent in Marseille she sent information about shipping which sailed under false, neutral, flags to provide fuel for Erwin Rommel's panzer army in Africa. They were sunk by the Royal Navy.

She spent a lot of her time rebuilding her networks, which had been losing more and more agents to the German security forces. The arrests in the Vichy Zone Libre were by French police. The Germans, knowing that there was much radio contact from there to England, introduced detector vans, manned by German operators and French police. This prompted new rules for Marie–Madeleine's agents. No longer than 20 minutes on the air, change broadcasting frequencies frequently. This, she says, infuriated her operators, who had been used to chatting to Whaddon's outstation at Nash for hours at a time.

There were some in her own ranks who wanted to take more direct action against the invaders. Coustenoble for one wanted to get rid of Admiral Darlan – the power behind Pétain's Vichy throne. Coustenoble – and others – argued that it was on Darlan's orders that *Alliance* members were being arrested – and sometimes tortured – by French police. Marie–Madeleine vetoed the plan. Things were bad enough as it was without pitching France into an open civil war.

At the end of 1941 Marie–Madeleine was summoned to neutral Spain to meet her SIS contact for the first time. To get into Spain she was smuggled across the border in the luggage van of a train. Many French resistance members worked for the SNCF – the French railways. She travelled in a mail bag – the diplomatic pouch of Vichy France. The bag was 4 foot long by 2 foot wide (118 by 70cm). Marie–Madeleine was 5' 6" (170cm). Not only did she have to double herself into the bag, she had to remain inside for ten hours, in increasing discomfort which finally became excruciating pain, lying in silent, immovable, agony as the border patrol flashed their torches into the luggage compartment... and then passed on.

Having arrived in Madrid, the first hurdle she had to overcome was her sex. SIS believed that they were dealing with a man, as she always referred to herself as such in her messages, believing 'the English' would have no confidence in a young woman (she was then 31 years old) running the *Alliance* network.

While she was waiting to be debriefed, the Japanese launched their attack on Pearl Harbour and the Germans declared war on America.

The SIS agent who debriefed Marie–Madeleine over the course of several days – 'Major Richards' – was more interested in her news than her sex. The conversations were mainly in English. Marie–Madeleine told him the latest: her headquarters staff at Pau had been arrested – some had been tortured, some radio sets seized. Her mother had been arrested. Richards had news to add: word had come via Nash that *Alliance's* Paris cell had been betrayed: more agents had been seized. Marie–Madeleine would need to rebuild *Alliance* – and her family. On the plus side, such voyages as hers would soon be a thing of the past. The RAF was devoting more planes for drop–offs and pick–ups:

"The next time we meet, we'll pick you up from home."

'Then, when we had covered the subjects of military intelligence, radio operations and, airdrops with the minute precision that I had learned to expect from the British, they moved on to what information they wanted.'

What the British wanted was more, and more detailed, information about shipping and first and foremost, submarines. U–boats were the number one problem now.

"Shipping, shipping, shipping."

"But the Royal Navy is invincible."

"Perhaps, but it isn't inexhaustible. Think about D–day."

"D–day?"

"D–day. The landings which will overcome fortress Europe. We've got to get there."

"When will this D–day be?"

"Now that America's in, it's a certainty – but the timing depends on events. Submarines today, tomorrow, perhaps, the air, and then secret weapons."

Marie–Madeleine was in Madrid for a couple of weeks, over Christmas 1941. Then it was back in the diplomatic bag to France. This time she had it easy; she was only in the sack for four hours.

Later in the war, Marie–Madeleine would be flown to England as a break from the mentally crippling work of running *Alliance*. The average time that an agent lasted was 6 months – when she was flown out she had been running *Alliance* for three and a half years. By this time she was chain-smoking sixty cigarettes a day. She was feted by SIS in London, being chauffeured in one of Pop Gambier–Parry's sleek limousines. Marie–Madeleine, ever observant, commented on the:

'...long black Packards, driven by the slim blonde nymphs of the British secret services, moulded into their fetching uniforms.'

She was taken to Whaddon by Lord Sandhurst, who, it will be remembered, was in charge of SIS's agent radio operations. She described the transmitting room as:

'A tower of Babel where messages in many languages were taken by men and women operators who then passed them to the War Office. Lord Sandhurst appeared to me to be a chap one would have imagined more used to pig–sticking than managing secret transmissions ...my illusions about the English were confounded.'

There is more, much more, in the tale of Marie-Madeleine Fourcade, Navarre and the Alliance network than I have space to tell here. If you are interested, Lynne Olson's *Madame Fourcade's secret war* is a must read.

10: Penicillin

Antibiotic: a substance, for example penicillin, that can destroy or prevent the growth of bacteria and cure infections.
Oxford English Dictionary.

I write in this book about many key scientific breakthroughs which were made in the Intelligence Zone. Some, such as computing and radar, were developed almost purely because of the war; others, such as atomics, were hastened by it.

The discovery of penicillin, the first known antibiotic, was another world-changing advance which was made in the area. The demands of war would facilitate the drug's mass production.

Alexander Fleming, the Scottish doctor who discovered penicillin was born in 1881. He served with the British army's RAMC (Royal Army Medical Corps) in France in the First World War. The first war, like the second, was a time of rapid progress in medicine, with advances in brain surgery, plastic surgery, blood transfusion and the use of antiseptics. The RAMC was where many of these advances were made.

Based in Boulogne, Fleming was horrified by the numbers dying in field hospitals because of infections in their wounds. Around one in every seven wounded men died that way; hundreds of thousands across the battle fields. The standard method of treating wounds was to apply antiseptic to them; but that, as can be imagined, was a harsh approach which sometimes did more harm than good. It was almost useless against deep infections such as often occurred in the multiple wounds where men had been peppered by shrapnel. Fleming was to devote much of his subsequent life to trying to find a means to kill the bacteria which caused the infections. In his own words:

'I play with microbes. There are, of course, many rules to this play but when you have acquired knowledge and experience it is very pleasant to break the rules and to be able to find something nobody has thought of.'

His first major discovery (in 1921) was the antiseptic Lysozyme.

In 1928, he was working at St Mary's Hospital, in Paddington, in London. Here he routinely prepared culture dishes and populated them with bacteria on which to experiment. In late July 1928, he went for a holiday. When he returned in early September he was surprised to find that one of the dishes had an extra growth in it, which was killing off nearby bacteria cultures. This was because a mould spore had settled on the dish from the atmosphere (probably from other experiments in the building) and grown. As he put it:

> 'It was astonishing that for some considerable distance around the mould growth the staphylococcal colonies were undergoing lysis (being destroyed). What had formerly been a well-grown colony was now a faint shadow of its former self... I was sufficiently interested to pursue the subject.'

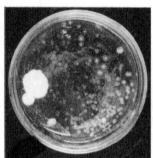

Fleming's discovery. The large penicillin growth to the left has inhibited or killed surrounding bacterial (staphylococcal) colonies

It is as well for the world that he did pursue the subject. He had made what was perhaps the most important discovery in the history of medicine The mould growth was penicillin; the first identified antibiotic. It would – and still does – save the health and lives of millions.

Fleming experimented with penicillin; curing an eye infection in his laboratory assistant with it. He could not, however, purify and extract enough of it to go much further. His research in London lapsed at that time. One of his former students however, Doctor Cecil Paine, continued to use it for eye operations (when working in Sheffield), with some success. How this happened, along with the wider story of penicillin and antibiotics, can be found in *Miracle Cure* by Milton Wainwright.

The first of Doctor Paine's case notes relate to a three year old infant, Peter, who had already spent three months being unsuccessfully treated in a nearby hospital. The disease that he suffered from was relatively common in infants. It could sometimes be treated by washing the eyes with a solution of silver nitrate, but often resulted in a complete loss of sight. Nothing had worked in Peter's case. Paine irrigated the boy's eyes with a solution of crude penicillin. The treatment was a complete success and Peter was allowed home shortly before Christmas in 1930. This was the first tiny sign of how antibiotics would revolutionise medicine, curing, preserving life, and alleviating suffering; in children and adults alike.

Doctor Paine was offered a new post which took him away from penicillin. He did, however, explain his successes to the Professor of Pathology at Sheffield, Howard Florey; and it was Florey who was to move penicillin into the mainstream. Florey, an Australian, became the Professor of Pathology at Oxford University in 1934 and it was there that he gathered a team of scientists to work on penicillin, including a Jewish refugee from Germany, Ernst Chain.

The task of producing and purifying penicillin continued to be extremely difficult. The earliest attempt to use it failed because of a lack of raw material. There followed several successes; enough to prove that penicillin was 'capable of achieving miracles' (in Milton Wainwright's words). For example, a six year old boy with a hip infection who was on the point of death was cured in a matter of days. This was in June 1940, as resistance to the German armies in France collapsed and the Nazi troops stood on Cap Gris Nez in sight of England and began to shell Dover.

In August 1940, the first paper on penicillin appeared in *The Lancet* – Britain's foremost medical journal. Florey's Oxford laboratory had been by now transformed into a mini factory. Added to this the urine of treated patients was being recycled to extract more of the precious drug. The result was enough penicillin to treat four or five patients; little more than a drop in the ocean which was needed. Britain already had thousands of wounded in hospital and, as the Battle of Britain raged overhead and German aircraft bombed English cities, more and more arrived. The British medical industry was fully occupied with its war duties; having also lost many of its men to conscription and some of its facilities to bombs. It had little spare capacity to produce penicillin.

This was, of course, at a time when a German invasion of Britain seemed extremely likely. Florey and some of his colleagues were so worried that they smeared spores of the penicillin-producing fungus inside the linings of their coats, in case they had to destroy all the cultures and take to the hills (such as they are) around Oxford.

In July 1941, Florey along with Norman Heatley – who had done important work on scaling up penicillin production - flew to neutral America to enlist the help of the New World. Their breakthrough was welcomed there with open arms. America introduced key improvements to the production process such as finding and using more productive (fungi) strains and the use of corn steep liquor as a growth medium. These allowed a radical increase in production. This in turn shaped much of the world's modern pharmaceutical industry (Pfizer's development of deep-tank fermentation was perhaps the main reason why it is today the world's largest pharmaceutical company).

While Axis soldiers still continued to die from bacterial diseases, penicillin saved thousands of British, American and Russian lives in world War Two. Since the war, It has saved more lives than were lost in the entirety of that conflict.

Fleming, Florey and Chain would share a 1945 Nobel prize (in physiology or medicine) for their work on penicillin.

***

By the 1990s, there was enough penicillin in existence to allow a 5 gram dose for every man, woman and child on the planet. It has saved humanity from much pain, suffering and early death. To take Britain as an example, the average lifespan has increased from about 60 to about 80 since the war. In many other countries, the rise has been even more dramatic. Antibiotics are the major reason why this is so; and penicillin remains the most important of the antibiotics.

11: The great administrator forges the Grand Alliance

Germany invades Russia

Germany invaded Russia on the 22nd of June 1941. Although Germany had not declared war the attack was no surprise to the British Prime Minister, Winston Churchill; who had been forewarned of it by Bletchley Park. Churchill had immediately passed the information to the Russian leader, Joseph Stalin, who ignored it; just as he ignored several other warnings that he was given during the ten days before the invasion. One of these alerts was a message from a communist spy in Berlin, Willi Lehmann. That message still exists. Across it, Stalin has scrawled the word 'disinformation.' The convolutions of Stalin's mind led him to believe that the invasion was 'merely' a provocation. The Russian dictator was faltering. A week after the attack he disappeared for two days leaving his country leaderless, allegedly saying as he left the Kremlin: "Everything's lost. I give up. Lenin founded our state and we've fucked it up!"

Happily the British Prime Minister was made of sterner stuff than the Russian dictator. Here was a straw, a lifeline, a hope. A slim hope, perhaps; for what could stop the Germans defeating Russia quickly, as they had in 1917? The hopelessness of a cause was rarely enough to deter Churchill from trying. He spoke on the BBC on the night of the invasion, promising Britain's full support to the Soviets. His words were not complimentary. This is hardly surprising given that until the previous day Russia had been allied with Hitler and planning how to plunder Britain's empire. Churchill said:

"The Nazi regime is indistinguishable from the worst features of Communism. It is devoid of all theme and principle except appetite and racial domination. It excels in all forms of human wickedness, in the efficiency of its cruelty and ferocious aggression. No one has been a more consistent opponent of Communism than I have for the last twenty-five years. I will unsay no words that I've spoken about it."

Having delivered this lifestyle-warning, Churchill administered the medicine:

"But all this fades away before the spectacle which is now unfolding... we have but one aim and one single irrevocable purpose. We are resolved to destroy Hitler and every vestige of the Nazi regime. We have offered to the Government of Soviet Russia any technical or economic assistance which is in our power and which is likely to be of service to them. We shall bomb Germany by day as well as by night in ever-increasing measure, casting upon them month by month a heavier discharge of bombs and making the German people taste and gulp each month a sharper dose of the miseries they have showered upon mankind."

This was not the glow of the glow worm. This was the roar of the British lion.

Here, at last, was a possible chink in Hitler's armour. Britain and France had (with important help from the United States) won the First Word War against Germany and her allies; could Britain and Russia win the second? To do so the Soviets would need tanks, aircraft, ammunition, fuel, food and much else besides. A lifeline from Britain must be organised quickly: a task right up Churchill's street. Russia was about to discover the truth of what Air Commodore Samson had said a quarter of a century earlier; 'One of these days the nation will understand what a great administrator he is.'

Aid to Russia – the convoys and the rail link

The first convoy of ships from Britain to Russia, *Dervish*, sailed from Liverpool just six weeks after the German invasion. Among its cargo it carried thirty nine Hurricane fighter aircraft and the pilots and personnel to support them. Hurricanes were one of the two fighters which had broken the Luftwaffe in the Battle of Britain. In fact they had brought down more German aircraft than even the Spitfire. Russia would get almost 3,000 of them from Britain during the war, as well as 1,200 Spitfires.

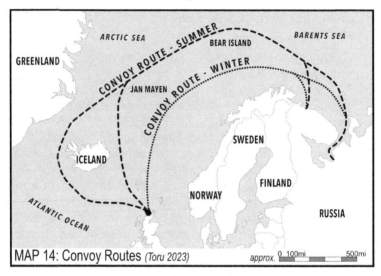

MAP 14: Convoy Routes *(Toru 2023)* approx.

Churchill demanded a convoy every ten days. Their route was along the coast of Nazi-occupied Norway, where heavy German naval units and hundreds of aircraft lay in wait. U-boats permanently patrolled the area in force. In summer they sailed in endless daylight, in winter they sailed in gales and freezing conditions, when ships could be capsized simply by the weight of ice forming on their superstructure. In those conditions a sailor who went into the sea was likely to die within minutes of entering the water.

Tanks were taken from the British production lines and put on board ships. It has been said that around a third of the tanks defending Moscow in the battle for that city at the end of the year (1941) were British. Although I cannot verify that statement, it certainly tallies with the fact that Britain delivered 750 tanks to Russia in 1941. The British tanks probably pulled more than their fair weight as, unlike Russian tanks at that time, they came with radios. This meant that they could act in unison rather than being picked off piecemeal. Further (British) radio sets were fitted into Soviet tanks at the front line, by a team or Russian technicians trained and supervised by an expert (Edgar Harrison) from Whaddon.

Aid to Russia would severely hamper the British war effort, both in the short and the longer term. Aircraft, tanks and armaments were sent straight to Russia from British factories instead of to Britain's front line in North Africa, or to her far-eastern garrison, Singapore.

Supply train between the Persian Gulf and Russia

On top of the Arctic convoys, Churchill offered Russia a second lifeline – along an existing rail line across Iran from the Persian Gulf to Russia. Russia agreed. British Empire (mostly Indian) and Russian armies entered Iran, deposed the Shah and occupied the country. The British sorted out the logistics and set the deliveries in motion. Along this railway would flow – mainly American – food, ammunition, weapons and other supplies in staggering amounts.

To take but one example. The saying that 'an army marches on its stomach' has been attributed to Napoleon. This little witticism takes for granted that the army are already shod. That hadn't always been the case in Russia. In the First World War, back in 1917, the collapse of the Czar's armies (and the birth of the communist state) was partly down to footwear. The victorious German troops had been at that time amazed to see that many of their opponents had rags, not boots, round their feet. Not this time round; in the second war, America supplied Russia with no less than 15,000,000 pairs of boots.

Without the Allied supply lines there is very little doubt that Russia would have lost the war.

Of course, the immense supply of materials from Britain and America was only one factor in Russia's ultimate victory in the east. The Russian T34 tank was another. Intelligence from Bletchley Park was another (I will return to that subject later). Then there was the Russian spy Richard Sorge; who Ian Fleming thought 'the best spy of all time'. Sorge gave Stalin information about Japanese plans which allowed him to switch troops from Siberia to counter-attack at Moscow, under the inspired leadership of general Zhukov.

Then there was the incredible endurance of the Russian soldier. The bravery and endurance of even the best-led soldier is ultimately pointless though, unless he is fed, clothed, and supplied with arms and ammunition.

Churchill's initiatives and British and American factories fed, armed and supplied a significant proportion of the Russian army and swung many a battle their way.

Placentia Bay – the sharing of the flame

The invasion of Russia and the start of Lend-Lease spawned a series of summit meetings that would bring the plans of Britain, America and Russia into alignment. These meetings would send Churchill travelling east and west throughout the war. The first of his main conferences was in August 1941, when he travelled in HMS *Prince of Wales* to meet President Franklin Roosevelt, who was aboard the USS *Augusta*. The British and American ships met in the Bay of Placentia, off Canada.

Churchill's main aim in the meeting was to get the President to commit American troops on the ground. Instead, the Americans agreed to provide United States Navy escorts for the Atlantic convoys from America to a point in the mid-Atlantic, or Iceland. There they would be met by ships of the Royal Navy who would take them onwards to Britain or Russia. This was part of the all-important 'mood music' which swung the American public – still in the majority isolationist - towards fighting.

At this meeting, Roosevelt asked Churchill to summarise Allied war aims. Churchill stated these, in brief, as being the defeat of Hitler followed by an alliance of nations – hopefully all of them - to ensure that war did not happen again. Winston dusted off the Declaration of Saint James, which the President and Prime Minister further modified between them. This was issued as a joint document and called the Atlantic Charter. This was the founding document of what was to become the United Nations (Roosevelt's title).

Churchill's gift to the future. The world's greatest wordsmith pens the world's pledge to live without war. Churchill's draft of page 1 of the Atlantic Charter.

Churchill said of the charter: "We gladly accorded the first place to the United States." That was fair enough as America would be providing a permanent home for the United Nations and the lion's share of its funding: but there was a great deal more to the order of precedence than that. Henceforward the United States of America would increasingly become the moral arbiter as well as the prime military power of the world.

Thus Churchill came back from Canada with his beacon for the future of humanity and the pledge by America to aid in the overthrow of the Nazis. America was, of course, also by now committed to providing food, fuel and weapons to Britain and through her, to Russia: but the meeting was a bitter disappointment to Churchill. He had wanted American troops on the ground.

The tact of Bomber Harris

The RAF's Air Vice-Marshall Sir Arthur Harris was in Washington at the time. His mission was to buy Liberator long-range bomber aircraft for convoy escort. He was also buying American trainer aircraft and sites in the USA for pilot training (the RAF was undergoing massive expansion). He met many American industrialists, service chiefs and politicians, from the

President down and was rewarded with much goodwill, lots of help with training facilities and aircraft - and not many Liberator bombers. The Americans were busy bringing their own air force up to speed and had few spare Liberators. As far as American despatch of their own troops or airmen, Harris had no illusions whatever. He wrote to his boss (Wilfrid Freeman) on September the 15th 1941 of:

'Our wishful thinking… about the probability of US entry into the war. They will come in when they think we've won it… but if they come in in any other circumstances, short of being kicked in, I'll stand you a dinner and eat, as my share, a pink elephant, trunk, tail and toenails.'

As so often, Harris (of whom, as the leader of Bomber Command, we shall hear a lot more), was pithy, funny and wounding; and apt to express what many others thought but were afraid to utter.

The President had very good reasons for not coming in… yet. Apart from building up his country's armed forces, he had still to win over the isolationist majority. He had to bring his people round to fighting by degrees. Most of his electors were of European stock - and a lot of them had gone to the states to get away from the troubles of that old and violent continent. Britain had taken the strain for the last couple of years and was under no immediate threat of invasion. She could – bankrolled by American Lend-Lease - take it a bit longer.

But that did not mean the Americans were idle. They put their formidable powers to work bringing their armed forces up to strength. American factories poured out weapons, American dockyards built ships and millions of American conscripts went through training.

Isolationism and unpreparedness aside, there was another consideration which was staying Roosevelt's hand. The third factor was the anomaly of de Gaulle's position and the governance of France. America still recognised Pétain's Vichy as the legitimate government of France. The way to get at Germany would probably be through France. Vichy wasn't asking to be liberated; if the Allies were to land on French territory, they might well be met by French bullets. (This was not fantasy, but an accurate prediction of what later happened in North Africa).

As for Churchill, he would just have to forget American troops for the moment. He had Russia as an ally now. True, providing aid to Stalin was a terrible drain to Britain in ships, tanks and aircraft; but supporting the eastern front was vital to defeat the Nazis. And it was a pretty good bet that America would enter the war by and by.

Churchill and Roosevelt had seen it all before. America had declared war on Germany last time – in 1917 – because the Germans had tried to provoke Mexico into attacking the USA. This time around, Nazi attacks on America would probably start at sea; it being almost impossible for German U-boat commanders to know whether they were firing at British or American ships.

The second act. Japan attacks Britain and America

Both Germany and Japan were carving themselves empires; and this had made them allies. The Japanese had already taken Korea, Manchuria and parts of China; Germany next wanted them to invade Russia from the east, while they attacked from the west. This pincer-movement would allow the two countries to carve up the vast Soviet Empire between them. Japan refused. It had already, years earlier, tried to attack Russia (through Manchuria) and had suffered a bloody nose at the hands of the highly-gifted Russian tank general, Georgy Zhukov. Instead it decided to attack British, American and Dutch possessions in Asia.

The Japanese assaults began on December the 7th 1941. All were surprise attacks, as Japan had not declared war on Britain or America.

First came air attacks on the British colonies of Malaya and Hong Kong. The British battle ships, the *Repulse* and the *Prince of Wales* were sunk in these attacks. The *Prince of Wales* had, as we have seen, been in the battle against the *Bismarck* and had also been Churchill's base in his meeting with Roosevelt at Placentia Bay a couple of months earlier. The two great ships had no air cover; British aircraft carriers being already fully

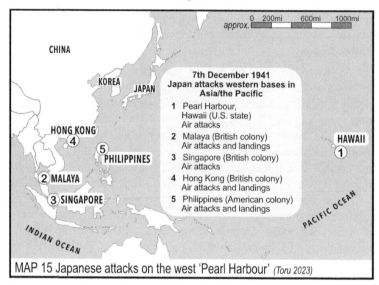

MAP 15 Japanese attacks on the west 'Pearl Harbour' *(Toru 2023)*

deployed in the Atlantic and Mediterranean against Germany and Italy. Twelve hundred men died in these sinkings.

This was followed by large scale troop landings, which quickly overran Hong Kong, Malaya, Singapore and most of Burma. The British defences were a product of complacency and lack of planning. Thirty thousand Japanese troops captured 80,000 British troops. This was a national humiliation – one of the greatest defeats in British military history.

And yet the defenders had their reasons. The Japanese deployed over ten times as many tanks and over twice as many aircraft as the British; and the Japanese aeroplanes were better; they had single wing fighters while most of the British planes were biplanes which were slower and poorly armed. Half of the RAF aeroplanes in the Far East were destroyed in the first days, allowing the Japanese to bomb almost at will. The British were nearly on the ropes. All of their aircraft carriers were fighting in the Atlantic and the Mediterranean. Their heavy tanks and their frontline aircraft were defending the British Isles or fighting in Africa or Russia. Quite apart from being out-thought and out-fought by their enemy, the security of their bases in the east had been sacrificed to keep Russia in the war.

Around an hour after the start of the attacks on Malay and Hong Kong, the Japanese air force struck the American air and naval bases at Pearl Harbour, sinking many American ships and killing 2400 men. Although the Japanese incoming attack aircraft were 'seen' by American radar operators, no defence was made against them. It shouldn't have been that way.

British radar technology was in advance of American; and although these advances had been handed over by the Tizard Mission of 1940, few if any of them had been integrated into American defences. The most obvious omission was that American aircraft had not been fitted with the British IFF (Identification Friend or Foe) transponder. This device 'told' the radar operators when incoming aircraft were friendly. At Pearl, the incoming Japanese bombers were thought to be American aircraft and therefore no defensive air strikes were made against them.

As a result of Pearl Harbour, Britain's radar supremo, Robert Watson-Watt, was summoned to America and flew there on the day after the attack. He was asked to do a full assessment on American radar equipment and procedures. The report he produced was called by General Gordon Saville, the (outstanding) director of Air Defence at the United States Army Air Force headquarters: "A damning indictment of our whole warning service". British procedures and technology were rapidly introduced to American aircraft and ships.

Historically, of course, the Pearl Harbour attack was the most important of all, as it brought America into the war. Uncle Sam had been caught napping; but he was awake now and angry. The young, strong, colossus would soon stand at the head of the world. His anger boded ill for his enemies.

Later in the day, Japanese troops began a seaborne assault on the American colony of the Philippines, which they would quickly overrun.

A week or two later, the Japanese began to occupy the Dutch East Indies.

As a result of these attacks America and Britain were at war with Japan. There was an added bonus for Churchill, too, for Germany declared war on the United States a couple of days later. Roosevelt didn't need to court public opinion anymore; his provocations had borne fruit. America had, in Bomber Harris's words, been 'kicked in'. The pink elephant was safe.

A fundamental purpose of this book is to show the key role British intelligence played in the war. Intelligence has two definitions. One of them is 'the collection of information of military or political value'. Bletchley Park had no serious rivals here. The second is 'the ability to acquire and apply knowledge and skills'. Britain's world lead in 1941 in the physics of atomics, radar and communications fall within this second definition. As for individual intelligence, no one was sharper than Churchill. His brain had engineered the alliance with America. His brain had organised the convoys to Russia. His brain had welded together Britain, the United States and Russia to build an alliance with the clout to win the hot war.

There were three Allies now; Britain, America and Russia. This was such a fundamental change in the Second World War that Churchill devoted one volume (*The Grand Alliance*) of his history of the war to it. It is partly for that reason that I, too, will finish this volume at this point.

Henceforth the advances made in the Intelligence Zone would not only be critical to the British war effort, but to the United States and Russia too. Nor had world-shaping innovations ceased in the Intelligence Zone; the expanding war would be the impetus that drove perhaps the greatest invention of all; the computer. At one and the same time, the balance of world power would shift increasingly towards America. These are themes that I cover in the sequel to this book; *A New World After Pearl*.

Dear reader,

I hope that you have enjoyed this book. It has been the result of many years of research. If you bought it on online and like it, please leave a review. Better still, buy copies for your friends – they'll probably like it too!

I have researched it as closely as possible. If, however, you have seen anything which you have good reason to believe to be inaccurate, please tell me. If I agree, I will amend it.

My contact email is intzoneuk@gmail.com

Thank you. And thank you for reading it.

Alan

March 2023

As I've explained earlier, there is a sequel to this book *A new world after Pearl,* which continues the story from 1942 to 1945. The map opposite shows the chapters both in this book and in that sequel.

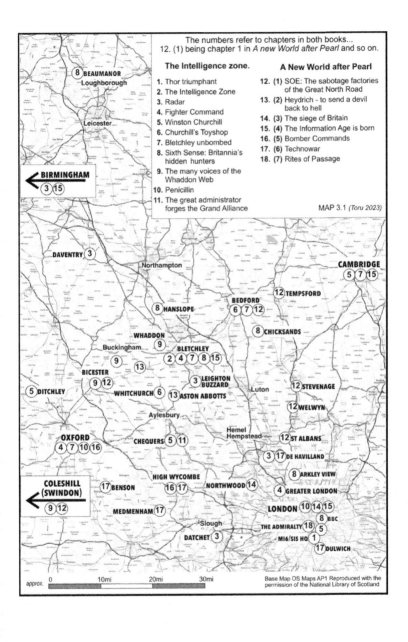

The numbers refer to chapters in both books...
12. (1) being chapter 1 in *A new World after Pearl* and so on.

The Intelligence zone.

1. Thor triumphant
2. The Intelligence Zone
3. Radar
4. Fighter Command
5. Winston Churchill
6. Churchill's Toyshop
7. Bletchley unbombed
8. Sixth Sense: Britannia's hidden hunters
9. The many voices of the Whaddon Web
10. Penicillin
11. The great administrator forges the Grand Alliance

A New World after Pearl

12. (1) SOE: The sabotage factories of the Great North Road
13. (2) Heydrich - to send a devil back to hell
14. (3) The siege of Britain
15. (4) The Information Age is born
16. (5) Bomber Commands
17. (6) Technowar
18. (7) Rites of Passage

MAP 3.1 *(Toru 2023)*

8 BEAUMANOR
Loughborough

Leicester

BIRMINGHAM
3 15

DAVENTRY 3

Northampton

CAMBRIDGE
5 7 15

12 TEMPSFORD

BEDFORD
8 HANSLOPE 6 7 12

8 CHICKSANDS

WHADDON
9
Buckingham
9
13
BICESTER
9 12
5 DITCHLEY

BLETCHLEY
2 4 7 8 15

3 LEIGHTON BUZZARD
WHITCHURCH 6 13 ASTON ABBOTTS
Luton

12 STEVENAGE

12 WELWYN

Aylesbury

Hemel Hempstead
12 ST ALBANS

OXFORD
4 7 10 16
CHEQUERS 5 11

3 17 DE HAVILLAND

HIGH WYCOMBE
COLESHILL
(SWINDON)
9 12
17 BENSON
16 17
NORTHWOOD 14

8 ARKLEY VIEW

4 GREATER LONDON

MEDMENHAM 17
Slough
DATCHET 3

LONDON 10 14 15
8 BBC
THE ADMIRALTY 18 5
MI6/SIS HQ 1
17 DULWICH

approx. 0 10mi 20mi 30mi

Base Map OS Maps AP1 Reproduced with the permission of the National Library of Scotland

Acknowledgements

My thanks to those who have read and commented on this book over the period of the five years that it took me to write it; John Ahern, David Biggins, Colin Bell, Mark Owen, Steve Parkinson and Roger Spittles.

I also thank the authors of the source books that I have used. I have tried to contact the authors, or the copyright holders, of all of the major works that I cite.

And I thank the museums which relate to this book. I have set up a separate website www.theintelligencezone.com to list them. Especially, I thank the volunteers in them who have helped me in verifying the accuracy of the various chapters. These volunteers give freely of their time and effort for the benefit of the community and we all owe them our gratitude.

I hope and trust that my thanks will be practical; for I am sure some of my readers who visit my website will subsequently wish to visit the museums themselves. They will be sure to meet many fine staff. Should you speak to them, please mention this book and give them my regards. There is a fair chance they will have met me or will meet me in the future.

Finally, on a personal note, I would like to acknowledge and thank the University of the Third Age (U3A); the Buckingham branch of which is valiantly trying to teach me to speak German. This is another institution run by volunteers which adds to the education and well-being of the community.

Bibliography

Chapter 1. Thor triumphant
Books

Boyd, Julia. *Travellers in the Third Reich : The Rise of Fascism: 1919-1945.* Pegasus Books, 2018.

Cox, Geoffrey. *Countdown to War: A Personal Memoir of Europe, 1938 - 40.* Coronet Books, 1988.

Delmer, Sefton. *Black Boomerang.* Viking Adult, 1962.

Delmer, Sefton. *The Counterfeit Spy.* Coronet, 1976.

Delmer, Sefton. *Trail Sinister.* Secker and Warburg, 1961.

Delmer, Sefton. *Weimar Germany: Democracy on Trial.* London, Macdonald And Co.; New York, American Heritage, 1972.

Fleming, Peter. *Invasion 1940 : An Account of the German Preparations and the British Counter-Measures.* Akadine Press, 2000.

Pickles, Dorothy Maud. *France between the Republics.* Contact publications, 1946.

Riess, Carl. Joseph Goebbels. Fonthill Media, 2015.

Smith, Michael. Foley: *The spy who saved 10,000 Jews.* Biteback Publishing, 2016. – I have not used any of this book in my work (I came across it too late). However, I would highly recommend this story of a truly heroic SIS officer and 'Righteous among nations'. It plainly recounts the evil of the Nazi state and how Frank Foley saved many lives from its insane butchery. It also tells much more about this remarkable man.

Spears, Sir Edward. *Assignment to Catastrophe.* Heinemann, 1954.

Wall, Daphne. *The World I Lost: A Memoir of Peace and War.* Sortium Ltd, 2014.

Winterbotham, F. W. *The Nazi Connection.* Dell Publishing Company, 1979.

Media and Online sources

Borden, Mary. *"Journey down a Blind Alley."* Internet Archive, University of Michigan, 1946, https://archive.org/details/JourneyDownABlindAlley-nsia/page/n15/mode/2up

Lochner, Louis Paul. *"What about Germany."* HathiTrust, Dodd, Mead & Company, 1943, https://babel.hathitrust.org/cgi/pt?id=mdp.39015012841279&view=1up&seq=1

Reinhart, R. J. *"Gallup Vault: U.S. Opinion and the Start of World War II."* Gallup.com, 29 Aug. 2019, https://news.gallup.com/vault/265865/gallup-vault-opinion-start-world-war.aspx

Wikipedia Contributors. *"Operation Aerial."* Wikipedia, 16 Oct. 2022, https://en.wikipedia.org/wiki/Operation_Aerial

Chapter 3. Radar; The race against time
Books

Bowen E. G. *Radar Days.* CRC Press, 1998.– Gives a full technical background and is enjoyable to read too.

Brown, Paul, and Edward Herbert. *The Secrets of Q Central : How Leighton Buzzard Shortened the Second World War.* Spellmount, 2014. – An interesting account of the site and its effect on Leighton Buzzard.

Hanbury-Brown, Robert. *Boffin: A Personal Story of the Early Days of Radar, Radio Astronomy and Quantum Optics.* CRC Press, 1991. – A well written mix of technical and autobiography.

Latham, Colin, et al. *The Birth of British Radar : The Memoirs of Arnold "Skip" Wilkins OBE.* Radio Society Of Great Britain, 2011. – A 95 page account. Much of it very technical but shot through with stuff of interest to the general reader.

Watson-Watt, Sir Robert. *Three Steps to Victory: A Personal Account by Radar's Greatest Pioneer.* Odhams Press Ltd, 1957. – Turgid at times, at others fascinating. A key book.

Younghusband, Eileen. *One Woman's War.* Candy Jar Books, 2011.– An interesting account of one of the plotters.

Media and Online sources

"Fennessy, Edward (Oral History)." Imperial War Museums, 1992, https://www.iwm.org.uk/collections/item/object/80012509. – Sir Edward Fennessy on Bawdsey and Leighton Buzzard. Four 30 minute broadcasts of his radar work. Fascinating

Hanbury-Brown, Robert. *"Edward George Bowen 1911-1991* | Australian Academy of Science." https://www.science.org.au/fellowship/fellows/biographical-memoirs/edward-george-bowen-1911-1991

Chapter 4. Fighter Command
Books

Davidson, Martin, and James Taylor. *Spitfire Ace.* Macmillan, 2015.

Deighton, Len. *Blitzkrieg: From the Rise of Hitler to the Fall of Dunkirk.* Harpercollins, 1994.

Deighton, Len. *Fighter: The True Story of the Battle of Britain.* Random House, 2008.

Dixon, Jack. *Dowding and Churchill; the Dark Side of the Battle of Britain.* Pen & Sword Military, 2009. – Dixon flew in Bomber Command during the war.

Fiedler, Arkady. *Squadron 303 : The Story of the Polish Fighter Squadron with the R.A.F.* S.N, 1945.

HMSO. *The Battle of Britain August - October 1940.* HMSO, 1941.

Johnson, 'Johnnie'. *Wing Leader: Top-Scoring Allied Fighter Pilot of World War II.* Goodall Publications Ltd, 2019.

Orange, Vincent. *Dowding of Fighter Command.* Grub Street, 2008.

Winterbotham, F. W. *The Nazi Connection.* Dell Publishing Company, 1979.

Younghusband, Eileen. *One Woman's War.* Candy Jar Books, 2011.

Media and Online sources

Cooling, Benjamin Franklin, editor. *Case Studies in the Achievement of Air Superiority*. 1994, https://media.defense.gov/2010/Oct/12/2001330116/-1/-1/0/AFD-101012-038.pdf.

Dowding, Air Chief Marshal Hugh. *"The Battle of Britain."* London Gazette, vol. Supplement, no. 11th September 1946, Sept. 1946, https://www.thegazette.co.uk/London/issue/37719/supplement/4543/data.pdf.

Kirkland, Faris R. *"French Air Strength in May 1940."* Air Power History, vol. 40, no. 1, 1993, pp. 22–34, https://www.jstor.org/stable/26279444.

Simkin, John. *"Rudolf Hess."* Spartacus Educational, 2017, https://spartacus-educational.com/GERhess.htm.

Wikipedia Contributors. *"History of the Armée de l'Air (1909–1942)."* Wikipedia, https://en.m.wikipedia.org/wiki/History_of_the_Armée_de_l'Air_(1909–1942).

Wikipedia Contributors. *"The Blitz."* Wikipedia, 7 Jan. 2023, https://en.wikipedia.org/wiki/The_Blitz#Night_attacks.

The Battle of Britain. Directed by Guy Hamilton, United Artists, 1969.

Chapter 5. Winston Churchill
Books

Andrew, Christopher M. *Her Majesty's Secret Service : The Making of the British Intelligence Community.* Penguin Books, 1987.

Atkin, Nicholas. *The Forgotten French.* Manchester University Press, 2013.

Churchill, Winston. *The Gathering Storm.* Penguin Books, 2005.

Churchill, Winston S. *The Grand Alliance : The Second World War, Volume 3.* Rosettabooks, 2010.

Churchill, Winston, and Denis Kelly. *The Second World War.* Penguin, 1989.

Cox, Geoffrey. *Countdown to War.* Coronet Books, 1988.

Gilbert, Martin. *Churchill : A Life.* Holt, 1992.

Gretton, Peter. *Former Naval Person.* Sapere Books, 2021.

Jenkins, Roy. *Churchill.* Grupo Planeta Spain, 2014.

Le Vernoy, Alec. *No Drums, No Trumpets.* Michael Joseph, 1988.

Packwood, Allen. *How Churchill Waged War.* Grub Street Publishers, 2018.

Pickles, Dorothy Maud. *France between the Republics.* Contact publications, 1946.

Probert, Henry. *Bomber Harris.* Stoddart, 2001.

Reynolds, David. *In Command of History.* Random House, 2012.

Sir Edward Spears. *Assignment to Catastrophe: The Fall of France, June 1940.* Heinemann, 1954.

Snow, C. P. *The Physicists.* House of Stratus, 2010.

Tree, Ronald. *When the Moon Was High.* Macmillan, 1975.

Media and Online sources

Bilge, Kerem. *"Admiral William Leahy, Ambassador to Vichy – Association for Diplomatic Studies & Training."* Adst.org, 2006, https://adst.org/admiral-william-leahy-ambassador-to-vichy/ .

"Russia (British Empire War Assistance) (Hansard, 16 April 1946)." Api.parliament.uk, https://api.parliament.uk/historic-hansard/commons/1946/apr/16/russia-british-empire-war-assistance.

Sterling, Christopher H. *"Getting There: Churchill's Wartime Journeys."* International Churchill Society, 1 May 2013, https://winstonchurchill.org/publications/finest-hour/finest-hour-148/getting-there-churchills-wartime-journeys/.

Chapter 6. Churchill's toyshop
Books

MacRae, Stuart. *Winston Churchill's Toyshop.* Amberley Publishing Limited, 2010.

Pawle, Gerald. *The Secret War 1939 - 45.* Companion Book Club, 1958.

Snow, C. P. *The Physicists.* House of Stratus, 2010.

Winston, Frederick. *The Prof in Two Worlds.* London : Collins, 1961.

Media and Online sources

Physics, American Institute of. *"Nicholas Kurti – Session I."* www.aip.org, 24 Sept. 2021, https://www.aip.org/history-programs/niels-bohr-library/oral-histories/4725-1

Chapter 7. Bletchley unbombed
Books

Andrew, Christopher M. *Her Majesty's Secret Service : The Making of the British Intelligence Community.* Penguin Books, 1987.

Bennett, Ralph Francis. *Ultra and Mediterranean Strategy.* William Morrow & Company, 1989.

Briggs, Asa. *Secret Days : Code-Breaking in Bletchley Park.* Frontline Books, 2012.

Churchill, Winston. *Their Finest Hour.* Bantam Books, 1949.

Deutsch, Harold C. *The Historical Impact of Revealing the Ultra Secret.* PN, 1977.

Greenberg, Joel. *Gordon Welchman.* Frontline Books, 2014.

Jeffery, Keith. *The Secret History of MI6.* Penguin Group, 2011.

Jones, R. V. *Most Secret War.* Penguin UK, 2009.

Kahn, David. *Seizing the Enigma.* Frontline Books, 2012.

Lewin, Ronald. *Ultra Goes to War : The First Account of World War Ii's Greatest Secret Based on Official Documents.* New York Pocket Books, 1980.

Mckay, Sinclair. *The Secret Life of Bletchley Park : The WWII Codebreaking Centre and the Men and Women Who Worked There.* Aurum Press, 2012.

Montagu, Ewen. *Beyond Top Secret U.* Corgi, 1979.

Sebag-Montefiore, Hugh. *Enigma : The Battle for the Code.* Wiley, 2004.

Smith, Michael. *Debs of Bletchley Park.* Aurum Press Ltd, 2015.

Smith, Michael, and Ralph Erskine. *The Bletchley Park Codebreakers.* Biteback Publishing, 2011.

Warner, Oliver. *Cunningham of Hyndhope, Admiral of the Fleet.* London : Murray, 1967.

Welchman, Gordon. *The Hut Six Story : Breaking the Enigma Codes.* M&M Baldwin, 2018.

Winterbotham, F. W. *The Ultra Secret.* Futura, 1975.

Winterbotham, Frederick William. *The Ultra Spy.* Macmillan, 1989.

Media and Online sources

Stengers, Jean. *"Enigma, the French, the Poles and the British 1931 -1940."* Revue Belge de Philologie et D'Histoire, vol. 82, no. 1, 2004, pp. 449–66, https://doi.org/10.3406/rbph.2004.4836.

Chapter 8. Sixth sense: Britannia's hidden hunters
Books
Abrutat, David. *Radio War.* Fonthill Media, 2019.

Beesley, Patrick. *Very Special Intelligence : The Story of the Admiralty's Operational Intelligence Centre 1939-1945.* Seaforth Publishing, 2015.

Boyle, David. *Operation Primrose : U110, the Bismarck and the Enigma Code.* Real Press ; Createspace, 2015.

Coles, Alan, and Ted Briggs. *Flagship Hood.* Robert Hale Ltd, 1985.

Hinsley, F. H., and Alan Stripp. *Codebreakers: The inside Story of Bletchley Park.* Oxford, Oup, 2001.

Mullenheim-Rechberg, Von. *Battleship Bismarck.* Naval Institute Press, 2012.

Pidgeon, Geoffrey. *The Secret Wireless War.* Arundel Books, 2018.

Raymond, John. *Bring Back My Stringbag.* Pen & Sword Books Ltd, 1979.

Sinclair Mckay. *The Secret Listeners : The Men and Women Posted across the World to Intercept the German Codes for Bletchley Park.* Aurum, 2013.

Taylor, John A. *Bletchley Park's Secret Sisters.* Castle Books, 2005.

Media and Online sources
Preston, Paul. *"Franco and Hitler: The Myths of Hendaye 1940."* Contemporary European History, vol. 1, no. 1, Mar. 1992, pp. 1–16, http://eprints.lse.ac.uk/26101/.

Wikipedia Contributors. 2022. *"B-Dienst.".* Wikipedia. September 1, 2022. https://en.wikipedia.org/wiki/B-Dienst.

Wikipedia Contributors. 2019. *"Spain during World War II."* Wikipedia. Wikimedia Foundation. December 5, 2019. https://en.wikipedia.org/wiki/Spain_during_World_War_II.

Chapter 9. The many voices of the Whaddon Web
Books
Abrutat, David. *Radio War.* Fonthill Media, 2019.

Fourcade, Marie–Madeleine. *L'Arche de Noé; Tomes 1 & 2.* Ldp, 1971.

Howe, Ellic. *The Black Game : British Subversive Operations against the Germans during the Second World War.* Queen Anne Press, 1988.

Olson, Lynne. *Madame Fourcade's Secret War : The Daring Young Woman Who Led France's Largest Spy Network against Hitler.* Random House, 2020.

Pidgeon, Geoffrey. *Edgar Harrison : Soldier, Patriot and Ultra Wireless Operator to Winston Churchill.* Arundel Books, 2008.

Pidgeon, Geoffrey. *The Secret Wireless War.* Arundel Books, 2018.

Sisman, Adam. *Hugh Trevor-Roper.* Hachette UK, 2012.

Taylor, John A. *Bletchley Park's Secret Sisters.* Castle Books, 2005.

Media and Online sources

Wikipedia Contributors. 2023. *"Battle of Crete."* Wikipedia. January 3, 2023. https://en.wikipedia.org/wiki/Battle_of_Crete#Aftermath.

Chapter 10. Penicillin

Books

Wainwright, Milton. *Miracle Cure : The Story of Penicillin and the Golden Age of Antibiotics.* Blackwell, 1990.

Chapter 11. The great administrator forges the grand alliance

Books

Meissner, Hans Otto. *The Man with Three Faces.* Ace Books, 1956.

Schofield, B. B. *The Arctic Convoys.* London : Macdonald and Jane's, 1977.

Woodman, Richard. *The Arctic Convoys, 1941-1945.* Barnsley Pen & Sword Maritime, 2007.

Media and Online sources

"Lend-Lease, Major Supplies from the Western Allies to Russia." n.d. WWII Forums. http://www.ww2f.com/threads/lend-lease-major-supplies-from-the-western-allies-to-russia.488.

"Russia (British Empire War Assistance) (Hansard, 16 April 1946)." n.d. api.parliament.uk. https://api.parliament.uk/historic-hansard/commons/1946/apr/16/russia-british-empire-war-assistance.

List of terms and acronyms

ATS – Female member of the British army in WW2

AXIS – the alliance of fascist powers (principally Germany and Italy and later Japan)

BBC British Broadcasting Corporation. The state-owned radio and television service

GC & CS The government Code and Cypher School. The department of the SIS/MI6 which dealt with cryptography and was at Bletchley Park (later renamed GCHQ)

GPO – General Post Office. At the time, the state-owned monopoly for postal and telephone services

HF/DF (huff-duff). High Frequency detection. The equipment which was used to determine the physical source from which enemy transmissions were coming

Luftwaffe – the German air force

MI5 – The British domestic (as against overseas) intelligence service

MI6 – see SIS

NID – Naval Intelligence Division (of the Royal Navy)

RAF – Royal Air Force

RFC – Royal Flying Corps. Merged with Royal Navy Air Service (RNAS) to become the Royal Air Force in 1918

RN – Royal Navy

RNAS – Royal Navy Air Service. The navy's flying arm. Merged with the RFC in 1918 to become the Royal Air Force

RSS – Radio security service. The civilian counterpart (GPO and secret services) of the military listening ('Y') services

SIS. The Secret Intelligence Service, also known as MI6. Britain's external intelligence service (i.e. dealing with overseas intelligence)

SOE – Special Operations Executive – organisation set up for overseas sabotage

Ultra – The highest classification of British security. Often used to refer to Bletchley Park's output

USAAF – United States Army Air Force (preceded the USAF)

WAAF – Women's Auxiliary Air Force (female member of the RAF in WW2)

WRNS (WREN) – female member of the Royal Navy in WW2

Y services. The listening services the British armed forces and secret services used to puck up Axis messages. The letter 'y' came from the original 'WI', which was short for Wireless Interception.

Index

Index

Index

Printed in Great Britain
by Amazon